Solar Rain

The Earth Changes Have Begun

Mitch Battros

with Tony Stubbs

Solar Rain: The Earth Changes Have Begun
by Mitch Battros
with Tony Stubbs

First printing: Fall 2005

ISBN: 0-9771348-3-0

Published by:
Earth Changes Press
PO Box 31775
Seattle, Washington 98103
Fax: 206.632.0863

To order more copies of this book, please contact the publisher or visit the publisher's websiteat:
www.earthchangesTV.com

Edited and designed by Tony Stubbs (www.tjpublish.com)

Printed in the United States of America

Table of Contents

Acknowledgments

This book is dedicated to you, the reader.

I would like to thank the following people for contributing their time and creativity in the development of Earth Changes TV, which has been the foundation for this book, and all those that will follow. Harry Tchinski who was the original creator of our ECTV concept. Sherry Todd-Grantham who helped build Earth Changes TV as our webmaster and graphics designer. Lois Green and Melissa Morton-Thomas for producing Earth News newsletter (hard copy). Bill Smith and Scott Johnson for working the cameras in the ECTV studios. John Kesiela as our first and only Director of Earth Changes TV, the television show. Anna Haight, our Chief News Editor, and Petra Gradisar, our number one volunteer all the way from Slovenia. And last but not least, Chuck Warren, who is our current webmaster and has built what you see today on Earth Changes TV.com

It has been quite the journey. From being the new kid on the block who produced what many would describe as 'on the fringe' of scientific information, to being acknowledged by thousands as the No. 1 news source for 'space weather' and 'earth science.' With all humility and gratitude, I thank you for helping make Earth Changes TV, which has been the launch pad for *Solar Rain* and the forthcoming *Cosmic Rain* (spring 2006), the pioneering instruments for a fast-changing world.

Preface

On June 5, 2005, I announced on the ECTV website that I had a fully paid ticket available for the Belize cruise, and invited people who wanted to go to e-mail me, telling why they should be the person to go.

On June 7, I posted the following piece on the website:

I am sitting here in awe from the response received from the more than 200 people to join our ECTV Cruise to Belize. I simply was not prepared for the quality, compassion, enthusiasm, experience, creativeness, spirituality, and vision produced by those who responded. No not some…"everyone". Remember, this is a group who can make arrangements to join our cruise with just five days notice.

I am sitting here with an aching head trying to pick one gifted person to join this once-in- a-lifetime journey. Folks, I truly do not think I could ever do this again. It is too draining. So here's the deal… the success and popularity of this spontaneous event demands it to re-appear, so it will indeed occur on our next excursion, but I will not be the one to choose. This task will go to my chief editor, Anna Haight. I think she is far better equipped to handle the agonizing decision of eliminating even one single person from the list.

I could not be more thrilled to find out the unique character and distinction of the ECTV followers, members and fans. You have brought my appreciation to what I stand for to a new level. To witness the talent, insight and brilliance which you possess, along with your ovation and appreciation for what we do here at ECTV, has both bolstered and humbled my very essence.

This is the one most theme which almost every one of you mentioned and I wish to share with all. It appears my desire to maintain an unyielding devotion to balance the scientific community with the ancient wisdom of our ancestors, is what you appreciate most. Again, I could not be more jubilant and fulfilled. This knowledge has reinforced my drive to continue in the halls of NASA and NOAA, yet maintain my balance with the brightest minds in ancient text, culture and prophecy. Yes, it is true; as a result of diligence, perseverance and a strong portfolio of research and factual data, I have been allowed in the halls of our most esteemed scientific communities. This has allowed me to interview the top minds in the world regarding the field of 'earth science' and 'space weather'.

Introduction

In most scientific journals, descriptions of the Sun and the Earth may go something like you will see in this introduction. The Sun-Earth connection is not a new theory. It has been long known there is some relation between what happens on the Sun and its slow methodical effect on the climate on Earth. But what this book is about to lay out will turn current charts, graphs, and formulas on their heads. The word that groups all these scientific methodologies into one is *paradigm*. Webster's Revised Dictionary defines *paradigm* as: "A set of assumptions, concepts, values, and practices that constitutes a way of viewing reality for the community that shares them, especially in an intellectual discipline."

Solar Rain lays out, chapter by chapter, a much closer causal effect. So close, in fact, that what happens on the Sun can affect what happens on the Earth before many of you will finish the first three chapters.

Now lets start from the beginning........

A long time ago, a negatively charged particle, called an electron, orbited a positively charged particle, called a proton, in an eternal dance of attraction. These two particles, when joined together, make an atom we call hydrogen. Combined, this pair of atoms now exerted more gravitational attraction, and pulled in a third, then a fourth, and so on over unimaginable eons. Eventually they would form a ball of hydrogen atoms 865,000 miles in diameter that is our star, the Sun. So what goes on inside?

The most popular theory is that of nuclear fusion, whereby at the center of this ball, the force of trillions of atoms being attracted into the center compresses the atoms and triggers chemical reactions that convert the hydrogen atoms into other elements and produce immense heat. The resulting convection currents then carry the atoms away towards the edge of the huge ball, so this mass of trillions of trillions of atoms is in constant, seething motion. It's estimated that in about ten billion years, all the hydrogen atoms will have been converted into other elements and this solar soup will cool down, so it's roughly middle-aged. In the meantime, it will still be causing chaos in the surrounding billions of miles for a long while yet.

Of course, this process repeated itself countless billions of times elsewhere in space to produce other stars that gravity pulled together into vast structures we call galaxies. And our star is an unremarkable accretion of hydrogen atoms on the edge of an unremarkable galaxy amongst billions more that make up what we call the universe. Some even speculate that our universe isn't alone in Creation, but no one really knows.

Another theory—the Electric Sun theory—is that constant plasma flows cause massive magnetic fields that actually hold the Sun together. The bottom line is that we don't really know.

Also a long time ago, a few different types of atoms began to be attracted to each other and formed a huge disk around the equator of the Sun. These atoms were more complex, having a nucleus of several protons surrounded by an equal number of electrons in various orbits, and perhaps some neutral particles adding their weight to the central nucleus. So far, we've identified over a hundred different structures, and new ones keep coming to light, some so unstable that they exist for only a fraction of a second before assuming another structure. These collections grew over the vastness of time and gravity drew them towards the huge Sun. However, their centrifugal motion through space prevented them from being sucked into the Sun, so they existed in perfect balance. Then, at various distances from the Sun (predictable by Bode's Law—see later chapter) the atoms condensed into planets. One such accumulation of atoms is what we to-day call home—planet Earth.

In sufficiently large and pure quantities, some types of atoms we call conductors exhibit a curious and profoundly important property—outer electrons are more loosely attracted to the atom's nucleus. If there is a surplus of electrons in one area and a paucity in another area, the outer electrons hop to other atoms, moving towards the deficit in an attempt to neutralize the imbalance. If the imbalance is sufficiently large, the electrons will actually jump across otherwise non-conducting space, causing havoc to whatever gets in the way, especially living tissue. Benjamin Franklin was the first to speculate that when storm clouds churn, they create excess free electrons, which then leap down to the planet's surface as lightning.

As electrons move through a conductor, they give out energy. If this cannot be absorbed internally, it is radiated outwards as heat and light, an effect Thomas Edison harnessed to invent the incandescent light bulb. There is another phenomenon associated with the movement of electrons that cannot be seen—the production of what we call a magnetic field. This mysterious invisible field can be noted only by its effect on a class of materials whose internal lattice structure can be aligned to create their own magnetic field, i.e., magnets. Then we can observe the two magnetic fields interacting, either attracting or repelling each other. This force can be strong enough to be harnessed to perform useful work, such as turning an axle. Conversely, if a conductor is moved through a magnetic field, a flow of electrons, or current, is induced in the conductor, which can be transmitted for several miles and converted back into a magnetic field, or heat and light at a distance remote from the source.

Thomas Edison was the first inventor to harness this effect commercially, and he used a steady flow, or direct current. Due to internal resistance in the conductor, this form of electrical transmission needed thick conductors and was feasible over only short distances of a few miles. Another inventor, Nikola Tesla, reasoned that a rapidly alternating current would achieve the same effect but that internal friction would be less, allowing higher voltages to be transmitted over longer distances and using thinner conductors. Telsa won the ensuing 'battle of the currents' and today, alternating current is the standard.

Tesla also reasoned that man could emulate nature's lightning, and transmit enormous current through space, without the need for physical conductors. A simple antenna at the remote receiving location would capture the electrons pumped out by the large antenna at the transmitter. However, he was unable to obtain funding to explore wireless transmission, which resulted in the now-familiar sprawl of electrical towers and high-voltage wires criss-crossing the countryside. In some rural areas of North America, the fact that these wires can run for hundreds of miles will prove pivotal to our story.

The center of Earth is a seething cauldron of molten iron, rotating within the cooler mantle. This movement generates a magnetic field that has fluctuated throughout history. At one time, its strength was about five gauss, and today it stands at about one tenth of that. Many speculate that the planet is preparing to flip magnetic poles, which will cause chaos in navigation equipment and among animals that use the field in migration. Despite a few local anomalies due to underground deposits of iron ore, the Earth's magnetic field is generally stable and well-behaved. In contrast, the Sun's magnetic field is chaotic. Rivers of incandescent plasma course around and within the body of the Sun generate magnetic fields that twist and spiral internally and out into the Sun's atmosphere, called the coronasphere.

The latter effect provides pathways for plasma streams to climb high above the Sun's surface in huge arcs. Occasionally, enormous bubbles of plasma, weighing billions of tons, are ejected from the surface and hurled into space at speeds approaching two billion miles per hour. These Coronal Mass Ejections (CME) are themselves moving currents and thus generate their own magnetic field as they careen through space. If a CME leaves the equator of the Sun, it can traverse the Plane of the Elliptic, or the disk the Earth's orbit defines. Two days later, it will arrive at the orbit of the Earth, and if the Earth happens to be there, the solar shock wave will impact the planet, followed by the magnetic field of the plasma.

As the magnetic field sweeps across the planet, it induces a current in long-distance transmission lines and steel pipelines transporting oil. This current generates a voltage difference of 2 to 10 volts per mile, which can add 5,000 volts to the potential already handled by a 500-mile line. That can cause hotspots in electrical transformers and burn out the coils inside them. It can also cause explosions in pipelines.

This is where the story opens in chapter one. But as we will see, this just the tip of the iceberg. The Sun's influence on Earth's atmosphere and infrastructure is huge, and there is nothing we can do about it except predict and prepare for the impact.

The May 2001 issue of *Popular Science* carried an article that confirmed the equation I published in 1999 that explains how solar events affect Earth and our weather. Of course, the 'record breaking' weather we were then experiencing here in the US and around the world came as no surprise to many of you. It is of no coincidence extreme weather follows solar flares and CMEs. The equation, of course, is:

Sunspots => Solar Flares (CMEs) => Magnetic Shift => Shifting Ocean and Jet Stream Currents => Extreme Weather

The *Popular Science* article went on to say, "The data suggest that the reflectance has decreased slightly during the past five years, as the Sun's magnetic activity has climbed from solar minimum to maximum during that time. Many scientists have noted changes in climate that seem to mimic the 11-year solar cycle and this research could support the theory that the Sun's magnetic field plays an indirect role in Earth's climate."

Scientists and engineers reassure the apocalyptically fearful that a solar flare's impact on Earth is affected by a complex array of variables, and the eruptions may not necessarily have cataclysmic effects; in addition, they've been preparing for this for years, developing warning systems and plotting ways to keep power grids and global communications on-line, and to protect air traffic from disruption.

But by the same token, nobody is sure exactly what will happen when the Sun goes ballistic. "It's the luck of the draw, really," says Paul McCurley, an engineer for the Edison Electrical Institute, a utility industry trade group.

The previous to last solar maximum, around 1990, provided a glimpse of how disruptive bad solar weather can be. In March 1989, at radio telescope facilities in British Columbia and Ontario, needles on recording devices suddenly flew off the scale, and alarm buzzers sounded in a startling cacophony. The astronomers present quickly discerned the cause: Eight minutes before, 93 million miles away, the Sun's magnetic field had unleashed a huge blast of energy toward Earth. "It was like a solar hurricane," Dominion Radio Astrophysical Observatory scientist Ken Tapping opined to a Canadian newspaper. (Some solar scientists, it should be noted, object to such alarming metaphors, noting that solar flares don't rip out trees or knock down houses.)

But there wasn't much time for them to ponder the awe-inspiring magnitude of the event. They hurriedly began pumping out fax and computer messages to government agencies in Canada and the United States, warning that within the next 36 to 48 hours, the flare's next phase—a plasma cloud filled with excited subatomic particles, and associated magnetic storm—would reach our planet.

Sure enough, in the early morning hours of March 13, the solar storm arrived. The Earth's atmosphere expanded as it absorbed the heat, buffeting satellites and knocking them out of position. Within seconds, the Sun's surplus energy surged through power lines across the upper Northern Hemisphere. Lights in Stockholm fluttered, and in Toronto, burglar alarms shrieked en masse. Quebec's electrical system took the worst hit; throughout much of the province, refrigerators ceased humming and clocks stopped ticking. The flare's bizarre effects spread even farther and wider; in the South, the U.S. Navy experienced disruptions in its communications, and on the other side of the Atlantic, the Concorde supersonic jet was diverted from its usual altitude of 55,000 feet because of the possible hazard to passengers from the flare's gamma and x-ray radiation.

Having been a voice in the wilderness for years concerning the role played by the Sun, I was delighted at the resulting flood of confirmation. One of the strongest endorsements came forward from Mukul Sharma, Assistant Professor of Earth Sciences at Dartmouth University. He has strong evidence confirming what I have been calling a 'Mega Cycle' since September 1999 regarding the Sun. His research shows the Sun's magnetic activity is varying in 100,000-year cycles, a much longer time-span than previously thought, and this solar activity may in turn cause the 100,000-year climate cycles on earth. This research helps scientists understand past climate trends and prepare for future ones. "Surprisingly, it looks like solar activity is varying in longer time spans than we realized," says Sharma. "We knew about the shorter cycles (11 year) of solar activity, so maybe these are just little cycles within a larger cycle. Even more surprising is the fact that the glacial and interglacial periods on earth during the last 200,000 years appear to be strongly linked to solar activity."

Another great endorsement soon followed. A 2002 analysis of observations from the Solar and Heliospheric Observatory (SOHO) revealed detailed and unexpected weather patterns not only on the Sun's visible surface but down below as well. Dr. Deborah Haber and Dr. Bradley Hindman from the University of Colorado presented their results at the AAS meeting in Albuquerque. "For the first time, we can see large-scale weather systems developing on and just below the surface of a star," said Haber.

Monitoring these solar patterns could also play an important part in improving our ability to predict weather on the Sun that affects us on Earth by making it possible to forecast Coronal Mass Ejections and solar flares that can cause geomagnetic storms and disrupt electronics on satellites. "We can't predict them now, but we hope we'll be able to do that," Haber added.

A statement like that sure makes me think they monitor ECTV site very closely. I am thrilled to know that well respected international news agencies are showing allegiance to the growing body of evidence of the Sun-Earth Connection.

Dr. Lucie Green, of Mullard Space Science Laboratory (MSSL) in Surrey stated in September 2002, "Prediction of space weather is still a long way off but our research is helping us understand why CMEs happen in the first place." The BBC reported that scientists hope it will one day be possible to predict when the Sun is likely to emit CMEs as part of space weather forecasts.

The cynic in me wonders if NASA is planning to announce 'their new' discovery and go public with breaking news of how they figured out the Sun is the cause of weather. I expect they will also announce the new upcoming 'Super-duper Doppler' that will forecast space weather and its correlation with our own.

The German philosopher Arthur Schopenhauer (1788 - 1860) said, *"All truth passes through three stages. First, it is ridiculed. Second, it is violently opposed. Third, it is accepted as being self-evident."* *One day, the contents of this book will be deemed self-evident.*

So What Is the Sun-Earth Connection and Why Is It Important?

Historically there has been a fascination with the Sun since time began. Our ancestors would often gaze at the Sun wondering what energy or destruction would be bestowed upon lifeforms. The oldest of our ancestors knew very well what an angry Sun can do. They also knew it was the life source of their existence.

This knowledge was passed down through the ages telling of great harvest, energy, health. The Egyptians would bestow the title 'Sun God' upon their leader Ra. This similar pattern has filtered through every known society known to Earth. It was clear to all, the Sun could give life, and it could take it away. If you can't control something, at best you try to predict it and work within its vagaries.

This went on for millennia, until the Industrial Revolution allowed men to boast that they had finally "conquered nature." We seemed to have gained dominion over shelter, warmth, transportation, new source of fuel for transportation. Long gone was the need for fire and steam engines. For all practical purposes, the Sun had simply become a 'neighbor,' never again to be feared or worshiped. One could argue that an attitude of self-mastery now prevailed—a costly and devastating mistake.

Proof exists that our ancestors living decades and centuries prior to our current generations appear to have had a much higher knowledge of our solar and star system then many college level astronomy students. The Mayan culture of Central America is one of many examples. They knew hundreds of years prior to our modern scientific body of today, there is, and always has been an undeniable Sun-Earth Connection.

As we'll see in Chapter 5, the Maya were talented astronomers, religiously intense in their observations of the Sun, moon and planets. Now, new research shows something in the heavens may have influenced their culture and ultimately helped bring about their demise.

In an article in a recent issue of the journal *Science*, a team of researchers led by a University of Florida geologist reports finding that the Yucatan Peninsula, seat of the ancient Maya civilization, was buffeted by recurrent droughts. More importantly, the research shows, the droughts—one of which is thought to have contributed to the collapse of the Maya civilization—appear to have been caused by a cyclical brightening of the Sun.

"It looks like changes in the Sun's energy output are having a direct effect on the climate of the Yucatan and causing the recurrence of drought, which is in turn influencing the Maya evolution," said David Hodell, a UF professor of geology and the paper's lead author.

The paper, co-authored by Mark Brenner, a UF assistant professor of geology and director of UF's Land Use and Environmental Change Institute, and Jason Curtis, a UF geology researcher, was based on analysis of a sediment core* from Lake Chichancanab on the north central Yucatan Peninsula in Mexico.

For the latest research, Hodell, Brenner and Curtis returned to the lake and collected a new series of cores. The researchers discovered layers of calcium sulfate, or gypsum, concentrated at certain levels in the cores.

Lake Chichancanab's water is nearly saturated with gypsum. During dry periods, lake water evaporates and the gypsum falls to the lake bottom. The gypsum layers are 'proxies,' representing drought episodes. The researchers found the recurrence of the deposits was remarkably cyclical, occurring every 208 years, although they varied in intensity.

---

* Cores are samples of lake sediment retrieved by driving a hollow tube into the lake bottom. The sediments are deposited layer by layer, like a wedding cake, with the oldest layer at the bottom. Such cores provide a timeline that allows researchers to obtain a continuous record of changes in climate, vegetation and land use.

"The 208-year cycle caught our attention because it is nearly identical to a known 206-year cycle in solar intensity," Hodell said. "As part of that cycle, the Sun is most intense every 206 years, something that can be tracked through measuring the production of certain radioactive substances such as carbon-14."

The researchers found the drought episodes occurred during the most intense part of the Sun's cycle. Not only that, but they found the droughts occurred at times when archeological evidence reflected downturns in the Maya culture, including the 900 A.D. collapse and abandonment of cities, and a slowing of building and carving activity.

Hodell added, "The energy received by the Earth at the peak of the solar cycle increases less than one-tenth of 1 percent, so it's likely that some mechanism in the climate is amplifying the impact in the Yucatan."

Archaeologists know the Maya were capable of precisely measuring the movements of the Sun, moon and planets, including Venus. Hodell said, "I am unaware, however, of any evidence the Maya knew about the bicentenary cycle that ultimately may have played a role in their downfall. It's ironic that a culture so obsessed with keeping track of celestial movements may have met their demise because of a 206-year cycle. The cycle continues to the present, which happens to fall into about the middle of the 206-year period."

Co-author Brenner added, "Even a severe drought today, however, isn't likely to have the same impact on the culture as in ancient times. North Korea currently is suffering an extreme drought, but the country has the benefit of international aid. Nobody stepped in to help the Maya out, and as conditions worsened, it probably created a lot of stress among various Maya cities competing for resources."

In the famous venue of the slow, awakening giant, the world's solar scientists are playing 'catch-up' to a new (which is actually very old) understanding of the symbiotic and close-knit relationship between what happens on the Sun and what can be almost immediately reflected as a problem on Earth. Until now, and partly due to my 'Equation' published in 1997, scientists would measure the events that would occur on the Sun and its relation to events on Earth in terms of decades and centuries. Instead, my Equation suggests that what occurs on the Sun is made manifest on Earth within 'hours and days.' This new concept shifts the current paradigm from what has traditionally been measured in the way of cycles that relate to *climate*, measured in decades, centuries, and millennia, to the almost instant causal principle of *weather.*

I have taken intense precautions to carefully weave the threads of science (new), with ancient text (old), to deliver the most accurate and factual science based material bringing you to the window of change. Here you will see the making of a new paradigm which is rare and is unfolding in our lifetime.

Below is a 'real time' example of a current event that unfolded in front of the eyes of the world, which is a template example of what I believe will be the new 'Sun-Earth Formula' to be used throughout the world.

New M-Class Flare and Hurricane Dennis

A new second M-Class flare has fired off from the Sun (today) Saturday July 9th. This comes on the heels of Thursday's, July 7th M5 flare. It will be Thursday's flare which could cause serious problems.

I am expecting a spike in the Kp Index within a few hours (by late morning Sunday 10th July). This will indicate Thursday's solar flare, and now confirmed CME which followed, has hit the Earth's magnetic field. In turn, this interaction will cause the magnetic field to shift. When this occurs, a shift in the jet stream will follow. (see equation).

Sunspots => Solar Flares => Magnetic Field Shift => Shifting Ocean and Jet Stream Currents => Extreme Weather and Human Disruption (Mitch Battros)

Now here is where it could get pretty nasty ... I believe it is quite possible we will witness the effects of charged particles emitted from the Sun (solar flares and CME), hitting Earth's magnetic field. As charged particles hit Earth's magnetic field, our field goes into an immediate defensive posture, wrapping itself around the Earth like a 'cocoon.'

See depiction: http://www.earthchangestv.net/images/sunearth_01G.gif. It is when this natural phenomenon occurs, we may observe Hurricane Dennis strengthen to a possible Category 4 with sustained winds of 155 mph.

When this Sun-Earth causal connection unfolds, it drives the jet stream down towards lower latitudes. This in turn drives ocean currents. Depending on where the brunt of the geomagnetic storm influence hits, there could potentially be a devastating surge on Hurricane Dennis, driving the winds to a possible Category 4.

As I immediately could see this new formula unfolding right in front of our eyes, I instructed everyone via the ECTV newsletter to:
1. Keep your eye on the Kp Index: http://www.sec.noaa.gov/rt_plots/kp_3d.html
2. Today's new M-Class Flare: http://www.sec.noaa.gov/rt_plots/xray_5m.html
3. Hurricane Dennis: http://www.nhc.noaa.gov/

Speaking in terms of research, this could be a measured outcome study for the scientific community to view in 'real time.' There could be many variables for this event to 'not happen.' However, if this scenario does hold true, we may have just witnessed the birth to a new use of 'space weather' to help local forecasters apply the Sun-Earth formula in daily weather forecast.

A spectacular demonstration of the importance and sometimes devastating effect of the Sun's power and immediate consequences on man and Earth occurred in Quebec, Canada in March 1989, which is where we begin.

Chapter 1

The Month the Lights
Went Out in Quebec

What is known as the 'solar dynamo' is responsible for the 11-year solar cycle (also called the 22-year solar cycle, the sunspot cycle, magnetic cycle). No matter how you view the Sun, it exhibits significant changes over the 11-year solar cycle. All types of solar energy output are modulated by this cycle. However, the Sun can appear dramatically different over much shorter timescales than 11 years; some phenomena can vary drastically in minutes. It is also true that the Sun can produce extended cycles which go far beyond the known 11- and 22-year predictions. These are what I call "mega-cycles" (see Chapter 4 for more on this topic).

Giant sunspots appear, some growing as large or larger than the planet Jupiter, or maybe 15 Earth diameters across. Sunspots cause solar flares and, usually, the biggest flares come from the biggest spots. The effects on Earth are many and varied: Radio blackouts disrupt communications; solar winds carry protons that penetrate Earth's upper atmosphere, exposing astronauts and high-altitude air travelers to radiation doses equal to a chest X-ray; auroras appear all over the world, as far south as Florida.

There are three ranks of solar flares according to their x-ray power output: C-flares are the weakest. M-flares are medium, and X-flares are the most powerful. Each category has subdivisions: X1, X2, X3 and so on, with a typical X-flare registering X1 or X2. On November 4, 2003, sunspot 486 unleashed an X45 flare—the most powerful ever recorded (see photograph). Fortunately, it exploded as it had just slipped behind the western limb of the Sun, saving Earth from a direct or partial hit. Thank goodness for us, this record-breaking solar flare blasted harmlessly out into space, but in March 1989, planet Earth was not so lucky.

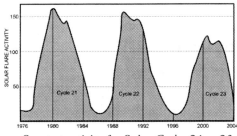

Sunspot activity for Solar Cycles 21 – 23

An X-class Flare

Photo: NASA

Solar flares start as flows in the endlessly churning seas of hydrogen plasma that make up the Sun and most die down uneventfully, but every 11 years, the flows become torrents, drawing more and more matter into them and rapidly becoming self-sustaining. Being charged particles, they are electric currents and generate powerful magnetic fields whose lines of force arc upwards for millions of miles, creating conductive pathways for plasma to escape the Sun's interior.

Around March 11, 1989, as Cycle 22 was getting underway a flare erupted (see plot of solar flare activity during the last three solar cycles). Scientists saw it 8 minutes later, but the full impact was still two days away, and this one was headed straight towards where our planet would be by then. Meanwhile, the residents of Quebec were still trying to get back to normal following the worst ice-storm in Canada's history.

The Great Quebec Ice Storm of the Century

It began in January 1989, when a large, persistent low-pressure front over Texas began to drift north. Many meteorologists blamed it on El Niño, a topic we discuss in a later chapter. On Monday, January 5, people were dragging themselves back to school and work after the Christmas and New Years' holidays. First came the drizzle, then a ¼ inch of rain. Below freezing temperatures quickly transformed the rain to a glass-like ice that coated everything it touched. Soon, roads became treacherous, and the first two victims were a 36-year-old Toronto man and his 61-year-old mother, ironically driving to a funeral. By dawn Tuesday, ¾ inch of rain had fallen, coating everything with about one inch of ice. Normally, storms such as this blow out to sea quickly, but a huge high-pressure dome to the west blocked the usual west-east flow, allowing this one to stall over the area for four days.

Yes, it was beautiful. Crystallized trees and growing layers of icicles hanging from gutters looked straight off a Christmas card, but no one realized the cost that would be exacted as layer upon layer of ice had tree branches and power lines groaning under the weight. Another ½ inch of rain Tuesday added another inch of ice, so by Wednesday, January 7, tree branches began to snap off like toothpicks, bringing down power lines and crushing cars, houses and people alike.

Power poles followed, since they are designed to handle a two-inch layer of ice on the lines, which was reached on Wednesday. Ultimately, there would be up to a whopping seven inches on everything. That bitterly cold night, people used fireplaces, talked by candlelight and went to bed under many extra blankets, hoping that it would soon be over. However, they were kept awake by the constant explosions as large branches and entire trees crashed to the frigid ground.

Downed lines began to black out ever-larger areas of Eastern Ontario and Western Quebec, and the affected areas quickly linked up to form a huge swathes of both provinces. Pretty soon, the Emergency Measures Unit office at Ottawa-Carleton's municipal headquarters began to buzz. This was turning out to be no ordinary winter storm. Representatives from regional and local government, hospitals, public health, police, ambulance, fire and Red Cross assembled to closely monitor what was fast becoming a runaway situation. "No one predicted something of this magnitude," said Merv Beckstead, Ottawa-Carleton's chief administrative officer.

Stores had long since run out of heaters, fuel and generators, and with no respite in sight, Hydro management was forecasting system-wide disruption of up to two weeks. In hindsight, that would prove hopelessly optimistic. By the early hours of Thursday, January 8, the area of devastation was still widening, and the decision was taken to declare a state of emergency. This allowed regional government to apply for federal and provincial financial aid, and to call for military assistance. It also warned residents that the situation was serious and allowed for an 'Emergency Vehicles Only' curfew on the roads—the first time this had ever been done in the history of a region that was used to bad weather.

Continued rain and sub-freezing temperatures prolonged the misery, and Hydro workers were in a bind, because within hours of being replaced, a line would break again under the weight of new ice.

The story of the Hogan family was typical. Sue Hogan awoke early in the morning and smelled smoke. Her husband Dave went downstairs to check on the wood and oil furnace they had been using for backup heat during the blackout. It was ablaze, so he hollered up the stairs for everyone to get out. Their sons, Ben, 8, Adam, 13, and Gord, 15, groggily threw on some clothes and fled outside. The fire department could do nothing, and the Hogans watched as their home went up in flames. Sadly, they lost their beloved pet beagle but felt fortunate the family of five had escaped unhurt. Neighbors immediately responded with offers of lodging, food and clothing, and Sue was amazed that the community was so behind them. Such displays of caring would be repeated all across Eastern Canada as random acts of kindness broke out everywhere.

For example, nine-month pregnant Tasha Geymonat and her partner Jody McKellar of Edwards were headed for Riverside Hospital at 7:32 a.m., but the icy roads were simply too dangerous to continue, even for their Chevy Blazer. They called the paramedics, and Marc Lafleur and Bill Magladry helped deliver a healthy 8 lb. 4 oz baby boy in the back of the SUV. Such acts of heroism became commonplace as shops, banks, schools, public transport and everything else without backup generators shut down.

Weeks and weeks living in an emergency shelter can fray anyone's nerves, so area hotels slashed their rates. Cell phone companies offered free service, and restaurants offered free meals to emergency workers, as they did in New York following September 11. One grateful resident said, "A country is much more than its weather. It's the people." They were finding out what it meant to be Canadian.

Early Friday morning, the army arrived and brought a sense of security to the devastated area. Dressed in green fatigues, they continued to roll in and by 6 p.m., a solid base of soldiers had swelled to thousands, both regulars and reservists. They cleared debris blocking roads, provided emergency medical assistance, helped utility workers to restore power, set up fuel and food dumps, evacuated residents and went door-to-door making sure people were safe. For example, they found a mother with two young children who all had the flu. They'd lost all their food in the freezer, and were shivering cold and hungry. Close to pneumonia and possible death, they were rescued from their own home, which had become a freezing prison. Once in a warm shelter, lots of hot chicken soup helped them begin their recovery.

Sadly, the Army also had to deal with looters. The supplies pouring in from across the nation and the U.S. presented a tempting target, especially in-demand items such as portable generators, dozens of which were stolen. Some generators may have been liberated out of genuine need, but most found their way onto the black market for a profit. Others price-gouged on essentials such as batteries, flashlights and gas. And many posed as Red Cross volunteers allegedly collecting for money to run the shelters. To prevent looting, police dropped all but essential services, but many residents took matters into their own hands, standing guard over their homes with loaded rifles.

Among the hardest hit were the thousands of dairy farmers, because when cows aren't milked regularly, they become vulnerable to mastitis, an infection of the udder. And due to transport problems, they had to dump millions of gallons of milk, leading to massive financial losses of \$5 – \$6 million. Government officials worked hard to get them generators for their mechanized milking systems, but breakdowns were common since the equipment had been mothballed for so long. The farmers got little sleep as they focused on the health of their herds, and on damage to property and equipment. And some farmers lost cows to electrocution due to downed power lines.

Utility workers faced an overwhelming task. In Ontario alone, freezing rain took down about 5,000 poles in rural areas, which meant that about 100,000 households, about 300,000 people, were in the dark. Rural Quebec and urban areas were even harder hit, bringing the total to 4 million people. People were torn between staying in their icebox homes to protect against looters and going to shelters, leaving pets behind to fend for themselves. But in the end, plummeting temperatures forced the issue. The disruption hit the elderly particularly hard, plunging many into despair, which volunteers worked hard to dispel. The elderly were also more prone to hypothermia, carbon monoxide poisoning, motor vehicle accidents, slips and falls on the ice leading to broken hips and head injuries. Many died from heart attacks while clearing ice and trees or shoveling snow, from failed oxygen equipment, and from weather-related traffic accidents.

On Monday, January 12, a week after the first drizzle, the temperature finally climbed above freezing, and the worst was over. But utility workers faced months of hard work to rebuild an infrastructure that had taken decades to build. In the end, 470 major transmission towers (at $500,000 each) and 37,000 wooden utility poles had been brought down by weight of the ice. Many Quebeçois were without power a month later.

Eventually, the losses due to the ice storm would amount to $1.5 billion for Ontario and Quebec. Most insurance claims were for automobile damage due to accidents and falling trees, homes damaged by falling trees, fire and flooding, business losses due to closures, and farm losses, due to livestock death and equipment damages. A huge loser, of course, was Hydro-Quebec itself, which had to restore the infrastructure, against the backdrop of lost revenue amounting to millions, coupled with the need to buy more expensive electricity from neighboring utilities.

However, things were just getting back to normal in mid-March when Mother Nature's next whammy hit the area.

The Great Magnetic Storm of Cycle 22

Astronomers had been tracking 'Active Region 5395' on the Sun when, on March 10, 1989, it suddenly belched out a huge cloud of super-hot plasma. Three days later, residents in higher latitudes enjoyed a magnificent Northern Lights display. Even people in Florida got to enjoy the show that had never been seen so far south, and went to bed on the night of March 12, awed by the display.

At 2:44 a.m. the next morning, stray electrical currents generated by a powerful magnetic field surged through the electrical circuits of the Hydro-Quebec control center. Giant capacitors along the 735kV lines that had been designed to absorb the 10 kV spikes tried and regulate the current that ran 115% above normal, but were over-whelmed. To prevent damage, automatic breakers tripped and took them off-line. These had been the primary line of defense, so the entire grid was now vulnerable, and immediately things rapidly fell apart. All five lines into Montréal tripped, and a surge in load tripped the supply lines from the 9,450 MW generators at La Grande. This resulted in a sudden drop in frequency, and automatic load-shedding kicked in, but compensators could not recover from the loss of about half the system's generating capacity. As each piece went off-line, the load was offloaded onto other generating plants, which also tripped out. Within 20 seconds, the entire Quebec power grid collapsed, too quick for human operators to react. Of course, generators were still spinning, ready to crank out their 21,500 MW, but they were all dis-connected from those who badly needed electrical power on a frigid Canadian morning. Their current was going nowhere ... and people shivered.

Sorting out the mess took nine hours, while most of Quebec was in darkness. This silent disaster disrupted the lives of six million people, yet somehow the 50 million people on the Eastern Seaboard of the U.S. remained unaffected thanks to some capacitors on the Allegheny Power Network that did their job. Long term effects were costly, as the huge oil-cooled transformers that had burned up cost millions to replace, which took months. Meanwhile Hydro-Quebec had to reroute power, and, as it had done two months earlier, and purchase more expensive fossil fuel power from other companies.

How Does It Happen?

The vulnerability of a power system to geomagnetic disturbances stems from the widespread nature of the event. Power systems can easily handle local problems, such as lighting strikes or equipment failures, but because modern power grids are interconnected, a planet-wide phenomenon is amplified across thousands of miles, as a small volt-age-per-mile spike becomes a 'killer-volt' effect.

Magnetic field variations that occur during a geomagnetic distur-bance create slowly varying Geomagnetic Induced Current (GIC) in long-distance power lines. These slow DC effects are superimposed on the 60 Hz AC that is being transmitted through the lines.

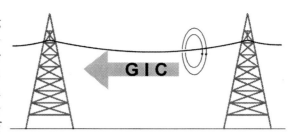

GIC flowing through voltage step-down transformer windings produces extra magnetic flux in the coils, possibly saturating the core of the transformer. This results in a spiky AC waveform with increased harmonic levels that can cause relays and other equipment on the system to malfunction, leading to progressive trip-outs of individual lines, and ultimately to complete collapse of the whole system.

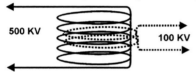

This simplified graphic reveals why we need transformers on power lines. Transmission is more efficient (lower line loss) at high voltages, much like the high pressure in a fireman's hose can move more water, faster than your garden hose. Several transformers step down the voltage from 500 kV to the 120 V in your house. In the example, if the solid coil had, say 10 turns and the dotted coil had two turns, the voltage would be stepped down by a factor of five. To help the current be induced magnetically from one set of coils to the other, the coils are wound around a large magnetic core. The magnetic flux in the core creates heat, which is dissipated by oil-cooling and large cooling fins on the outside of the transformer. The large thermal mass of a transformer core means a negligible change in core temperature but localized hot spots can damage the more vulnerable transformer coil windings. GIC can burn out the heavy-duty coils, because saturation of the transformer core produces extra eddy currents, which generates extra heat in the transformer.

The costs to power system operators involve not only replacing damaged equipment but also the loss of revenue from the sale of power. The March 13 Quebec blackout cost over $13 million, with damaged equipment accounting for about half. For example, the transformer at the Salem, NJ, nuclear generating station that burnt out cost several million dollars to replace. Normally, delivery time for such specialized equipment is about a year, but a replacement was available, so delivery and installation took only 6 weeks. Even so, the disruption meant the purchase of replacement power from neighboring utilities at a cost of about $17 million—far more than the cost of the transformer. So not only are we talking about Mother Nature causing major disruption to our lives, we're also talking about enormous costs ... all because the Sun hiccups occasionally.

All told, Cycle 22 would spawn five great magnetic storms that impacted our planet—February 1986, March 1989, March 1991, November 1991 and May 1992. Less severe storms also occurred in September 1989, March 1991 and October 1991, but they were still strong enough to hinder utility operations. These events caused the industry to become more aware of the destruction that geomagnetic storms can wreak on an unprepared infrastructure. They also led to calls for better warning, to allow power companies to reduce system loads, delay maintenance, and ground sensitive equipment to protect the network. Since such events are unstoppable, such protection is the best (and probably the only) way to prevent costly and dangerous blackouts due to GIC.

Modern power systems are interconnected in such a way that they are increasingly vulnerable due to advances in technology. When a solar storm damages one system, systems connected to it can experience failure as well, so preventative measures have been implemented to avoid events such as the 1989 Quebec blackout. For example, Hydro-Quebec spent over $1.2 billion installing additional transmission line capacitors that trap GIC flow in order to prevent it from causing damage to the system. Hydro-Quebec also installed monitoring equipment to detect voltage fluctuations and immediately notify operators so that they can shed load to other parts of the network and disconnect the links between power grids, thus preventing cascade failure.

Utilities are also relying more on space weather forecasting to help remain operational during geomagnetic storms. Once they receive advance warning of a geomagnetic storm, operators can implement 'safe-mode' protocols. Learning the lessons cost them billions, but space weather is no longer dismissed as some whacky fringe science; it is now seen as 'being aware of the larger environment in which we live.'

The prediction and advance warning of geomagnetic storms rests on numerous technologies developed to monitor and gather data. One of the most reliable forecasting tools is NASA's Solar and Heliospheric Observatory (SOHO), launched in December 1995 to provide a detailed picture of the Sun's magnetic structure. This satellite provides x-ray images of large solar eruptions, and is a valuable tool for space weather forecasting, providing two to three days advanced warning.

NASA's Advanced Composition Explorer (ACE) satellite is another forecasting tool, positioned about one million miles from Earth. It monitors the content of the solar wind, and provides one-hour advanced warnings of space weather disruption. In November 2001, ACE reported on two solar energetic particle (SEP) events that turned out to be the largest of Cycle 23.

So what is actually going on with that huge ball of burning hydrogen 93 million miles away, whose power output *each second* is more than mankind has consumed in its entire history? And how can that affect us so far away? This is the story we pick up in the next chapter.

Chapter 2

What *Is* the Sun-Earth Connection?

On November 25, 2000, the *Sydney Morning Herald* carried the headline:

Strong solar storms to wreak havoc in US

The article began: "Across the United States this weekend, fire alarms and anti-theft devices may be triggered for no reason, pictures on television screens may flicker and fade to black, and entire communities could be plunged into sudden darkness."

The article reported on the rash of major geomagnetic storms expected to strike beginning that day and lasting for several days. Officials of the U.S. government's Space Environment Center announced that the solar radiation and geomagnetic storms would be category G3, on a scale of G1 (minor) to G5 (extreme). (The scale is described below.) They also predicted that "power system voltage corrections may be required, false alarms may be triggered on some protection devices, surface charging may occur on satellite components, drag may increase on low-Earth-orbit satellites, and corrections may be needed for orientation problems."

The list of possible calamities didn't end there, however. "Power grid failures are more likely at higher latitudes in both hemispheres, and the geomagnetic storms will continue for at least several days, affecting the whole planet. This is a global event, but we won't know the magnitude until it actually starts," a spokesman stressed. "A flare on the surface of the Sun on Thursday has spawned a large cloud of plasma, which is heading towards the Earth. From its appearance, we have been able to determine that it *is* Earth-directed and will be a major event. We expect the magnitude of the storms to reach six or seven on a scale of nine. As a result, orbiting satellites may experience 'orientation problems.' This may affect some communications, but television networks and cellular phones should be working normally. Any interruptions should be brief. Most vulnerable are power grids, which may be worst-equipped to withstand the geomagnetic onslaught from space. In 1989, most of the power grid in the Canadian province of Quebec went down for an extended period of time due to such a storm.

"On the bright side, night-time skywatchers in areas far beyond the Arctic could be treated to a spectacle they have never seen before. The Aurora Borealis could be seen in North America as far south as Oregon and Illinois. Most of Europe will be able to see it too."

So what's going on? This chapter explores the workings of the Sun, and how this affects our planet, so far away in one sense, yet in the Sun's backyard astronomically speaking. First we look at the 'nuts-and-bolts' of solar mechanics, and later, at what today's leading experts are thinking and saying.

Section 1: How the Solar System Works

Let's start with a few facts about this pretty ordinary stellar body we call the Sun:

- *Average distance from Earth:* 93 million miles, or 8 light-minutes
- *Radius:* 418,000 miles, diameter 836,000 miles, or 106 Earth diameters
- *Mass:* 2 x 10^{27} tons (that's 2 followed by 27 zeros), or 330,000 Earth masses
- *Makeup:* 74 percent hydrogen, 25 percent helium, 1 percent other elements

- *Average temperature:* 5,800 °K at the surface, 15.5 million °K at the core
- *Average density:* 1.41 grams per cm³ (density of water is 1.00)
- *Rotational period:* 25 days at the equator, 35 days at the poles
- *Distance from center of Milky Way:* 25,000 light-years
- *Orbital speed and period:* 138 miles per second and 200 million years.

Now we know its vital statistics, let's get to know how it works. The Sun warms our planet and provides the light that is absolutely essential for life on Earth via the plant process of photosynthesis. Classified as a G2-type star based on its temperature and the wavelengths in its light emission spectrum, it's an 'average' star, one of billions making up our galaxy.

It came into being over 4.5 billion years ago, and will continue to burn for many billion more. Even though it's mainly just gas—mostly hydrogen and helium—its huge mass means it has enormous gravity, enough to keep all the gaseous atoms together and hold even the most distant planet in its orbit, perfectly balancing the centrifugal force pulling it away.

In the beginning, the solar system was more of a huge disk of space matter, but then, according to the laws of physics, 'clumps' developed, which slowly formed into the planets we know today.

Sun's Interior

Far from being just an amorphous ball of gases, however, the Sun has a well-defined internal structure, made up of three major zones:

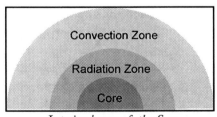

Interior layers of the Sun

- *Core*, from the center and out to 25 percent of the radius. Unimaginable gravitational forces pull the mass inward and create an intense pressure sufficient to force hydrogen atoms to fuse into a helium atom in a nuclear fusion reaction that generates enormous energy in the form of photons.
- *Radiation Zone*, extends 55 percent of the radius from the core. Here, the photons carry the energy from the core outward.

The journey takes thousands of years, however, because the photons move by hopping from one gas molecule to another, with about 10^{25} absorptions and re-emissions.

- *Convection Zone*, extends the final 30 percent of the Sun's radius to the surface. Here, huge convection currents carry the energy outward in massive rising movements of hot gas, that cool and fall back towards the core. Because of the huge distances involved, photons still take between 100,000 and 200,000 years to reach the surface.

Sun's Atmosphere

Above the surface is an atmosphere, also consisting of three parts:

- *Photosphere*, the region we see from Earth. About 200 miles deep, its average temperature is about 5,800 °K. It appears bubbly, like the surface of a simmering pot of soup, as convection currents bubble to the surface, only these bubbles can be 600 miles across.

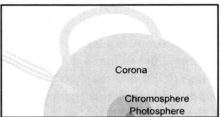

The Layers of the Sun's Atmosphere

- *Chromosphere*, about 1,200 miles deep. The temperature is much greater than the photosphere, rising to about 10,000 °K, probably heated by convection within the photosphere that is constantly pushing upward several thousand miles.

- *Corona*, the extremely hot outermost layer that extends several million miles outward into space, which we see during a solar eclipse. No one knows why, but the temperature of the corona is about 2 million °K, possibly due to the effect of the Sun's magnetic field. The corona exhibits bright hotspots, and darker cold areas called *coronal holes*. These appear as large, dark areas when viewed in x-ray wavelengths, and are caused by unipolar magnetic fields on the Sun's surface. They can last for years, with magnetic field lines extending far out into the solar system. As open field lines, they allow a continuous outflow of high-velocity solar wind.

Sunspots, Prominences, Flares and CMEs

Sunspots

From time to time, darker, cool areas called sunspots appear on the photosphere, always pairs, with an intense magnetic field, about 5,000 times greater than the Earth's, whose lines of force leave one sunspot, arc up into space and re-enter through the other spot. The magnetic field results from rivers of gases in the Sun's interior that behave like electric currents, hence generating strong magnetic fields. Sunspot activity follows an 11-year cycle, probably because the equator rotates more quickly than the poles, magnetic field lines in the interior become twisted. The twisted field lines break through the surface, forming sunspot pairs. Eventually, the field collapses and sunspot activity decreases. Then the cycle starts again. (See below.)

Prominences and CMEs

Occasionally, a cloud of plasma will rise up from the chromosphere and follow the magnetic lines from sunspot pairs, arcing into space (see photos). They can last for months and can reach 30,000 miles or more above the surface. Sometimes, they erupt and eject millions of tons of plasma out through the corona into space at several hundred

SIZE OF EARTH

Photo: NASA / SOHO

This SOHO image shows a prominence on July 24, 1999 that was particularly large and looping, extending over 35 Earths out from the Sun.

miles per second. Such eruptions are called Coronal Mass Ejections (see below).

Solar Flares

Sometimes a sunspot group will vent a violent, temporary explosion, probably due to a sudden magnetic field disturbance. This releases electrons, visible light, UV light, radio frequency energy, and gamma and X-rays, the energy being comparable to up to 40 billion Hiroshima-size atomic bombs.

Coronal Mass Ejection (CME)

On March 9, 2000, a spectacular CME lifted off, as shown in this UV light SOHO photograph, probably due to the twisting of the Sun's magnetic fields. (In comparison, the Earth would be about the size of a pinhead.) From the surface to the top of the prominence is almost two million miles. When this bubble broke away from the surface, it became a CME. Fortunately, this one did not interact with Earth.

CMEs occur when plasma in the corona, which is structured along an arching magnetic field, suddenly breaks away and is violently released. A large CME can contain up to a billion tons of matter that can be accelerated to several million miles per hour in a spectacular explosion. Plasma and other solar material streaks out through the interplanetary medium, impacting anything in its path.

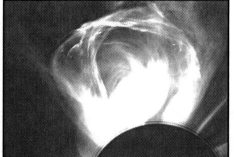

A Coronal Mass Ejection (CME)

Photo: NASA / SOHO

CMEs are sometimes associated with flares but usually occur independently. We don't really know why they happen, but they can occur at any time during the solar cycle. However, they are more frequent as solar activity rises and peak around Solar Maximum. They are propelled outward at speeds of up to 1,000 miles per second, often overtaking the background solar wind. In this case, they compress the solar wind and create a shock wave that can trigger a major geomagnetic storm on Earth. The effects depend on the CME speed, the strength of its magnetic field, and the angle at which it impacts Earth's magnetic field.

The Sun's Magnetic Field

The structure of the Sun's magnetic field changes dramatically during the 11-year cycle. Scientists theorize that during the lull, the lines of magnetic force run north and south between the magnetic poles in an orderly field. However, as the Sun rotates, the Convection Zone at the equator spins faster than it does at the poles. Beneath the Convection

Zone, the Radiation Zone spins as a sold mass. The different ways that these two zones move causes the Sun's magnetic field to stretch at the equator.

As the solar cycle continues, these lines of magnetic force continue to stretch around the equator until unpredictable activity occurs—sunspots form and solar flares eject powerful bursts of energy out into the Solar System. Prominences also erupt from the surface, and huge CMEs careen out into space. Following this Solar Maximum, the magnetic field collapses, activity subsides, and the Sun re-

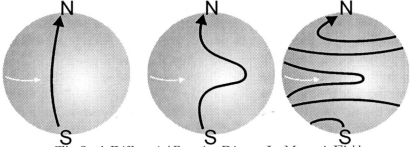

The Sun's Differential Rotation Distorts Its Magnetic Field

turns to the Solar Minimum. Then the cycle begins again. The last Solar Maximum occurred around 2000, and the next is due around 2010.

From Sun to Earth
Once considered a perfect vacuum, the interplanetary medium is actually a turbulent, chaotic region ruled by the solar wind, which flows at between 600,000 and 2,000,000 miles per hour, depending on the conditions on the Sun. Its effect is evident in the tails of comets, which always point away from the Sun.

The solar wind flows harmlessly around most planets, but interacts with those having a magnetic field by flattening the magnetic field lines on the sunward side and stretching them out on the downwind side. This distorts the magnetosphere, within which lies the ionosphere, a layer of upper atmosphere containing ions, or free electrons, released by solar x-rays and UV light. The solar wind varies over periods as short as seconds, so the ionization interface of about 10 Earth radii in the direction of the Sun, which separates interplanetary space from

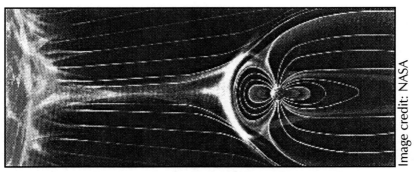

Distortion Impact of a CME on the Earth's Magnetosphere

the magnetosphere, is very dynamic, resulting in the 'wavy blanket' appearance of auroras. As the magnetosphere extracts energy from the solar wind, internal processes produce geomagnetic storms. The solar wind shock wave can push the magnetopause inward by as much as four Earth radii, from its usual 10 radii to six. This SOHO image shows the Sun's magnetic field releasing plasma towards the Earth, and how the solar wind shapes the Earth's magnetosphere. The magnetic cloud of plasma can be 30 million miles wide by the time it reaches Earth.

Geomagnetic Storms

When the solar blast and its associated magnetic field reaches Earth's magnetosphere, it causes a geomagnetic storm that can last as long as two days. Highly energized charged particles in the plasma reach deep into the magnetosphere, producing the familiar aurora. During a geomagnetic storm, a portion of the solar wind's energy is transferred to the magnetosphere, causing Earth's magnetic field to change rapidly in direction and intensity, and energize whatever lies within it. Before going into more detail, we need to know more about the Earth's atmosphere.

Earth's Atmosphere

The Earth is surrounded by a blanket of air that reaches over 350 miles into space. In addition to providing the air we breathe, this is essential to life on this planet, since it absorbs the energy from the Sun, recycles water and other chemicals, buffers against solar electrical and magnetic forces, and protects us from the high-energy radiation and frigid vacuum of space.

Four distinct layers have been identified, separated by buffer zones about 2 miles (10,000 feet) deep:

- *Troposphere*, from the surface to about 10 miles, where the temperature drops to about -52 °C.
- *Stratosphere*, up to about 30 miles. Dry and less dense, temperatures increase to 0 °C due to the absorption of UV from the Sun by the ozone layer.
- *Mesosphere*, extending to about 50 miles. The temperatures fall as low as -100 °C despite absorbing energy from the Sun.

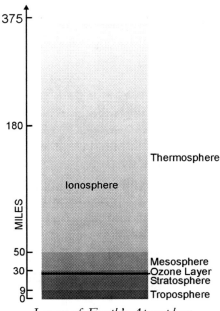

Layers of Earth's Atmosphere

- *Thermosphere*, going up to about 375 miles. Due to solar energy absorption, temperatures can climb to almost 2,000 °C. Within this layer is a band between 50 and 180 miles called the ionosphere, consisting of charged particles.

The Ozone Layer, Our Protector

Ultra-violet light is the part of the electromagnetic spectrum, with wavelengths between 280 and 400 nanometers (billionths of a meter), and is not normally visible. The longer wavelengths (315 – 400 nm) are termed UV-A, and are relatively benign. However, the shorter wavelengths (280 – 315 nm) are far more damaging, causing skin cancer, DNA damage and harm to plants. The ozone layer in the upper stratosphere is a natural shield against UV-B, but many human-developed compounds, especially CFCs, are causing the layer to break down, particularly over the South Pole.

During high proton emissions, the increased number of energized particles entering Earth's middle atmosphere erodes the ozone layer and depletes atmospheric ozone, which allows more UV-B to reach the surface. For example, in 1982, a massive proton event reduced ozone density to 30 percent of normal. Fortunately, it was only temporary.

This is no longer an academic discussion topic; already residents of the southern-most tip of South America cannot leave their skin exposed to sunlight for more than a few minutes without running a high risk of skin cancer. (We return to this topic in a later chapter.)

Solar Influences

As Earth's orbit and the path of a solar flare of CME intersect, we experience many disruptions to radio communication, navigational systems, satellites, electrical transmission, climate and even our own bodies.

Radio Communication
Short-wave radio communication systems reflect radio signals off the ionosphere for long-distance transmission, and storms in the ionosphere can cause it to absorb some radio frequencies. Solar activity frequently disrupts ground-to-air (including air-traffic control), ship-to-shore, and ham radio. It can also impact military detection and early-warning systems such as over-the-horizon radar, and submarine detection and locating systems.

Navigation
Systems such as LORAN and OMEGA use transmitters located around the world emitting very low frequency (VLF) signals that allow a receiver to determine its position. Solar events and geomagnetic storms can cause the system to give position information that is off by several miles. GPS signals are less prone, but are still affected by sudden variations in the density of the ionosphere.

Satellites
Geomagnetic storms and increased solar UV emission heat the thermosphere, causing it to expand. As the heated air rises, satellites orbit-

ing up to about 700 miles experience increased drag, causing them to slow down and lose altitude. They must then be boosted back into orbit or they will continue to fall and burn up in more dense atmosphere. For example, during the great geomagnetic storm of March 1989, four navigational satellites belonging to the U.S. Navy had to be taken out of service for a week, and higher-than-expected solar activity caused Skylab to re-enter Earth's atmosphere prematurely.

Static charges can also build in satellite and spacecraft circuitry, resulting in electrical arcs between components, possibly burning them out.

Geological Exploration

Many geologists use the Earth's magnetic field to analyze subterranean rock structures in the search for oil, gas, water and mineral deposits, and geomagnetic storms can disrupt their delicate instruments. Other techniques, however, actually depend on geomagnetic storm anomalies to reveal what's beneath the surface.

Electrical Transmission

Moving a conductor through a magnetic field, or moving a magnetic field across a conductor both induce an electric current in the conductor. Geomagnetic storms induce slowly varying direct current that is often lethal to electrical transmission equipment. Geomagnetic storm warnings allow power companies to go into 'safe-mode' and minimize damage and power outages.

Pipelines

Rapidly fluctuating geomagnetic fields can induce currents in pipelines constructed of conducting material. These cause flow meters to give erroneous information, and dramatically increase corrosion. In Russia, for example, a corroded gasoline pipeline began leaking and the resulting explosion destroyed a village, with huge loss of life.

Climate

The Sun's radiation drives circulation within our atmosphere. Over an 11-year cycle, output of the Sun varies by 0.2 – 0.5 percent, which is enough to cause climate changes on Earth. Tree-ring records also confirm the impact on plant growth. Solar activity has been fairly regular over the last 300 years, but during the 17th and 18th centuries, sunspot activity was minimal, triggering a mini-ice age in northern latitudes.

Another Sun-Earth link currently under study concerns stratospheric winds near the equator that blow in different directions depending on where we are in a solar cycle.

Bio-Hazards

Intense solar flares release super-high-energy particles that can be lethal to astronauts in space, who are not protected by the atmosphere. High-energy particles can lead to long term chromosome damage and possibly cancer in living cells, and large doses can be instantly fatal. Solar protons with energies greater than 30 MeV are also particularly hazardous.

Scientists are increasingly discovering links between magnetism and the health and well-being of living beings. Pulsed magnetic fields are widely used to treat just about every medical condition outside the U.S., where large pharmaceutical companies do not have a stranglehold on 'acceptable' healthcare modalities, i.e., can be patented. In those countries, extensive literature documents the evidence of how changes in the ambient magnetic field affect biological systems. In fact, humans have long worn therapeutic magnets, beginning with Cleopatra who enjoyed their rejuvenation properties. Researchers have also documented the impact that fluctuations in the geomagnetic field have on human biology.

All homing pigeon racers know that geomagnetic storms degrade their birds' navigational abilities and lament the losses when only a fraction of their birds return home. So nowadays, they routinely consult geomagnetic alerts when scheduling races.

Migratory animals such as dolphins and whales have an internal compass composed of magnetite wrapped in bundles of nerve cells that allows them to 'see' lines of force. However, it is not known whether magnetic variations alone are responsible for mass beachings, or whether undersea acoustic tests conducted by the U.S. Navy are also disrupting the animals' natural SONAR faculties.

Section 2: What the Experts Are Saying

On March 16, 2000, at the height of cycle 23, I wrote an ECTV column titled, *Mainstream Scientists Confirm Climate Change Due to Sun.* I reported on the findings of two highly respected scientists, solar physicists Willie Soon and Sallie Baliunas of the Harvard-Smithsonian Center for Astrophysics, who wrote that the cause of our climate change is due to *the Sun and solar cycles.* Apparently, they found a clear drop in the temperature of Earth's atmosphere after the Sun's magnetic field activity is most intense, because at this point in the solar weather cycle, magnetic activity drops off dramatically, and the Sun's coronal holes enlarge significantly.

I found this turn of events very encouraging. If it can happen in the field of solar weather, it can happen in the field of asteroids, comets, and why not an admission to life on other planets.

On October 20, I followed up with another column titled *NASA Shifts Theory from Humans to Sun* about NASA's sudden about-face regarding the cause of our extreme and record-breaking weather. NASA issued a report suggesting humans may have very little to do with what many call the 'greenhouse effect.' Their report opened with: "Is human activity warming the Earth or do recent signs of climate change signal natural variations?" Well, well, I thought. Once again it is good to see the fundamentalists finally catch on. When a paradigm such as this one shifts, it will always come with those in power kicking and screaming. The new understanding is similar to my equation:
Sunspots => Solar Flares => Magnetic Shift => Shifting Ocean and Jet Stream Currents => Extreme Weather

Even though I published my famous equation in July 1999, NASA finally got round to saying, "Studies by paleoclimatologists reveal that natural variability caused by changes in the Sun and volcanic eruptions can largely explain deviations in global temperatures. The Earth has gone through warming periods before without human influence."

The article also suggested: "It's not only solar events that initiate weather flux, but it is also us humans." I have absolutely no problem with this statement. I have made it several times myself. What I do challenge is the percentages. In my studies, I suggest the vast majority is related to solar activity with a much lower contribution (7% to 15%)

attributed to fossil fuel and other human pollutants. Still this is indeed a significant amount that we *do* have control over and we should maintain responsible stewardship.

I can't tell you how good it felt to be validated. But wait, there was more! NASA went on to state what I have been saying since I started ECTV in April 1995. All along, I have stated: "I believe all science is nothing more than subjective conjecture, based on any given facts. In other words, an opinion." The NASA article stated: "It may surprise many people that science—the *de facto* source of dependable knowledge about the natural world—cannot deliver an unqualified, unanimous answer about something as important as climate change."

The article concluded: "Because such conclusions are based on a scientist's professional judgment, (conjecture) disagreement is inevitable. There is enormous room for differences of opinion among equally competent scientists of good will. There are always people—and reasonable people—who fall on both sides of the argument. And there are reasons for that. So the best we can hope for is a consensus."

Is the Weather Getting More Extreme?

Let's look at some headlines from British newspapers at the peak of Cycle 23:
- 1999 was "the hottest since records began in Britain in 1659" (*Observer*)
- Autumn 1999 was "the sunniest Autumn since 1940" (*Western Mail*)
- Ireland had "the wettest September since records began in 1892" (*Daily Mirror*)
- January 1999 was "Britain's wettest month ever" (*People*)
- January 6, 1999: "London's warmest January day since records began 150 years ago"
- July 1998 was "the hottest month in the history of the world" (*Daily Mail*)
- 1997 was "the third warmest year since records began" (*Guardian*)

Elsewhere, we saw:
- 05/19/00—Central United States Hit by Violent Weather
- 05/19/00—Somalia Floods Leave 3,500 Homeless
- 05/19/00—Wild Weather Hits Northeast

- 05/20/00—At Least 10 Dead as Philippine Floodwaters Subside
- 05/20/00—Kuwait Temperature Hits Springtime Record 45 °C
- 05/21/00—Massive Floods Threaten East Timor's Critical Coffee Harvest
- 05/22/00—Heavy Rains, Floods Kill 11 in Colombia
- 05/23/00—Record Heat Blasts California.

Warmest, wildest, wettest, sunniest! Records being broken all around the world. What's going on? On October 22, 1999, Robert Hager reporting for *NBC Nightly News*, said, "The U.S. government says that the weather is getting rougher and more expensive. Already, La Niña has cost $21 billion worldwide and the system is forecast to last even longer. Scientists say weather extremes are the wave of the future.

"1999 has had its share of weather fluctuations. Record wet in North Carolina from floods has cost $6 billion so far. Before that, the record dry in the mid-Atlantic area cost $1.3 billion. Kevin Trenberth of the National Center for Atmospheric Research says to look for more of the same. 'The best estimate is the kinds of extremes we've been seeing in the last few years will be very much the wave of the future,' he said."

On July 21, 2000, I wrote an ECTV column titled *"New Sunspot Count of 402 Sets Record High,"* in which I warned readers to watch the next 48 hours for extreme weather all around the world, and for an increase of forest fires.

Remember, there is a compounding effect to earth changes. In other words, because of the already increased weather phenomena, the new and even stronger solar events enhance what is already expected to be "record breaking" events.

FEMA has already begun its mobilization procedures to address what they believe to be national crisis proportions over the next several months.

In addition to causing heat waves and droughts, solar events may also cause more moisture to evaporate into the air. So when it does rain, the rain may be heavier. Even snowstorms may be heavier, and all this affects people's lives. Ants Leetmaa, director of NOAA's Climate Prediction Center, describes the kind of headaches expected that winter in the north United States: "People should be prepared to pay more for fuel oil and energy. ... There'll probably be more airline delays, more storminess as you go through there. You're probably looking at more snow removal costs."

In 1999, Mt. Baker, Washington set a new record for the most snowfall ever measured in the United States in a single season, according to NOAA. The Mt. Baker Ski Area reported 1,140 inches (that's 95 feet) of snowfall for the 1998/99 season, breaking the previous record of 1,122 inches, set during the 1971/1972 season

The 1999 Record Snowfall Dwarfs the Mt. Baker, WA, Ranger Station

at the weather station on the slopes of Mt. Rainer, about 150 miles south of Mt. Baker. (Interestingly, the 1971/72 winter coincided with a Solar Minimum, so something else is going on besides solar activity.)

It's Not Just About Weather

In February 2001, Larry W., an ECTV contributing editor, wrote a column titled, ***"Volcanic Eruptions and Sunspots"*** in which he pointed out that there were 16 volcanic eruptions in 1998, 14 in 1999, and over 30 in 2000—double the volcanic eruptions from the previous year. Since 1995, sunspot numbers have steadily increased up to present date. Volcanic eruptions on Earth seem to be following sunspot numbers on the Sun. Larry asks, "Is there a connection or is this coincidence?"

A year later, on February 3, 2002, I penned a column titled, ***"Sunspots, Solar Flares, Earthquakes and Volcanoes"*** in which I reported that on Friday, February 1, the Sun exhibited a sunspot count of 256, which was 100 higher than the reported maximum expected for Cycle 23. A powerful X-Class flare had just been unleashed, and was partly headed towards Earth. As a direct result, the Earth experienced several volcanic eruptions, most notably Mt. Colima in Mexico.

The logs of www.volcanolive.com report that for the two weeks of February 1 – 15, 2002, the following volcanic and seismic activity occurred:

- Saturday, 2, Colima volcano (western México). Thousands warned to get ready to evacuate, as the volcano could erupt within the next 48 hours.
- Sunday 3, Turkey. Magnitude 6.2 earthquake kills 21 and injures 150.
- Monday 4, Colima volcano (western Mexico). Vented white plumes of smoke from the crater Sunday.
- Monday 4, Turkey. Earthquake aftershocks of up to 6.2 kill at least 35 people and injure more than 100.
- Wednesday 6, Colima erupts, spewing red-hot rocks, prompting evacuation.
- Thursday 7, Mt Etna (Sicily, Italy). Eruptions resume, venting smoke and gas.
- Sunday 10, Chikurachki Volcano (Kurile Islands, Russia). Begins spouting ash and smoke.
- Sunday 10, Mt Merapi volcano (central Java, Indonesia). Erupts, with 194 events of glowing lava avalanches.
- Sunday 10, Ijen volcano (Java, Indonesia) undergoes continuous seismic tremors, and shallow earthquakes.
- Tuesday 12, Fuego volcano (Guatemala). About 400 explosions per hour (up from 75), plus glowing lava flows.
- Wednesday 13, Mt Ruapehu volcano (North Island, New Zealand). Shows signs of increasing activity.
- Thursday 14, Fuego volcano (Guatemala). Increasing ash and steam emission, prompting evacuation warnings.

Coming so closely behind the massive flare, is this spike in activity coincidence? Many don't think so. The *Christian Science Monitor* recently ran an article by Alex Salkever that examined one of the great paradoxes about our planet that Albert Einstein said was probably the greatest unsolved mystery in science.

The Earth is believed to consist of a core just over 2,000 miles across (made up of a solid inner core and a liquid outer layer), the mantle (almost 2,000 miles thick), and the crust (about 25 miles thick).

The Earth's magnetic field stems from the flow of electrical current within the core, as the outer core rotates around the inner core. However, due the core's high temperature and conductivity, scientists cannot understand why it did not become electrically neutral about 20,000 years into the planet's history. Why is it still generating a magnetic field after 3 billion years? No one knows.

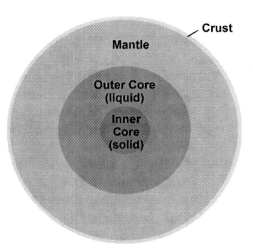

Structure of Earth's Interior

And why is the magnetic field concentrated at the poles rather than being evenly distributed? And why does it flip every so often? Scientists theorize that interior convection currents drive a 'dynamo effect' whereby a spinning conductor generates a magnetic field.

Until recently, scientists could not model the Earth's interior, but today's supercomputers allow for complex models that begin to explain what might be going on. The Glatzmaier-Roberts model indicates that the magnetic field waxes and wanes over several millennia, dropping to zero and flipping over. The implications of not having the magnetosphere to protect the planet are currently unknown, but without protection from solar winds, life would be more vulnerable to solar activity.

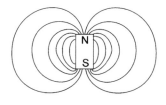

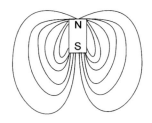

We saw earlier how a CME traveling faster than the solar wind creates a shock wave ahead of itself. More research is needed into the effect of that shock wave, and of the CME's intense magnetic field itself, on the Earth's magnetosphere. What

(Upper): Normal Bar Magnet Field; (Lower): Field When Near a Repeling Field

internal stresses and strains occur within the core and the mantle? And could these account for the increased seismic activity following a major solar event? We pick up this question in a later chapter.

Measuring the Sun-Earth Connection

Sun-watchers use a variety of measurements to gauge activity: Sunspot count, X-ray emission level, intensity of planetary geomagnetic disturbance, and the solar storm scale.

1. Sunspot Count

Observers at participating observatories count the number of sunspot groups and multiply by 10, and then add the number of individual sunspots. Results vary greatly, depending on the quality of atmosphere above and the experience of the astronomer, so a center in Zurich then calculates the mean of all the counts from around the world.

During the Solar Minimum, we expect the count to be low, say below 10, the average Solar Maximum peak over the last 200 years is about 125. Quiet 11-year cycles can peak below 100, and the most vigorous peak in 1959 topped out just over 250, with 200 sustained for a full year. Our current cycle (23) maxed at 165, and as of 2004, we should have been down around 25, but as we will see in Chapter 3, we were still spiking to 150, higher than the maximum of many cycles.

2. Solar X-ray Monitor

The X-Ray Solar Status Monitor downloads data periodically from the NOAA FTP server. The previous 24 hours of five-minute X-ray levels from the GOES-8 and GOES-10 satellites) are analyzed, and an appropriate level of activity for the past 24 hours is assigned as follows:

- **Normal:** X-ray flux is inactive < 1 microwatt/sq. m
- **C-class:** X-ray flux is active >= 1 microwatt/sq. m
- **M Class Flare:** X-ray flux >= 10 microwatt/sq. m
- **X Class Flare:** An X Class flare has occurred (X-ray flux >= 100 microwatt/sq. m, or 0.1 milliwatts/sq. m
- **Mega Flare:** An "off the scale" X-ray event with X-ray flux >= 1 milliwatt/sq. m.

On November 4, 2003, giant sunspot 486 unleashed the most powerful CME on record. The blast saturated X-ray detectors onboard GOES satellites for 11 minutes, rendering them blind, but it was later calculated to have been a massive magnitude X-45. When the radiation hit Earth's atmosphere, it caused a severe radio blackout, noticed by radio listeners across North America. The previous record-holder was an X-20.

3. Geomagnetic Field Status Monitor

Geomagnetic disturbances can be monitored by ground-based magnetic observatories recording the three magnetic field components that are combined to give us the Kp Index. The name *Kp* originates from **K**ennziffer **p**lanetarische, or planetary index. The global Kp Index is obtained as the mean value of the disturbance levels in the two horizontal components of the magnetic field, observed at 13 subauroral stations. Irregular disturbances of the geomagnetic field caused by solar particle radiation within a 3-hour interval are averaged to come up with the index value.

The previous 24 hours of three-hour planetary Kp Index data is analyzed and an appropriate level of activity for the past 24 hours is assigned as follows:

- **Quiet:** the Geomagnetic Field is quiet (Kp < 4)
- **Active:** the Geomagnetic Field is unsettled/active (Kp = 4)
- **Storm:** A Geomagnetic Storm has occurred (Kp > 4)

The Geomagnetic Field Status Monitor downloads data periodically from the NOAA FTP server.

4. Solar Storm Scale

NASA has compiled a 5-level scale describing the effects at each level, along with the physical measurements in the logarithmic Kp scale, and average frequency of events at that level:

- *G 5 — Extreme.* Kp = 9. Four storm events per cycle at this Kp level (4 storm days per cycle).
  - *Power systems:* grid systems can collapse and transformers experience damage.
  - *Spacecraft operations:* extensive surface charging, problems with orientation, uplink/downlink, and tracking satellites.

- *Other systems:* pipeline currents reach hundreds of amps, HF (high frequency) radio propagation impossible in many areas for one to two days, satellite navigation degraded for days, low-frequency radio navigation out for hours, and the aurora seen as low as the equator.
- *G 4 — Severe.* Kp = 8. 100 events per cycle (60 storm days per cycle).
  - *Power systems:* possible voltage stability problems, portions of grids collapse and protective devices trip.
  - *Spacecraft operations:* experience surface charging and tracking problems, orientation problems need corrections.
  - *Other systems:* induced pipeline currents affect preventive measures, HF radio propagation sporadic, satellite navigation degraded for hours, low-frequency radio navigation disrupted, and the aurora seen as low as the tropics.
- *G 3 — Strong.* Kp = 7. 200 events per cycle (130 storm days per cycle).
  - *Power systems:* voltage corrections required, false alarms triggered on protection devices, and high 'gas-in-oil' transformer readings likely.
  - *Spacecraft operations:* surface charging on satellite components, increased drag on satellite, and orientation problems need corrections.
  - *Other systems:* intermittent satellite navigation and low-frequency radio navigation problems, HF radio intermittent, and the aurora seen as low as mid-latitudes.
- *G 2 — Moderate.* Kp = 6. 600 events per cycle (360 storm days per cycle).
  - *Power systems:* high-latitude power systems affected.
  - *Spacecraft operations:* corrective actions are required by ground control; changes in drag affect orbit predictions.
  - *Other systems:* HF radio propagation fades at higher latitudes, and the aurora seen as low as 50 degrees.
- *G 1 — Minor.* Kp = 5. 1700 events per cycle (900 storm days per cycle).
  - *Power systems:* weak power grid fluctuations.
  - *Spacecraft operations:* minor impact on satellite operations.
  - *Other systems:* the aurora seen at high latitudes (60 degrees); migratory animals begin to be affected.

Chapter 3

A Year in the Life of a Star

The previous chapter presented the theory of the Sun-Earth connection, and this chapter takes a look at what actually happened in the year 2004. I chose that year because it's recent enough for most of us to remember events as they unfolded, yet we now have a little perspective on those events. But be warned: this chapter reads like a thriller novel.

The Year That Was 2004 – A Disturbing Pattern Unfolds

Wednesday, Feb. 25: Starting with a Bang (almost)

Revealed today is the news that in January, Earth was almost hit by an asteroid. Designated 2004-AS1, it was first believed to be 30m across and had a 25% chance of contact. It eventually passes us by at a distance of about 12 million km, or 32 times the Earth-Moon distance, which is very fortunate because it turns out to be much larger than originally thought – about 500m wide.

On another front, the sunspot count shoots up to 107 and an X-class flare erupts from region 564, with a CME possible. According to NASA, Cycle 23's Solar Maximum should have ended in 2001, so this flare is a wild anomaly … and a portent that this will be no ordinary year.

Friday, Mar. 5: M-class Outbreak
The Sun remains active, undergoing an M-class flare.

Sunday, Mar. 7: CME Event
The rash of solar flares results in a CME that continues for an amazing 24 hours, rather than the usual pattern of a few minutes. The planet braces for freak weather anomalies.

Tuesday, Mar. 9: Expected Weather Disasters Arrive On Schedule
We are not disappointed. High temperature records are broken throughout California, and powerful cyclone *Gafilo* ravages Madagascar, killing seven. A freak 'snowstorm of the century' blankets South Korea, and helicopters have to drop food and fuel to thousands of drivers marooned on highways across the country. Extended auroral lightshows reach the northern U.S. as the solar CME's wind stream reaches Earth.

Friday, Mar. 26: Freak Hurricane in Southern Atlantic
Yesterday, the sunspot count jumped higher to 128, and today a freak cyclone forms in the Atlantic and barrels ashore in Brazil. Named Catarina, until today, this category 1 is only the third cyclone ever in the South Atlantic Basin. Hurricanes are rare over the southern Atlantic Ocean. Yet

Photo credit: NOAA

In this NOAA photograph, note the clockwise *circulation of Southern Hemisphere hurricanes.*

this storm with a well-formed eye about 300 miles east of southern Brazil has all the look of a hurricane. If, indeed, this is a tropical cyclone, it did not begin in the usual way; rather, it began as an ordinary "cool" trough that sat over warm seas for a few days. The atmospheric setting had to be "just right" to allow this trough to strengthen markedly while altering from cool-core to warm-core, and thus become tropical in nature.

The last time this occurred was in 1991 when a strong tropical depression formed off the west-central African coast and moved into the central South Atlantic.

Wednesday, Mar. 31: Intense Solar Activity Continues

Yesterday's sunspot count was at 124, the day prior 169, and today 121. These counts are *three times* higher than NASA's early prediction of this solar cycle. Therefore, it's no coincidence the storms and freak temperature shifts we've seen over the last 72 hours are directly related to solar activity. There is a good chance sunspot region 582 will produce M-Class flares within the next 24 hours and continued 'freak weather' is expected within the next 48 hours.

Monday, Apr. 5: M-class Flares Continue

Sunspot region 588 produces an M-Class flare. Shortly after, LASCO imagery indicates a partial-halo CME emerging from the Sun's southeast limb. This CME does not appear to be directed towards Earth, but it may deliver a glancing blow to the geomagnetic field. We can expect sudden winds, rapid temperature shifts, and possible hail and freak storms within the next 48 hours.

Tuesday, Apr. 6: Massive Hail Storm and Tornados

As predicted, severe hail storms are taking place in the southwest, mostly Texas, New Mexico and Louisiana. Also, severe winds are now taking form as tornados and touching down. At least 30 people have been evacuated from their homes. "It's flooding. It's hailing. You name it and we're getting it," said Kathy Kelly, a resident of Carlsbad, N.M.

Today's sudden storm filled dry creek beds with churning water and may have brought down a bridge on I-20 in west Texas, about 15 miles west of Pecos. No one was injured because police had closed the roadway earlier.

In southwest Texas, 30 people had to be evacuated as their homes flooded with water a foot deep in some areas. Tornado, thunderstorm and flash flood warnings were issued as the system moved slowly across the southern portion of both states. The system also brought up to 2 feet of snow to parts of New Mexico.

Monday, Apr. 19: Power Blackouts around the World
As the Earth's magnetic field weakens, it offers less protection against geomagnetic storms originating in the Sun. As a result, the following regions report power grid problems:

- *Kuala Lumpur:* A power outage lasting just under an hour hit the central business district on Monday morning. The power failure struck during the morning rush hour, causing traffic congestion in parts of the city. Power supplier Tenaga Nasional is investigating the cause of the 50-minute incident.
- *Singapore:* 80,000 homes were affected in Singapore's largest blackout in 12 years. The 66-kilovolt network operates 22,000 km of power cables.
- *Frisco, CO:* A rare power outage lasting about a half-hour partially disabled the 911 Communications Center for a half-hour Saturday, forcing dispatchers to rely on cell phones and teletype systems to communicate with emergency providers. As of Sunday afternoon, the power company could find no reason for the outage.
- *Los Angeles, CA:* Two commercial jets flew within 4.2 miles of each other at the same altitude during a power outage at LAX, despite the federal minimum of 5 miles. The power outage disrupted air traffic control for 1½ hours and delayed 80 – 100 LA-bound flights. The cause remains a mystery.

Saturday, May 1: Coronal Mass Ejection
A series of ten C-Class flares have raged over the last ten days. Normally, C-class flares are not newsworthy, but these are above C-9, which puts them on the border with M-class. One of the 10 C-class flares in sunspot region 601 generates a CME that is Earth-directed, so we will be "taking it on the chin" in about 48 hours.

Sunday, May 2: Geomagnetic Storms to Rage All Week
The past ten-day solar activity has undoubtedly been the source of the "freak weather" which has been recorded, from 'record-breaking heat' to freak tornadoes and extreme hail storms. I wish I could tell you it has come and gone, but the forecast is for more of the same. Watch for continued rapid temperature shifts within the next 48 hours as the

Sun pumps an unprecedented amount of energy into our atmosphere. Severe storms, high winds, hail and possible tornadoes are likely.

Monday, May 3: Bizarre Weather Outbreak

In the Texas Panhandle, Amarillo is dumped on with nearly 5 inches of snow early today. The last time this happened was May 6 and 7, 1917, when the city got over 9 inches. Further north, a week-long freeze in South Dakota inflicts irreparable damage on the alfalfa crop.

Monday, May 17: Sunspot Count Jumps to Triple Digits

Yesterday's sunspot count shot up to 148, today it is 147, in at least six regions. There is a good chance we will see M-class flares from region 609. Geomagnetic measurements have been unstable and "active." Watch for freak storms, beginning today and for the next 72 hours.

Thursday, May 20: Kp Index Jumps Dramatically; Storms Heading Our Way

Currently; there are six large sunspot regions, with region 609 being the largest, measuring about four Earth-diameters. The Kp Index rises sharply this morning as Earth enters a solar wind stream flowing from a coronal hole on the Sun. Geomagnetic storms and high-latitude auroras are probable.

Watch for high C-class and M-class solar flares, with a 5% chance of an X-class occurrence, ensuring continued 'freak weather' disturbance over the next 72 hours.

Friday, May 21: Tornado touches down near Spokane, WA

This afternoon, about 4:15 pm, during a storm that brings high winds, lightning and hail to northeast Washington before sweeping eastward into north Idaho, a freak tornado touches down in a rural area west of Fairchild Air Force Base.

Washington averages only one tornado per year somewhere in the state, but *three* have been reported in the past three weeks – one on April 27 near Sumas, another in East Wenatchee on Wednesday, and now near Spokane.

Tonight, we expect auroras in the northern skies, and a CME that could glance Earth's orbit.

Saturday, May 22: Freak Storms Breakout All Across US; M-Class Flare Occurs

An M-Class flare fires off, most likely from sunspot region 618. This comes on the heels of Thursday's sudden Kp Index surge indicating strong geomagnetic storms are pounding Earth's magnetic field. As a result, Earth's magnetic field warps around our planet much in the way of a cocoon, protecting us from harmful charged particles emitted from the Sun. When this occurs, there is a 'cause-effect' chain reaction that shifts ocean and jet stream currents. As a result, freak storms are flaring up with little notice, most often in the form of tornadoes and straight-line winds* (also called a *derecho*), that can pack a tornado's punch with winds over 100 mph, downing trees, lifting roofs and blowing big rigs off roads.

Typhoons are headed towards Japan, the Philippines and Singapore. In the United States, tornadoes are breaking out everywhere. From the Northwest through to the Northeast, states are experiencing harsh weather. The Upper Midwest has been pounded with a series of thunderstorms and the trend will continue through the weekend. Look for more severe weather overnight moving eastward from northern Illinois and Nebraska. Torrential downpours, gusty winds, frequent lightning and hail are the primary threats from these storms. The Weather Channel reports the jet stream that separates the tropical air mass from the drier and cooler air to the north will shift back and forth over the next few days. Cities south of this boundary, such as Kansas City, St. Louis and Cincinnati, will experience temperatures in the 80s and 90s with high humidity levels. Cities to the north, such as Minneapolis, Green Bay and Fargo, will be fairly cool.

One of the reasons for all this severe weather is that solar energy energizes the jet stream, which in turn drives storms by fueling and steering them.

---

* Straight-line winds are caused by severe downbursts within thunder systems. Strong downdraft (air inside a thunderstorm descending at up to 100 mph) spreads out at ground-level and causes damage equivalent to a strong tornado. These are responsible for most thunderstorm wind damage, and can be extremely hazardous to aviation and small watercraft.

Monday, May 24: Sunspot Count Rises

Today's sunspot count is at 118, and sunspot region 618 is expanding. The Space Weather Center states region 618 may produce X-class flares, which will be followed by single and possibly double-halo CMEs. If this occurs, watch for similar or increased 'freak weather' just as was experienced this past weekend. Again, watch for sudden temperature shifts, tornadoes, wind shears, straight line winds, and micro-bursts.

Tuesday, June 1: High C-Class Flare Fires Off; Electron Flux "All over the Chart"

The geomagnetic field is expected to be unsettled to active for three days (1-3 June), with isolated minor storm conditions on June 1 and 2 from the effects of a massive coronal hole.

Sunspot region 618, the largest of the current regions, is about to rotate off the western limb, but can still produce M-class flares. (On November 4, 2003, this sunspot region produced the largest solar eruption ever recorded (X-45) just after it rotated behind the western limb.) As this is happening, region 621 is just becoming visible on the eastern limb and will be in position for Earth-directed activity in two days. It may host possible M-class activity.

Sunday, June 13: Pelicans Abandon Habitat

The AP wire reports that 27,000 American White Pelicans have abandoned their summer nesting grounds at a national wildlife refuge in North Dakota. The questions are: (1) Why? and, (2) Where did they go? According to the U.S. Fish and Wildlife Service in Bismarck, they just up and left in the middle of the night. Of the many possible explanations, none is a clear favorite.

Many migrant animals such as whales, dolphins, birds, and turtles use the Earth's magnetic field as both a compass and map, and are thus extremely sensitive to disturbances. (Chapter 12 explores the issue in detail.)

Monday, June 14: More M-Class Flares

Sunspot region 634 unleashes an M-class flare as well as numerous C-class flares during the past 24 hours. Continued freak storms are expected across the northern hemisphere, probably in the form of straight-line winds, wind shears, and micro-bursts that can cause havoc, particularly around airports. (In 1991, the most likely cause of the crash of a Boeing 737 during its attempted landing at Colorado Springs was a micro-burst that slammed the airliner into the ground. This disaster prompted the FAA to mandate wind shear and micro-burst detectors at airports. Chapter 14 analyzes a severe-weather aviation incident at Denver Airport.)

Thursday, July 8: Freak weather kills 41 people, injures 150 across China

At least 41 people die and more than 150 are injured in freak weather-related incidents across China. Three people are killed and 143 injured when a hurricane lashes eastern China, dumping walnut-sized hailstones and felling trees. The gale, measuring force 12 (the maximum on the Beaufort scale), also hits Xiao county in Anhui province with unprecedented fury, destroying 18,000 houses.

Monday, July 12: M-Class Flare Fires Off as Predicted

An M-class flare fires off, and just as it ends, it spawns eight C-class flares.

What does this mean? Most likely severe to moderate geomagnetic storms. And what does this mean? Shifting ocean and jet stream currents, which in turn will cause freak storms, most likely in the way of wind shears, micro-bursts, straight-line winds, severe hail storms, and possibly tornados.

Hundreds of times a day across this country, wall clouds form in the late-afternoon convection currents of warm, moist air, and a few of them begin to rotate and spawn a tornado. But why is this more prevalent on some days than on others? The culprit is the energy being pumped into our atmosphere. During quiet solar periods, the input of solar energy is equivalent to a 60-watt bulb in every cubic meter of atmosphere. Intense solar periods are more like 300-watt bulbs, which heats up the thermosphere and stratosphere, which drives the jet stream faster in the troposphere. This, in turn, intensifies everything. Storms move faster, hurricanes spin more quickly and do more damage, and low pressure systems deepen, dropping more rain faster, leading to severe flooding.

Wednesday, July 14: Six M-Class Flares Launched Within 24 Hours

Recent solar events have taken us from 'stunned' to 'puzzled.' Within the last 24 hours, we've had an astonishing *six* M-class flares. This would be normal during a Solar Maximum, but that was over three years ago. Sunspot counts should be in low to mid-double digits, and often in single digits, but for some reason, this just isn't happening. Today's sunspot count is 129, just 20 points below the predicted maximum that should have ended almost four years ago. So what on Earth is going on? We explore this question further in the next chapter.

Monday, July 26: Measurements Still off the Scale

Today's sunspot count is 130, and four M-class flares have fired off in just the last 24 hours, with one M-8 flare. There's a 60% chance we will witness an X-class flare within the next 48 hours.

The Kp Index is running wild into the high 8s, meaning one hell of a geomagnetic storm that can blow out power grids, knock out satellites, and disrupt communications. Alerts may warn of power outages in the next 48 to 72 hours, and, of course, we expect continued extreme weather.

On the lighter side of this event, we should see some very impressive auroras, possibly visible at lower latitudes around forty north.

Thursday, Aug. 12: Tropical Storm Bonnie Makes Landfall

We're now officially in hurricane season, and the first named arrival, Bonnie, is a small storm as she comes ashore near Apalachicola around 10 a.m. EDT, packing just tropical storm-force winds. After a few minor thunderstorms, Bonnie weakens to a tropical depression, but then runs into an approaching cold front and dumps intense amounts of rain along the East Coast. She also spawns tornados in North Carolina that take three lives.

Friday, Aug. 13: Hurricane Charley Makes Landfall

Today, this Category 4 hurricane makes landfall at around 3:45 p.m. EDT at Cayo Costa, Fla., just north of Captiva Island, packing sustained winds of 87 mph and gusting to 109 mph. Once across Florida, Charley is expected to head off up the coast.

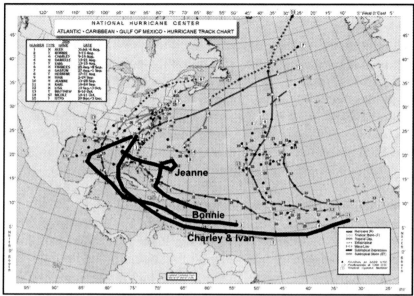

The 'Big Four' that made 2004 a 'Year to Remember' for Florida

Saturday, Aug. 14: Ten (10) M-Class Flares Within Ten Hours

The impossible continues to happen, as Earth is hit by *ten* (10) M-class flares all of which occur within a 10-hour period. The flares and geomagnetic storms will hit our magnetosphere within 48 hours, so we should expect heightened extreme weather. I would not be shocked to see hurricane Charley do some strange stuff. For example, it may weaken to a tropical or sub-tropical storm, but then gain strength, producing multiple tornadoes, hail storms and floods.

In fact, the course Charley takes at this time catches many by surprise. Instead of following the predicted track through the Tampa area, Charley turns abruptly to the northeast, at the same time going from a Category 2 (110 mph) to a Category 4 (150 mph) in only three hours. This rapid change in strength is so drastic that the National Hurricane Center (NHC) issues a special hurricane advisory outside of its normal schedule. [Based on later images, NHC believes that Charley got up to Category 5 (155 mph). So where did the energy come from? We know, don't we?]

Thursday, Sept. 9: Ivan Escalates

As of this morning, hurricane Ivan increases to Category 5. In the last 30 hours, the Kp Index doubled from 2 to 4, which may have contributed to Ivan's escalation, but it is two points short of my prediction of yesterday. This is good news, suggesting Ivan still has a chance of lessening. However, if the Kp Index were to reach 6, and the GOES X-Ray Flux were to reach an M-class flare levels, then I believe Ivan would remain a Category 5, perhaps even higher. Yes, a small chance it could have literally "gone off the chart" and become a mega-hurricane, warranting a new 'Category 6' classification.

Thursday, Sept. 16: Ivan Makes Landfall

Ivan crosses the Gulf coast of Alabama as a Category 3, causing flooding as far north as Pennsylvania.

Wednesday, Sept. 22: Hurricane Jeanne and a Geomagnetic Storm Hit

Yesterday, Ivan combined with a low-pressure system to create hurricane-force winds in Nova Scotia.

A remnant turns southward and makes a loop over the southeastern United States, redeveloping into a tropical storm in the Gulf of Mexico, and heading northwest towards Louisiana. Hurricane Ivan is blamed for at least 70 deaths in the Caribbean and 50 in the United States. Due to massive flooding, Ivan causes approximately $13 billion in damage to the United States, making it the third costliest hurricane in United States history. It is the only 2004 Atlantic hurricane to reach Category 5.

Just as predicted, a geomagnetic storm is in effect, as the Kp Index hits 5. This serves to energize the current crop of hurricanes and tropical storms—Jeanne, Karl, Lisa, and Meari.

Hurricane Jeanne is one wicked, deadly, and unpredictable storm, and I would not be surprised if Jeanne heads back towards the United States. She has already made the most unusual 90 degree turn when heading towards Florida, then turning sharply through a full right angle to Haiti, killing over 3,000 people and obliterating the town of Gonaives under huge mudslides. I have never seen such an event, and that 90 degree turn surprised most everybody, leading some to speculate about weather-tampering by "somebody."

[In fact, Jeanne made landfall in Florida just 2 miles (3 kilometers) from where Frances had struck 3 weeks earlier. Building on the rainfall of the previous storms, Jeanne brought near-record flood levels to the East Coast before turning east into the open Atlantic. Final property damage in the U.S. was almost $7 billion, making this the eighth costliest hurricane in US history.]

Wednesday, Oct. 20: Another M-Class Flare Just Fired Off

Today's sunspot count is 86, and coming from four pretty healthy sunspot regions. I would guess today's M-Class flare most likely came from region 682.

Monday, Oct. 25: Sunspot Count Jumps Past "Solar Max."

Today's sunspot count surpasses the last Solar Maximum by 28. NASA's predicted maximum for Cycle 23 was 150, yet today's count is 178! This occurs just days after NASA made their public statement that we may be entering the Solar Minimum, so the so-called 'maximum' is still alive and well; and over three years later than predicted.

In addition, an M-class flare has just fired off, most likely from sunspot region 687. I predict a 50% chance of an X-class flare from this same region within the next 48 hours.

So what does all this mean? More proof we are not in a typical 11-year cycle. Furthermore, I believe we are in for quite a ride. Watch for extreme weather around the world, extreme temperature shifts, straight-line winds, micro-burst, hail storms and even possible tornados.

Saturday, Nov. 27: Kp Index Literally "Off the Chart"

A geomagnetic storm is "in progress" and so powerful that it's registering off the Kp Index chart. I have only witnessed this twice before, and expect the FAA to issue a pilot and flight warning due to harmful radiation. Watch for satellite and power grid interference or outage.

This chapter has certainly made the point that when the Sun sneezes, we catch cold, or burn, or drown. Cycle 23 is turning out to be a maverick cycle, refusing to obey several hundred years of regularity, so something else is going on, something that I call a *mega-cycle*. We explore this in the next chapter.

Chapter 4

Cycles and Mega-cycles

We live in a world governed by cyclical change, where cycle times range from millions of years to seconds. At one end of the spectrum, earth changes take place extremely slowly. For example, the Indian subcontinent has moved hundreds of miles in 135 million years at a whopping 4 inches per year, crashing into the Eurasian plate with such force that the impact created the Himalayas. Today, a number of major tectonic plates bump and grind against each other, still forming the Himalayas and Rocky Mountains. And when they do, it can be disastrous for us. For example, in 1700, an estimated magnitude 9.0 earthquake and tsunami off the Puget Sound decimated the local native population, and in 1975, a 9.5 quake and tsunami destroyed Anchorage, AK.

The Indian plate is subducting under the Asian plate, but not smoothly. The Indian plate became blocked, so rather than smoothly slipping under the Asian plate, on December 26, 2004, the latter suddenly snapped up several feet along a 700-mile length. This displaced an enormous volume of water that formed a catastrophic tsunami that killed over 250,000 people. So an extremely slow cycle can undergo instantaneous change.

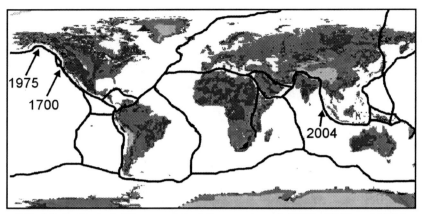

The Major Tectonic Plates and the Mega-quakes of 1700, 1975 and 2004

Ice Ages

Slightly faster than geological change is meteorological change, such as the vast Ice Ages that can last millions or tens of millions of years. In the last billion years, the planet has seen four of these mega-mega-cycles in which glaciers are possible because the average global temperature falls below 55 °F.

- Late Proterozoic (800 – 600 million years ago)
- Ordovician and Silurian (460 – 430 million years ago)
- Permian (310 – 250 million years ago)
- Late Neogene to Quaternary (the last 4 million years).

Today, we are still in the most recent Ice Age. However, within an Ice Age are many shorter cycles during which glaciers advance and

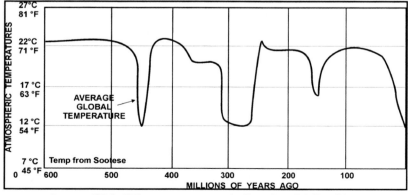

Average Global Temperatures over the Past 800 Million Years

46

retreat. The last 2 million years has seen over 20 glacial advance/retreat cycles of about 100,000 years each. More on this later in the chapter.

The emergence of the planet from such a cycle, maybe over a century or so, can spawn sudden disasters, as when enormous chunks of glacier break off from the Antarctic Ice Shelf and trigger a mega-tsunami. (Some researchers believe that one such tsunami was responsible for the biblical flood featuring Noah, when it's theorized that a huge ice-shelf broke off.)

Also, as sea levels fall when glaciers lock up water, and rise when glaciers melt, or due to seismic activity, large areas that lie beneath the oceans can be elevated. For example, in April 2005, geologists found the fossilized remains of a giant whale deep in the Wadi Hitan desert of Egypt. At one time, this completely arid area was underwater and teeming with the sea giants. Philip D. Gingerich of the University of Michigan announced his team had excavated the first known nearly complete skeleton of a *Basilosaurus isis*, 50-foot-long and 40-million years old. The first of the truly gigantic whales, *Basilosaurus* looked more like a sea monster, with short, sharp teeth for hunting sharks.

On a much smaller scale, the previous chapter discussed the solar cycle of 11 years, first noted by Friis-Christensen and Lassen, and named the Schwabe cycle. It was believed to be due to the magnetic field of the Sun coming under increasing stress because of differential rotation, until it collapses catastrophically, opening the way for higher levels of sunspot activity and the release of energy. After a few years of this, the Sun quiets down again, and the cycle starts over.

The chart, published in 1991 and corrected by the authors in 2000, shows how Earth's temperature (gray line) follows sunspot activity (black line). However, the black line shows that 11 years is only nominal and the cycle actually varies from 10 to 12 years. The search began in earnest to find the reason for the variation, and researchers found many contributing

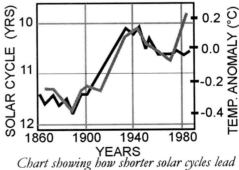

Chart showing how shorter solar cycles lead to warmer temperatures

factors that result in many other cycles involving Earth and the Sun that impact our climate (longterm impacts) and our weather (24 – 72 hour impact).

Gleissberg Cycle

In addition to the 11-year Schwabe cycle is another well-known cycle called the Gleissberg cycle, which is nominally a 78-year cycle but lengthens or shortens by up to two years. The intensity of activity was noted to vary from 11-year cycle to cycle, peaking every seventh cycle and then falling again. Activity peaked in 1947, was lowest in 1984 and should peak again in 2021, so we're currently in an upswing. Sunspot *frequency* is highest at the Gleissberg maximum but sunspot *intensity* seems higher at a Gleissberg minimum, probably because the corona is less dense, thus allowing for more energetic flares and CMEs. Faster CMEs create faster shock waves, which produce more energized protons that penetrate deeper into Earth's atmosphere. These shock waves also have a greater impact on Earth's magnetosphere and give rise to events such as the great Quebec blackout of 1989.

No one is sure why the Gleissberg Cycle happens, but the cycle seems to be tied to the orbit of Jupiter. Thus the cycle governs the ejection speed, acceleration and energy of solar proton emissions as they journey to the Earth.

200-Year Cycle

Another mega-cycle besides the Gleissberg is a 200-year supercycle. It has no agreed-upon value or name but varies between 180 and 220 years, the current cycle duration being 211 years.

The Gleissberg cycle has no subharmonics (other than the seven 11-cycles), but the 200-year cycle clearly consists of two parts of 100 years each, which oscillate between 80 and 120 years and intertwine with the Gleissberg cycle.

The 1930s was a warm spell, 1960s was a cold spell, 1990s again a warm spell, which culminated in 1998. If the 200-year Cycle holds, then the Sun is now headed back towards relatively lower intensity activity, so the current warming spell would end in the 2010s, with the 2020s being a cold decade. In fact, Theodor Landscheidt, director of the Schroeter Institute of Research in Cycles of Solar Activity, predicted a micro-Ice Age will begin in the 2030s.

Cycles within cycles mean that colder spells are not so cold as the earlier ones and warmer spells are a little warmer than the previous ones. This is caused by the 200-year oscillation. The Medieval era of 930 to 1300 was warm, followed by a mini- Ice Age beginning about 1400. Then another warm period began about 1760-1800, and is still growing today.

Different researchers, using different data and models come up with variations. Cole, for example, has determined 190 years as the value for the 200-year cycle and 78.5 years for the Gleissberg cycle.

The next section looks at a possible causative factor in solar cycles.

Solar System's 'Center of Mass' Cycle

There are other forces at work to undermine the Sun's stability, and when an unstable period coincides with a Solar Maximum, that Maximum may be higher than the norm. One agent for this perturbation is the mass of Jupiter. The Sun has a mass of 330,000 Earth Masses (EMs), whereas Jupiter has a mass of only 317 EMs, but that tiny mass is orbiting the Sun at the tremendous speed of 28,800 mph. (If you think that's fast, the Earth is orbiting the Sun almost three times faster, at a breakneck 66,000 mph.)

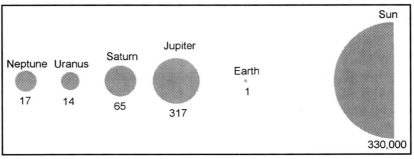

The diagram shows the relative contribution to the mass of the solar system of the larger planets (the planets not shown have relatively insignificant mass). When the planets are evenly distributed around the Sun, the Center of Mass (CM) of the solar system lies within the Sun itself. But if the planets line up as shown, the CM shifts slightly outside the Sun, and as it crosses the Sun's boundary, the solar system undergoes instability for a few years. Recently, this has happened starting in 1789, 1823, 1867, 1933, 1968 and 2002. This is obviously not a regular cycle, since the phenomenon has occurred at 34, 54, 66, 35 and 35 year intervals, respectively.

One prolific writer on this effect, Landscheidt, points out the impact on our planet of these years of instability. Using the North American lynx population as a proxy, due to the value of their pelts, the size of the lynx population has been well-documented over the last 200 years, and shows clear peaks of abundance starting in these six years and lasting three or four years. He also points out that these periods show unusual social unrest and spurts in progress:

- 1789 – 1793: French Revolution, modern U.S. Constitution
- 1823 – 1828: Collapse of the Spanish Empire, invention of the steam locomotive
- 1867 – 1870: Invention of the dynamo, combustion engine, typewriter, rotary printing press.
- 1933 – 1937: Great Depression, birth of Nazi Party, invention of television and jet engine
- 1968 – 1972: Summer of Love, revolution in China, rapid increase in the use of computers.

As of 2005, we are three years into the latest period of solar system instability, and may still see established institutions collapse and breathtaking inventions, such as cloning and nanotechnology.

Landscheidt also looks at how the Sun's 11-cycle affects terrestrial events, such as the health of the ozone layer. He finds that many researchers have observed that solar eruptions are followed by varied terrestrial phenomena, such as increases in the intensity of storms sweeping into the Gulf of Alaska, stratospheric warming, leading to troposphere penetration, strengthening of jet streams, and fluctuations in the size and depth of the ozone layer. The effect is even more marked, he observes, when Jupiter and the solar system CM are exerting a higher torque effect on the Sun, putting it under even greater stress.

When two cycles of instability interact, we clearly experience periods of mega-instability, and periods of super-stability. Also, there may well be cycles that we do not yet know about. For example, we know that the Sun is 25,000 light-years away from the center of our galaxy and orbits its center every 200 million years, traveling through space at the speed of 138 mps, or a whopping 500,000 mph. As it moves, it drags the rest of the solar system with it, but do we know where it's taking us? We may assume that space is uniform, but we don't know that, for we've been 'taking notes' for only a fraction of that 200-million-year orbital period. (I pick up this theme in my next book, *Cosmic Rain.*)

On May 15 , 2001, I wrote an ECTV column titled **Solar Cycles and Something Called The Photon Belt**, in which I speculated about the Photon Belt, a highly debated phenomenon amongst those in the field of metaphysics as well as some scientists. Back then I said this idea was a bit of a stretch for me … and still is. However, as we go through different regions of space, we may well encounter areas with varying energy levels. Gamma rays, for example, are normally harmless high-energy rays of shorter wavelength than x-rays, so have better penetrating properties. However, super-high gamma energy blasts, such as one emanating when a star collapses to form a black hole, could have a disastrous impact on life on this planet. The solar system's orbit around the galactic core could well take us through highly charged regions of gamma radiation or photons—we just don't know what lies ahead.

In the article, I also speculated that the so-called Photon Belt could be a phenomenon that affects our Sun, which in turn produces a greater frequency of, or more intense, CMEs, which in turn have greater impact on Earth's magnetosphere, causing more severe weather (which I call 'Earth Changes'). Why not? Through a series of connected chain reactions, a small cause can have an enormous effect, much like a single hand clap triggering an avalanche.

I have been influenced by a few special people who have sparked my curiosity of what they call the 'Photon Belt.' The article was meant to introduce the thought of such an event that will change the Earth's 'vibration' as well as our own. Could this be the event that lifts us into a new dimension, what the Hopi call the Fifth World and what the Christians call The Rapture? I sure hope so because I love the idea. All I know is that a lot of people are talking about it; a Google search on 'Photon Belt' yields 1380 pages, with about 10 website URLs per page.

We now know that the visible universe (what we can see) accounts for only ten percent of the mass of the universe, the remaining 90 percent being termed 'dark matter.' However, giving something a name doesn't mean that we know what it is, where it is, or what would happen if we bumped into a concentration of it, so any speculation about it is just that—speculation.

Mega-cycles

Since September 1999, I have been talking about a 'mega-cycle' in regard to the Sun's magnetic activity varying over a much longer time span than previously thought. I argue that this solar activity cycle may, in turn, cause very slow climate cycles on Earth, albeit faster than the vast cooling epochs. This would help scientists understand past climate trends and prepare for future ones. However, there were few takers for this new paradigm because it would upset the status quo that is so important to 'the establishment.'

What The Heck Is A 'Mega Cycle'?

In doing much research for this book, I was hard-pressed to get beyond the current 'paradigm' or standards as it relates to solar cycles. It became quite clear that NASA and NOAA make the rules and one would be set for a nasty awakening by challenging such a system. But being who I am, of course, I did just that.

Although early on in my research I could clearly see what was being reported regarding sunspot count and solar activity just did not fit the neatly packaged 11-year cycle so proudly disseminated. Finally in a fit of frustration, I did what NASA cannot do and stepped outside of what was known, and looked to our ancestors in the way of ancient text. What did they know about solar cycles? One thing for sure, they knew there were 'cycles outside of cycles.' Yes, there is a rhythm, but there is more than one beat. It is not just 11-beat – 11-beat – 11-beat. No, just like in any musical orientation, there are long counts and short counts.

Since the beginning of this book, new research studies have poured out confirming my hypothesis of a 'long count' or what I call a 'Mega-cycle.' On November 4, 2003, we witnessed the largest solar explosion ever recorded in modern times. I highlight 'modern times' hinting of the fact our Earth has seen this many times before as evidenced in ancient text and paleo-botany reports. Humans love to have easy to remember benchmarks, so they called this event the 'Halloween Storm.'

The Great 2003 Halloween Storm

Collectively we dodged a bullet in 2003. Our planet's strong magnetic field shielded us from the full brunt of what solar researchers now call the solar 'Halloween Storms,' when seven major solar outbursts jolted Earth's upper atmosphere, setting new records for extreme space weather:

- The largest X-ray solar flare ever recorded
- The fastest-moving solar storm ever, at nearly 6 million mph.
- The hottest storm ever to hit Earth, at tens of millions of degrees.

The storms erupted in late October and early November 2003 (hence the name), and threatened power transmission networks around the planet. It also threatened weather satellites in orbit above Earth, damaging 28 and actually killing two.

The solar storms continued outward, and burned out the radiation monitor aboard the Global Surveyor spacecraft orbiting Mars. And even the Cassini spacecraft near the planet Saturn recorded the intense energy from the Sun. Months later, the storms' energy reached beyond Pluto's orbit and washed over the Voyager spacecraft, far outside the solar system.

The Halloween Storms were anomalous because they came some three years after the so-called peak of Solar Cycle 23.

Daniel Baker, director of CU-Boulder's Laboratory for Atmospheric and Space Physics, an internationally known space weather expert, said, "The Halloween Storms of 2003 and similar events during summer 2004, and even events during the past few weeks, are evidence that solar storms are not tightly tied to peaks in the 11-year-long solar cycles. Most solar physicists contend that the present solar cycle (23) peaked in 2000 or 2001. The Sun has been throwing some unexpected curves at us," he said. "The message here is that the Sun can be very active during broad periods, and that we can expect frequent, irregular activity over a large part of its 11-year sunspot cycle.

"The Halloween solar storms of October and November 2003 were marked by highly energetic particles emanating from the Sun, as well as the acceleration of particles near Earth in a zone between two donut-shaped bands of radiation girdling the planet known as the Van Allen Belts. The normally quiescent region, which ranges from about

4,000 miles to 8,000 miles above Earth, was previously considered to be a 'safe zone' for satellites and immune from substantial amounts of radiation.

"During the Halloween storms, coronal mass ejections from the Sun hurled electrified gas clouds weighing billions of tons into Earth's magnetic field at several million miles per hour. The radiation made the safe zone between the Van Allen Belts thousands of times hotter and more energetic and hazardous to spacecraft.

"The hopped-up electrons inside the zone and the energetic protons emanating from the Sun disrupted an estimated 60 percent of operational near-Earth satellites. The powerful solar events also temporarily increased the volume of the solar system, or heliosphere, by 30 percent about eight months after the storms reached Earth. The storm effects were observed by spacecraft monitoring Mars, Jupiter and Saturn.

"Extreme space weather cropped up again over Earth when several solar storms pummeled Earth's magnetosphere in July 2004. The space environment has remained hot now for several years, and we just had a very powerful set of solar storms in January 2005. We can't afford to let our guard down when operating spacecraft in the near-Earth environment.

"Scientists are particularly concerned about the disruption of signals from a constellation of 24 Global Positioning System satellites, which orbit at roughly 10,000 miles above Earth and are regularly used to track the position of aircraft within inches as they move about the skies. The Halloween storms caused a temporary disruption of airline navigation systems by scrambling GPS communications, causing anxious moments for air traffic controllers.

"Scientists have come a long way in understanding the physics of space weather since 1859, when a solar storm known as the 'Carrington Event' slammed into Earth's environment. The famous event disrupted telegraph communications worldwide and even allowed New England residents to read newspapers by the light of Earth's supercharged aurora.

"We are more dependent than ever on technology, and therefore more susceptible to the effects of space weather. But scientists and engineers have made great strides in recent decades regarding this phenomenon. We understand much more about what is happening and can build more robust systems to withstand the effects."

NASA Worried over Sun's Activity

But wait, we are almost three years beyond NASA's predicted 11-year cycle known as Cycle 23. What could this mean?

I have received several notices telling of NASA's grave concern with the unusual increase in solar activity. Since I have not received an official response from NASA officials to my inquiries, just let me say there is quite a bit of 'chatter,' suggesting that Earth could be at some risk. The rumors suggest that the Pentagon has issued a 'gag order' to NASA, forcing them to say, "We cannot confirm or deny that recent and current solar activity is at dangerous levels." This should deflect awkward questions about their military spy satellites in space 'in the interests of national security' while George Bush conducts his war.

Over the past week, I reported 65 C-class flares, 16 M-class flares, and 2 X-class flares have occurred. Just the week prior saw another 2 X-class flares and 4 M-class flares erupted, and in addition to the solar flares, perhaps as many as 45 CMEs emerged.

Another area of concern is our power grids. As we saw in Chapter 1, if Earth experiences a direct hit from any one of these M-class or X-class flares, it could in fact cripple our infrastructure. There is good reason to be concerned over this issue. Some of you may remember how the 1989 X-class flare ripped through our magnetic field, knocking out power grids all across parts of the world.

Cycle 23 was unusual from the beginning. On July 18, 2000, I wrote a column titled, *New Sunspot Record, Extreme Weather Expected* in which I reported that a new sunspot record count of 342 had just occurred. This number was over double NASA's prediction of 150 for this solar cycle. This lends support to the theory of what many are calling a 'mega-cycle.' This phenomenon goes way beyond the 11, 22 and 200-year cycles we are more familiar with. It would be closer to thousands if not hundreds of thousands of years between events. I believe this is what we are experiencing.

Scientists are now starting to come forward with information about how and why these events are unfolding. As scientists feel increasingly secure from peer-badgering, we will see information beyond the shallow and cute terms like El Niño and La Niña. I believe what we will see is ongoing evidence of our weather being manipulated by none other than our Sun.

Sunspots are the one measurable quantity scientists can use to make such predictions as did NASA. A higher number of sunspots indicates the heightened solar activity that would follow, i.e., M-class and X-class flares as well as CMEs. In turn, the intensity of solar activity indicates how severely Earth's magnetic field will be affected. The severity of impact on the magnetic field in turns indicates how severe the ocean and jet stream currents will be affected, which in turn manifests as extreme weather in areas of the world hardest hit.

This is summarized in my equation:

Sunspots => Solar Flares => Magnetic Shift => Shifting Ocean and Jet Stream Currents => Extreme Weather

More recent disclosure of ancient text lends strong support for the existence of one or more mega-cycles. There are many references to such in the Aztec and Mayan Calendar (see Chapter 5). Could these events have been prophesied thousand of years ago? Did our ancestors experience this same events in their time? One thing can be said for sure: our Earth has seen this before, but we have not.

Sharma's 100,000-year Cycle

We've known about solar cycles since 1991, when Friis-Christensen and Lassen proved the link between mean surface air temperature in the Northern Hemisphere and the 11-year Solar Cycle and the 22-year oscillation of the Sun's magnetic poles. Others have also found 420-year and 1500-year solar cycles. We also know that over the past 2 million years, Earth has undergone mini-Ice Ages every 100,000 years but had no idea why.

Of course, I always suspected the Sun was behind this effect, so was delighted in June 2002 when Mukul Sharma, Assistant Professor of Earth Sciences at Dartmouth University, went public with strong evidence confirming the truth of my mega-cycle idea. He proposed a 100,000-year solar magnetic cycle that drives Earth's 100,000-year climatic cycle responsible for glacial/interglacial periods over the past two million years.

His research shows that the Sun's magnetic activity varies in 100,000-year cycles—a much longer time span than previously thought—and that this solar activity, in turn, may likely cause the 100,000-year climate cycles on Earth. This cycle may well be the driver of the 100,000-year climatic oscillation that is responsible for the recurring glacial maxima and minima of the past two million years.

"Surprisingly, it looks like solar activity is varying in longer time spans than we realized," says Sharma. "We knew about the shorter cycles (11-year) of solar activity, so maybe these are just little cycles within a larger cycle. Even more surprising is the fact that the glacial and interglacial periods on earth during the last 200,000 years appear to be strongly linked to solar activity."

Sharma's work is based on the fact that the production of beryllium-10, or ^{10}Be, in Earth's atmosphere is affected by the intensity of magnetic activity at the surface of the Sun, as well as the earth's geomagnetic field. This allowed Sharma to measure Earth's magnetic field intensity and create a 200,000-year history of how the Sun affects it.*

Based on his data, Sharma saw the obvious connection—"that variations in solar activity control the 100,000-year glacial-interglacial cycles," just as they also appear to control other climatic cycles within those longer cycles. Sharma and others point to the Sun as the causal agent of a warming global as when micro-Ice Ages ended in the Renaissance era and Victorian England. And things may continue to warm up, because Sharma found that Earth's mean temperature during the two preceding mini-Ice Ages was 2 °C (3½ °F) warmer than today's mean temperature.

He says, "I took sets of existing, independent data and made new comparisons and calculations. Then I went a step further to make a connection with the history of Ice Ages by looking at oxygen isotopes in the oceans, which reveal the history of how much ice was at the

---

* ^{10}Be, an isotope of Beryllium, has been increasingly used to date ancient geological forms such as glaciers. The more we learn about its production rates, the greater the accuracy in dating prehistoric landforms. The isotope accumulates in mineral grains over timescales far longer than typically found with ^{14}C, so-called 'carbon dating,' because it has a half-life of about 1.5 million years. When high-intensity solar magnetic storms rage, cosmic rays interact more with charged particles in the atmosphere, and less ^{10}Be is produced. Since the isotope's production rate and earth's magnetic field intensity are known for the last 200,000 years, Sharma could derive solar magnetic activity for this time period.

poles and are therefore a measure of average global surface temperature. I compared the estimated past variations in the solar activity with those of the oxygen isotopes in the ocean. Although there is a strong relationship between solar activity and oxygen isotopic variations, it is too early to say exactly what is the mechanism through which the Sun is influencing the terrestrial climate."

Sharma believes that more analysis is needed to test his theory. He asserts his calculations need to be verified for a million years, much more than his current 200,000 year analysis.

Summary of Possibilities

Discovering the 100,000-year cycle doesn't tell us *why* the Sun behaves like this, which will be thoroughly explored in my sequel book titled *Cosmic Rain*. Now that we have a better understanding of the Sun's causal effect on Earth's weather, climate, and rhythmic cyclical events, the natural follow-up question has to be "what causes the Sun's cycles?" And what are the implications for the mean Earth temperature increasing by 3½ °F (2 °C)?

Since the late 1800s, the average global temperature has increased by about 1 °F (½ °C), and some experts predict that it will continue to rise *much faster* than that, causing disruption to human societies and ecosystems that cannot adapt to rapid climate changes.

To get an idea of what that might mean, let's look at news headlines for a typical ten-day period in February 2000 following a run-of-the-mill CME, and see what happened:

Feb. 18	Africa experiences "freak" floods in Mozambique
Feb. 19	"Freak" floods in Kentucky force evacuation
	Violent storm hits Eastern Seaboard of United States
Feb. 21	Avalanches hit Europe due to warm temperatures following heavy snow
Feb. 22	Ohio declares a State of Emergency due to floods
	Cyclone Eline hammers Mozambique
Feb. 23	Record rain storms hit So. California
	Mayon volcano erupts in Philippines
Feb. 24	Australia hit with sudden floods
	Tornado-like winds pound So. California
	Landslides rake Java
	7.1 Earthquake hits Vanuatu Is.

Feb. 26	Icelandic volcano blows its top
Feb. 27	Wildfires burn in Florida, hundreds evacuated
Feb. 28	Cyclone Steve hits Australia
	Philippines volcano erupts again
	Unexpected ice melt in Russia traps hundreds

Words such as 'freak' and 'record-breaking' are often found in the headlines, but it's safe to assume that today's 'freak' will be tomorrow's 'normal' as we approach the peak temperatures of an interglacial period. This is not intended to stir panic—just the opposite, in fact. The more aware and prepared we are, the less the likelihood of falling prey to panic, shock and trauma. What is occurring is simply a natural cycle the Earth has seen many times. It's just that we have not. So what can we expect?

Continued natural, cyclical warming trends could have many damaging effects on life in the oceans and on land, forcing people and animals into new habitats. Weather patterns could change, causing flooding, drought, and storm damage. It could melt enough polar ice to raise the sea level, rendering coastal cities uninhabitable, and drought could cause crop yields to decline:

- *Harm to ocean life.* As a result of natural cyclical warming trends, the surface waters of the oceans could become warmer, increasing the stress on ecosystems such as coral reefs. Higher temperatures may also spread diseases that affect sea creatures.
- *Changes in land habitats.* The natural habitats of humans, animals and plants may become untenable, meaning that many species could not survive where they now reside. For example, some flowering plants need the winter cold as part of their lifecycle. And human needs for viable habitats may conflict with the needs of other species.
- *Weather damage.* Extreme weather conditions will become the norm, and changing rainfall patterns could cause flooding/drought oscillations. Higher incidence of hurricanes and tropical storms, plus increased intensity, will make the damage to Florida in August/September 2004 commonplace, encouraging us to be better prepared.
- *Rising sea level.* Continued melting large amounts of the vast Antarctic ice sheet would raise sea level around the world,

leading to coastal flooding, erosion, and the destruction of freshwater wetlands due to ingress by seawater. High sea levels would submerge coastal cities and small island nations, forcing relocation to higher ground. For low-lying countries such as Holland, this had international implications because the *entire population* may need to relocate to another country.

- *Threats to human health.* Tropical diseases, such as malaria and dengue, might spread to larger regions. Longer and more intense heat waves could cause more deaths and illnesses, especially among the very young and the very old as we saw in Paris in 2003. Floods and droughts could increase hunger and malnutrition.
- *Changes in crop yields.* High-latitude areas such as Russia would benefit from an increase in crop yields, but elsewhere, drought and higher temperatures would have a disastrous effect on crop yields in lower latitudes, because many crops are already at their limit of toleration.

(Chapter 13 explores such earth changes in much more detail.)

Mini-Ice Ages

We know that we are about 4 million years into the fourth great cooling epoch our planet has known, although no one knows why these mega-mega-cycles happen. We also know that, within this huge cycle, we are about 12,000 years into the warming phase of a 100,000-year cycle. The last glaciation in the continental United States peaked about 20,000 years ago, and we are now in a warming trend. By studying a

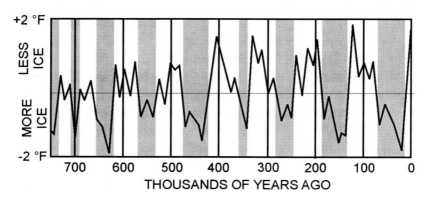

number of factors, such as oxygen isotope quantities and plankton trapped in glaciers, scientists can map out the most recent peaks, as Sharma did with beryllium-10. In the following chart, the vertical gray bands represent cooler parts of the Sharma cycles.

The above graph shows the general trend of changing ice volume on the Earth over the past 750,000 years. The relative extent of ice is based on Imbrie's estimates using changes in the amount of different isotopes of oxygen found in plankton. The gray portions are periods when glaciers may have reached down into the Mid-west U.S. It shows the 100,000-year periodicity of glacial advance and retreat. But where are we in our current cycle?

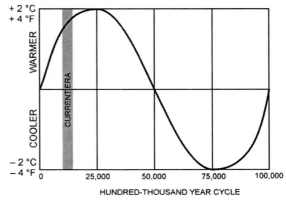

The graph shows, in crude form, a simplified, hypothetical plot of Earth's temperature that spans 100,000 years. If the midcycle begins at year 0, the temperature would peak 25,000 years later. We know that the last mini-Ice Age ended about 12,000 years ago, which becomes 'Year 0' on the graph X-axis. This means we are about half way to the peak, as shown by the gray line. So the planet can look forward to about another 12,000 years of warming, and then a 50,000-year cooling period, leading into widespread glaciation once more.

So is it going to get hotter? You betcha. Evidence points to temperature span of 4 °C (7 °F) between the global mean maxima and minima within the 100,000-year cycle. As we are halfway through the warming phase, it's about 2 °F (1 °C) warmer today than 12,000 years ago, and it will be another degree or so warmer in 12,000 years time, before things begin to cool down again. That may not seem a whole lot, but this planet is a complex system that exists in such an exquisite balance that a tiny change in just one variable can have a major impact throughout the system.

Is there anything we can do about it? Not a thing. Of course, we can make things worse by pumping the sky full of chemicals that destroy the ozone layer, which will mean increased incidence of skin cancer and asthmatic attacks, but the Kyoto Protocol can't do a *thing* about natural, cyclical warming trends. It's coming whether we like it or not.

What will it mean? We pick the story up in Chapter 13.

Chapter 5

Ancient Prophecies

This book is grounded in good science except for this chapter, which takes a side-trip to explore what ancient cultures had to say about earth changes and related issues.

The distinction between science and religion is purely arbitrary and based on a pact made in 17th century Italy between the Pope and the powerful Medici family. When Pisa teacher, inventor and scientist Galilei Galileo turned his telescope on the heavens in 1609, he got more than he bargained for. Just its 9x power was enough to confirm something he'd suspected for a while—that the Earth goes round the Sun, and not the other way round. In fact, he improved on Kepler's model of the solar system, and published his first account in 1616. This mightily angered the RC church because it conflicted with their view that God put Earth at the center of Creation as home to His finest creation—man. That we actually lived on a tiny satellite orbiting a much larger celestial body was completely untenable to the 'authorities' and they told Galileo to cease and desist. He did what any scientist would do and ignored them.

When his major work came out in 1632, the Inquisition was on him big time, and he was hauled off to Rome to 'speak' with the Pope. He was found guilty of heresy, declared 'anathema' and sentenced to house arrest. The Medici family stepped in with some luxury digs, in thanks for his telescope, which was helping them identify incoming sailing ships hours earlier than everyone else could, which gave them a trading advantage.

Probably the first true capitalists, the Medici family was heavily into science and technology, which the Church frowned on, so a deal was made. Scientists would be allowed to study the *physical* universe, but all matters pertaining to faith and one's relation to God were reserved to the Church. Thus unholy alliance still stands today, to the detriment of both sides, and it will be interesting when at some point, quantum physicists push so far across the quantum veil that separates the physical world from its nonphysical source that they literally bump into the creator of that source.

Other cultures did not enforce a division between science and religion, so scientists were priests, and priests were scientists. And the inner world of consciousness blended seamlessly with the outer world of matter, without conflict or paradox. Prayer was just one more tool in dealing with the world, and not something reserved for communication with one's deity.

Of all such cultures, I have long been interested particularly in the prophecies of the Hopi Indians, based in Arizona, and the ancient Central and South American peoples such as the Maya, because vast epochal cycles are central to their beliefs. I especially enjoy having their representatives as guests on my show. As a reminder, here's a map of their territory and some examples of their architecture at Chichen Icha, Tulum and Uxmal, every bit as magnificent as anything to be found in Egypt.

Mayan Model of the World

The Mayan body of knowledge claims that mankind has lived through five great ages, each ending in natural disaster:

- *First Age*, or the age of White-haired Giants, lasting about 4,000 years (15,600 – 11,500 BCE). It was ended by the Great Flood, the date of which is close to the Sumerian, Babylonian and Egyptian legends of around 11,000 BCE for the same event, due, it is claimed, to the massive slippage of the Antarctic icepack at the end of the last Ice Age. Who were these White-haired Giants? Refugees from Lemuria? We don't know, but a few survived the Flood and populated the Second Age.

- *Second Age*, or the Golden Age, ended with calamitous winds after about 4,000 years (11,500 – 7,600 BCE). Again, a few survived to people the next age.

- *Third Age*, or the age of the Red-haired People, survivors of the Second Age who came in ships from the east. It, too, lasted about 4,000 years (7,600 – 3,500 BCE). Who were the Red-haired People? Survivors of Atlantis?

- *Fourth Age*, lasting about 4,080 years (3,500 BCE – 580 CE), called the Age of the Black-haired People (which is what 'Sumerian' actually means), led by Quetzlcoatl, famous for his staff carved in the shape of a serpent, symbolic of DNA strands. Towards the end of this age, the 'gods' launched major wars against each other and Quetzlcoatl left, sailing east whence he came. (Quetzlcoatl bequeathed to them a form of hieroglyphic pictogram writing that was initially identical to the early Sumerian but they subsequently diverged, creating an intriguing link between these otherwise separate cultures. He also bequeathed his pyramid-building know-how to them.)

- *Fifth Age*, beginning in 580 CE. In 1140 CE, the Aztec arrived from the north and settled around Lake Texaco. In 1325, they founded the city of Tenochtitlan, today Mexico City. About the same time, the Mayan civilization mysteriously collapsed, leaving behind monumental buildings and huge cities, and their calendar, which the Aztecs adopted. (A later chapter explains how climate changes may have led to the demise of several ancient cultures.)

On April 9, 2001, my ECTV guest was author Carl Johan Calleman, author of *Enlightenment: The Mayan Calendar as Our Guide to the Future*. On the show, Carl explained how this is a very crucial time and it serves us best to let go of old ideas and let ourselves expand as life takes its twists and turns. I made the comment that perhaps what we are experiencing on the outside in the way of solar events and extreme weather may very well be a reflection of what many of us are experiencing in our inner self. I explained a process needed to help us along the path to perhaps a new world, or better put, a new way of being!

Carl believes the Maya people have told us of a frequency wave that occurs in cycles, each one taking us to a further place in evolution. Carl believes within months to a few years, we will have a comfortable knowledge of our working universe and how it works for us. Carl says, "In these years, we are growing up. By the year 2012, we will have evolved to the point of perhaps leaving this dimension to a higher vibration of being."

Then I asked him what form that would look like, giving as an example, "Would I be able to reach out and shake your hand? Would we have tangible bodies?" Carl's answer was simple: "I am not sure how it will unfold. We may still all be here (at least most of us) on this Earth, but interacting as a new one-world race, with connection with our ancestors and our spiritual elders."

Carl Calleman's book contains a Foreword by Mayan researcher José Argüelles that makes fascinating reading (reproduced with permission):

Since the Harmonic Convergence of August 16-17, 1987, and the concurrent publication of my book, the *Mayan Factor: Path Beyond Technology*, interest in Mayan civilization and the Mayan Calendar in particular has become widespread around the planet. Not only have there since appeared numerous books on the Mayan prophecies and civilization in general, but there has also been a revival of the traditional Mayan time knowledge as well, most notably through the efforts of Alejandro Oxlaj (Cerillo) of the Quiche Maya in Guatemala, and of Hunbatz Men of the Yucatec Maya in Mexico.

A deeper reason for this interest is that the Mayan Great Cycle of thirteen *baktuns* will end on the Winter Solstice (northern hemisphere) of 2012. It is awareness of this conclusive date which, acting like a signal in the human DNA, prompts so much interest and enthusiasm in the Mayan Calendar, as is demonstrated, for instance, by John Major Jenkins' *Maya Cosmogenesis 2012*.

Carl Johan Calleman's *Enlightenment: The Mayan Calendar as Our Guide to the Future* follows in the tradition of my book, *The Mayan Factor,* in being an in-depth philosophical investigation and interpretation of the Mayan Calendar, showing its absolute relevance as a tool and guide for this final stage of the 13-*baktun* Great Cycle. As Calleman well demonstrates, the Mayan Calendar is a multi-valued system, encompassing a deep philosophy of nature and natural rhythms, which in turn affords applications for historical analysis. In his analysis, Calleman is acutely aware of the religious and theological ramifications of his interpretations, not the least of which stems from the infamous book-burning of the Mayan texts by Christians in 1562. As Calleman writes, "The higher perspective generated by the Mayan Calendar is, however, not something that can be turned into a new dogma. ... Rather, the Mayan calendar provides a possible framework for the common exploration by individuals that share a respect for the contributions and views of others. The Mayan Calendar, properly understood, is thus in its essence, alien to all fundamentalism. This fosters a revival of the Mayan Calendar on a worldwide scale among all those aspiring to the unity of humanity." (pp.93–94)

This point of view is broadly ecumenical and universal and speaks of the most spiritual nature of the Mayan Calendar. It also speaks of Calleman's fascinating effort to create a grand synthesis of humanity's spiritual history—a history of the human mind—and an analysis of the present and near future that is based on a strict adherence to the Long or True Count, including the value of the 360-day *tun* cycles. Equally fascinating is Calleman's analysis and interpretation of the thirteen *baktuns* as alternating day-and-night cycles, and as related to the cosmology of the thirteen heavens. In this regard he sees that we are passing through a Galactic Underworld and that, after the 2012, date we enter into a Universal Underworld.

But for Calleman, as we approach the 2012 date, what is most important is that he sees a great spiritual awakening and unification occurring. "Based on our knowledge," he writes, "of the Mayan Calendar, there is then little doubt that, as we approach the completion of the Cosmic Plan, the number of enlightened people will increase vastly. The proof from the Mayan Calendar that the mind has a history then offers great hope to mankind." (p.236)

What I find interesting about Calleman's work is that it substantiates the premise of *The Mayan Factor*—that the Mayan civilization and the Calendar in particular are the overlooked factor in any consideration of the course and history of human civilization. Calleman has been able to explore and investigate from his perspective the depths of the Mayan Calendar demonstrating its fundamental spiritual and mental nature, which speak to a level of synthesis that the world sorely needs today. Even more importantly, Calleman sees the Mayan Calendar in relation to the divine or cosmic plan. "Thus the Mayan Calendar remains our most important tool for studying the cosmic plan, and this is clearly an analytical tool generated by the Western hemisphere." (p.239)

It is also interesting that the Mayan Calendar inspires in Calleman a genuinely holistic and global understanding of ourselves. For though the work I have pursued in my investigation of the Mayan Calendar differs in certain points from that of Calleman's—and it is wise to be open and fearlessly study all points of view—we share in common methods of applying fractal units of the calendar as tools of analysis. For both of us, it is clear that the Mayan calendar is well-disposed to fractal holographic applications based on the key numbers 7, 9 and 13. The reader will find Calleman's fractal-based interpretations utilizing many graphics to be thought-provoking and stimulating.

Finally, I would like to emphasize Calleman's perception of the two critical Venus passages that will soon be occurring—June 8, 2004 and June 6, 2012. These dates, marking the passage of Venus in front of the Sun are, for Calleman, an augur of the: "…final transformation of the human mind into a mind of light." Venus passages always occur in pairs. The last two pairs occurred in 1874/1882, and before that 1761/69. Of course, the dates of the 2004 and 2012 passages are most significant. The 2004 date must be seen as the herald of the

Great Calendar Change, July 25–26, 2004, while the second passage in 2012 initiates the Closing of the Cycle. For the 2004 date, Calleman is calling for a world wide meditation as a great opportunity to set the stage for the spiritual triumph of the Great Calendar Change.

On the True Count, the June 8, 2004 is 6 Ehecatl (wind) a sign of Quetzalcoatl. On the Dreamspell Count, that day is 3 Monkey, one of the Thirteen Clear Signs on the tomb of Pacal Votan. And it will occur but one week before the 52nd anniversary of the opening of Pacal Votan's tomb.

Pondering the meanings of Calleman's book, let us all search in our hearts and minds, and seek the higher unification of the spirit that is afforded by the study and practice of the Mayan Calendar in all its forms. Let us prepare to use the Mayan Calendar as a tool to study the course of events generated by the Cosmic Plan, for are we not in the end all fashioned of one soul? Calleman's text on the Mayan Calendar can only bring whoever reads it to a new threshold of understanding. Let us all move forward as one to the One!

A Mayan Warning

On July 18, 2003, the Mayan Elders gave through me a stark warning of upcoming dates to look out for. The previous night, I had interviewed Adam Ruble of Saq' Be', who told us of a message recently given to him personally by Mayan Elders, who wanted us to know the likelihood of *severe natural earth changes* which could occur between August 16 and December 15, 2003.

It appears that Carlos Barrios, highly praised Mayan Elder, had been very impressed with our interview back in April 2003 and wanted me to play an instrumental role in upcoming disclosures based on Mayan Prophecy and the Mayan Calendar.

They told me between those dates, there is a strong potential for natural disasters on a grand scale, although specific types, times or places were not given, but they did mention earthquakes, volcanoes, fires and floods.

Before I continue, a reminder to all: Just because I say it with passion and conviction does not make it 'The Truth.' It only makes it 'my truth.' It is because I have faith in the source and integrity of the Elders who have handed this knowledge to me, that I bring this to you. Perhaps one of the most powerful objective methods of integrity is a track record. So I would suggest it may be wise to give this a more conservative 'wait-and-see' approach prior to acceptance.

For the Mayan tradition, life and spirituality revolve around their sacred calendars. To them, there is no difference between time and space. The Maya refer to it as Najt (time-space). By understanding the various Mayan calendars, they are able to look into the spiral of the Najt and make predictions with great accuracy about the future. One of these ancient predictions relates to the upcoming period between August 16 and December 15, 2003. Don Jacinto Patsan from the Mam tribe in the highlands of Huehuetenango in Guatemala, brought forth this prophecy because it is important for humanity to understand at this time.

Don Jacinto and the Elders want us to know that this spiral of Najt is not totally rigid and inflexible. We humans possess the capacity to influence this spiral, and the power to affect in either a positive or negative way. We may do better to not think of this in terms of black and white, rather in shades of gray. The elders say the most important things are *unity* and *balance*. It may be wise to maintain our focus during this tumultuous period.

I am told the Ajq'ij (Mayan priests) are conducting Fire Ceremonies for this purpose. Adam has told me the Elders have suggested for us to light white and red candles at sunset to connect us to the Mayan ceremonies.

I have been reminded that, while this is a time of great danger, it is also a time of great hope for humanity to rise up together in unity and ease the transition to a new era. Perhaps this is truly the beginning of what I have been calling 'the transition.' I, for one, am excited and grateful to be alive in this particular period in our evolution. Sure, it's a bit scary, but if you share my understanding of what this is truly about, then you to have a light burning within, thirsting for our next level of existence. No, not in the way of death, or should I say, not in the way of death as we know it!

Before we move on from the Maya, I'm going to leave you with a question to ponder: The next solar maximum will come in 2012. Did the Maya synchronize their calendar's Long Count end date to the sunspot maximum of Solar Cycle 24? If so, how is that possible, when we only discovered sunspot cycles in the 17th century? Or is it all just coincidence?

Aztec Wisdom

On April 16, 2004, I wrote an article titled **Aztec Calendar Tells of the 6th Sun** based on the previous evening's interview with John Mini, author of *Day of Destiny*, who disclosed to our live audience that the time of destiny is indeed upon us. He emphasized the Aztec Calendar follows the Mayan Calendar very closely. However, with the Aztec's, the Sun was the most important factor, prophesying our current "cause and effect" relation with earth changes, such as weather, climate, earthquakes, volcanoes, tornadoes, freak storms, and drought. (On the cover of John Mini's book is the graphic of the original Aztec Sun Calendar, which shows the Sun with its tongue hanging out. This is meant to indicate that "the Sun will speak to us." And boy, oh boy, is it ever.)

But there was something more to our discussion. As we moved further into reviewing our current and future times, John made the significant reference as to the Aztec's message of 'internal change,' referring to our bodies and our minds. We spent at least 20 minutes in our interview carefully analyzing what the Aztecs may have meant by 'internal change.' John laid out his belief that they were referring to our cellular body and our emotional body. The sum of the whole person will be directly affected and influenced by the Sun.

John is an acupuncturist, as am I, so we had a wonderful flow of interactive discussion while a very large audience listened in. It is because of our selected form of therapy, we could more easily understand an eastern philosophy which treats the 'whole body,' unlike western medicine, which treats symptoms instead of 'causes.' In the field of acupuncture, we are first taught of the body's magnetic grid, more commonly known as the energy field that surrounds the body. When this energy field is out of balance, it manifest as illness—both mental and physical. The closest that modern medicine may come to embracing this knowledge is the symbiotic relationship known as "psycho-soma" (from psycho = mind; and soma = body). In eastern medicine, of course, no separation is perceived, and the whole person is treated through manipulating the body's energy meridians, or energy channels that run throughout the body.

So, returning to the Sun, it's my belief that current and future earth changes, as well as human changes, will be directly influenced by the Sun. The Sun will govern our transition into a new form of life, in the same way our Earth is experiencing its own natural cycle and transition. The good news is that we are moving towards a new, greater existence on the level of biblical and ancient prophecy. Perhaps the result will truly be a form of 'heaven on earth.' (I mean this in the most general terms, as I do not wish to describe it further in fear of not grasping the parameters it may take.) The not-so-good news is there will be significant shifts in both our physical body and mind, as well as in the Earth itself.

Ancient texts in all forms; from the Bible to the Dead Sea Scrolls, warn of trying times as we adjust, or morph, into our new state of being. As we'll see in Chapter 12, human changes could take the form of emotional and mental anguish such as depression, anxiety, fatigue, rage, and bewilderment. They could also include new viruses and diseases, an area of human health challenges to which John Mini and I directed much of our conversation. We discussed how to best stay healthy, how new (which is really old) medicines will be valued; ancient methods of excreting toxins, and how to increase our immune system.

Believe me, this is one show you will listen to over and over again. To hear audio of the program, go to www.earthchangestv.com/audioarchives.php.

Don't Worry; Be Hopi

Turning to the Hopi tradition, one of the most memorable speakers came on March 27, 2001. Hopi Elder Chief Dan Dan Evehema had this message for mankind:

"We Hopi believe that the human race has passed through three different worlds and life ways since the beginning. At the end of each prior world, human life has been purified or punished by the Great Spirit, or Massau, due mainly to corruption, greed and turning away from the Great Spirit's teachings. The last great destruction was the flood which destroyed all but a few faithful ones who asked and received a permission from the Great Spirit to live with Him in this new land. The Great Spirit said, 'It is up to you, if you are willing to live my

72

poor, humble and simple life way. It is hard but if you agree to live according to my teachings and instructions, if you never lose faith in the life I shall give you, you may come and live with me.' The Hopi and all who were saved from the great flood made a sacred covenant with the Great Spirit at that time. We Hopi made an oath that we will never turn away from Him. For us the Creator's laws never change or break down.

"We are now faced with great problems, not only here but throughout the land. Ancient cultures are being annihilated. Our people's lands are being taken from them, leaving them no place to call their own. Why is this happening? It is happening because many have given up or manipulated their original spiritual teachings. The way of life which the Great Spirit has given to all its people of the world, whatever your original instructions are not being honored. It is because of this great sickness-called greed, which infects every land and country that simple people are losing what they have kept for thousands of years.

"Now we are at the very end of our trail. Many people no longer recognize the true path of the Great Spirit. They have, in fact, no respect for the Great Spirit or for our precious Mother Earth, who gives us all life.

"We are instructed in our ancient prophecy that this would occur. We were told that someone would try to go up to the moon: that they would bring something back from the moon; and that after that, nature would show signs of losing its balance. Now we see that coming about. All over the world there are now many signs that nature is no longer in balance. Floods, drought, earthquakes, and great storms are occurring and causing much suffering. We do not want this to occur in our country and we pray to the Great Spirit to save us from such things. But there are now signs that this very same thing might happen very soon on our own land."

As with Mayan tradition, Hopi prophecy also talks of us having Four Worlds, with the Fifth World about to emerge from the ashes of the Fourth, the timing signified by Nine Signs:

1. The coming of white-skinned men, who take land that is not theirs and who strike their enemies with thunder (guns)
2. The coming of spinning wheels filled with voices (covered wagons)

3. A strange beast like a buffalo but with long horns that over-runs the land in large numbers (cattle)
4. The land is crossed by snakes of iron (railroad tracks)
5. The land is crossed by a giant spider's web (power lines)
6. The land is crossed with rivers of stone that make pictures in the Sun (mirages on asphalt and concrete roads)
7. The sea turns black, killing many living things (oil spills)
8. Many youth, who wear their hair long like our people, come to the tribal nations to learn our ways and wisdom (hippies)
9. A dwelling-place in the heavens, above the earth, falls with a great crash, appearing as a blue star (future demise of a space station?).

These are the signs of impending great destruction, or 'columns of smoke and fire such as the white man has made in the deserts (above-ground atomic testing). Following the destruction, 'there will be much to rebuild.' And very soon afterward, The Great Spirit (known as Pahana or Massau) will return, bringing with him the dawn of the Fifth World.

The Great Purification
On March 7, 2000 Robert Morning Sky talked about the Hopi tradition of the 'Great Purification.'

"The final stage, called 'The Great Day of Purification,' has been described as a 'Mystery Egg' in which the forces of the swastika and the Sun plus a third force symbolized by the color red culminate either in total rebirth or total annihilation, we don't know which. But the choice is yours—war and natural catastrophe may be involved. The degree of violence will be determined by the degree of inequity caused among the peoples of the world and in the balance of nature. In this crisis rich and poor will be forced to struggle as equals in order to survive.

"The reality that it will be very violent is now almost taken for granted among Traditional Hopi, but man still may lessen the violence by correcting his treatment of nature and fellow man. Ancient spiritually-based communities, such as the Hopi, must especially be preserved and not forced to abandon their wise way of life and the natural resources they have vowed to protect.

"The man made system now destroying the Hopi is deeply involved in similar violations throughout the world. The devastating reversal predicted in the prophecies is part of the natural order. If those who thrive from that system, its money and its laws can manage to stop destroying the Hopi, then many may be able to survive the Day of Purification and enter a new age of peace. But if no one is left to continue the Hopi way, the hope for such an age is in vain.

"How can there be peace? Nowhere is there peace, not even within the Hopi peaceful society. Every nation on earth, from people in high places down to the lowest cast, are not at peace. How can peace be accomplished when weapons are made to kill? How can there be peace if people hate, not love? Perhaps the only alternative now is Purification.

"Since mankind has lost peace with one another through the conflict because of the new ways, the Great Spirit, and the Great Creator has punished the people in many ways. Through all of this there was always a small group who survived to keep the original ways of life alive. This small group are those who adhere to the laws of the Creator, who keep the spiritual path open, out from the circle of evil. According to our knowledge we are not quite out of the circle.

"The men with ambitious minds will decrease, while the people of good hearts, who live in harmony with the earth, will increase until the earth is rid of evil. If the Hopi are right this will be accomplished and the earth will bloom again. The spiritual door is open, why not join the righteous people."

The Purification

The famous Hopi Prophecy Rock clearly depicts two paths:

- A 'two-hearted path,' with three individuals upon it. A two-hearted person is one who thinks with his head rather than his heart. Modern man is out of balance because he lives in a left-brain dominated society, leading to imbalance and conflict, and ultimately to the destruction of those on it.
- A 'one-hearted path,' or one that is in balance and harmony with the universe.

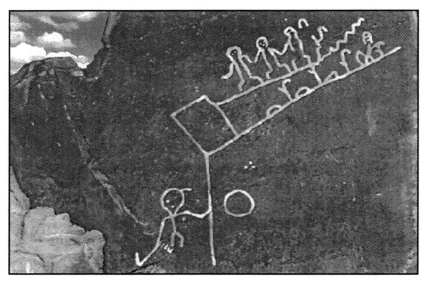

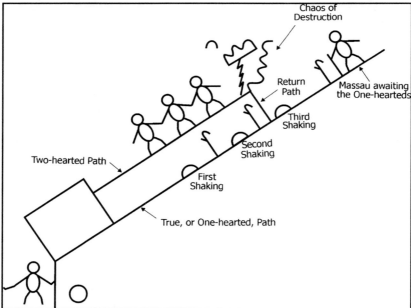

The Rock Prophecy shows a junction where the two-hearted people have a choice of choosing to start thinking with their hearts or continue to think with their heads only. If they choose the latter, it will lead to self-destruction, symbolized by the lightning strike from a cloud.

If people chose to think with their hearts, they will return to the one-hearted path and their own survival.

The Rock shows three half-circles that represent three world-shakings, as the Source strives to remind us of how we are all related. The first shaking occurs when man tosses bugs into the air (airplanes, first used in World War I). The second world-shaking occurs when man uses the Hopi migration symbol in war (swastika adopted by Hitler in World War II). The third shaking will be recognized by a red cover or cloak, which could point to Communist China. Hopi prophecy also says that signs of the third shaking will be:

- The trees die (acid rain or destruction of the rainforest).
- Man builds a house in the sky (space stations).
- Cold places become hot, and hot places will become cold (erratic weather).
- Lands sink into the ocean, and lands will rise out of the sea.
- The Blue Star Kachina appears.

Only by undergoing the Hopi process of Purification can we set foot on the Return Path to the One-hearted Path, and just hope that we haven't gone past that point. Purification involves a number of elements:

1. *Repentance*, or rethinking, of the Two-heated Way of Life. This involves commitment, deep knowing that we are all One, acceptance of personal power to create change, and following our inner guidance. It is good to do this in groups, because it reminds us that the whole is greater than the sum of the parts. Also, as individuals, we are so rooted in our Two-hearted ways that we need others to help point them out to us. Once we as a group have identified and committed to a One-hearted vision, we can begin to live it, first within the group, then increasingly in the outer Two-hearted world. Then like-minded groups may join together to form 'villages,' ready for when the Two-hearted Path collapses in ruins.

2. *Sovereignty*, or self-respect, and respect for the sovereignty of others. It is also about taking responsibility for our creations and good stewardship for whatever is in our sphere of influence. For example, the Fifth World view of the planet is as a

partner to be nurtured rather than as a resource to be consumed and discarded. Also, wealth and abundance will not be hoarded by those whose lands produce it, but will be shared equitably. Finally, any decision about stewardship will never be short-term but will consider the impact on future generations.

3. *Truthfulness.* Confusion over 'what should be' versus 'what is' separates us from the realities of life. We look for quick fixes, Hollywood endings and the latest fads rather than 'walking the talk' and 'doing the work.' One group may import 'what works' from another group and impose it on themselves, but disharmony may result. This leads to strife, conflict, and even war. Other cultures become too complex and collapse under their own weight, thrusting the people into anarchy until new ways are found. This is the inevitable outcome of the Two-hearted Path, and we are seeing its effects now as fewer and fewer Americans believe that government is 'by the people, for the people.' Our lives float between hope and fear, unrooted in 'what is.' From the moment of our birth, we are indoctrinated into membership of our culture, with prison or asylum awaiting dissenters. We leave school, trained to become 'another brick in the wall,' mindlessly perpetuating the Two-hearted Path. The Hopi language has no equivalent of, "I'm busy," or, "I'm sorry." Busy-ness and apology are not part of the One-hearted Path; and will not carry us through the collapse of the Fourth World and emergence into the Fifth.

We've already established that a significant shift is underway in consciousness in accepting weather and climate conditions. It is no longer a question of, "Are there 'earth changes'?" The only questions are: "How, what, when and where?" In other words, "What is it going to look like?" and to that we have no answers.

If you own your own house and fail to make mortgage payments, the bank can take the house back, but only after due process of law. Same if you rent; the house owner can evict you only after due process. Your real landlady, Mother Nature, offers no such protection. She can break your lease in a heartbeat and in any way she wants. A tornado in Seattle? An earthquake in New York City? Both unlikely, but not impossible.

This raises the issue of "safe areas." In 2000, I interviewed Will Carey, an expert in Permaculture on my show. I had just completed my opening monolog, part of which was showing the most current earthquakes of magnitude 5.0 or larger that had occurred within the last 72 hours. I may have mentioned something to the effect of: "Those living along the ring of fire may want to consider moving."

In response, Will pulled out four very detailed topographical maps of the United States, and asked, "So, Mitch, what makes you think living inland would be any safer than on the coast of California?"

I was thinking to myself: *Oh boy, I'm going to be torn to shreds right here, live on the air.* Thank goodness, Will was gentle with me. He started off with, "Now on this map, see all the rings that spread out from its center?"

He held up to the camera an area in the central plains. "Now Mitch, you don't want to live here. More people are killed by tornadoes here than any other natural cause. And see over here?" He was pointing to the Gulf of Mexico and Florida. "You don't want to live over here. Lots of hurricanes and floods. Can be a dangerous place to live." Then he pointed to the West Coast on yet another topo map and said, "See this over here? You don't want to live there. Lots of earthquakes and volcanoes."

By the time Will had finished, he had covered every single state on the map. The message was obvious. It's not *where* you live that will make the difference when the Earth Changes escalate. It will be *who* you live with. And yes, this includes yourself, and your ability to cope with rapid change and possible devastation. If you survive a major disaster, such as an earthquake, remember that the emergency services may be compromised, so be able to take care of yourself and those around you for up 72 hours.

Finally, I take comfort from the fact that wherever I am if disaster strikes is *exactly* where I'm *supposed to be. It is all part of a bigger plan, which as a limited human, I often cannot see.*

Perhaps ancient texts give us a definite affirmation that change is underway and escalating, but most prophecy stops short of giving us a more detailed outline. This is in perfect order. Why? The common thread that weaves in and out of every single prophecy by our ancestors is *US*. That is, *WE* have an influence on the energy around us.

When the Mayan Elders warned of what was to come between August 16 and December 15. 2003, they also said, "We have the opportunity to change our ways (thinking) and minimize what is to come."

Could that be true? Do we as humans really have such power? Are there enough conscious people in the world to make a profound difference at this time in history? My friend Gregg Braden wrote of this power in *The Isaiah Effect*. Also, the principle of *critical mass* applies, whereby enough people in unified contemplation on a matter can bring about the intended outcome.

So what happened with the Mayan Elders' warning for the latter half of 2003? A Google search on "world's greatest natural disasters" reveals the following for 2003:

- Algeria: earthquake (2,266 dead)
- Andhra Pradesh, India: Heat wave (1,300 dead)
- France: Heat wave (15,000 dead)
- Bam, Iran: earthquake (26,300 dead)

Was 2003 notable in any way? Not really, especially compared to 2004:

- Al-Hoceima, Morocco: earthquake (571 dead)
- Haiti and Dominican Republic: rains (2,400 dead)
- Philippines: typhoon (1,000 dead)
- Southeast Asia: tsunamis (260,000 dead).

So what's going on? Remember that the Elders said they would perform Fire Ceremonies in an attempt to mitigate the disasters. Did it work? Or did they merely postpone *the* major disaster in S.E. Asia by a year? We'll never know. Or did the fact that thousands of people listening to my radio show set their intent for disasters to *not* happen in the latter part of 2003 make a difference? We'll never know.

What we *do* know from scientific studies is that we *can* make a difference.

In June 1993, a group led by a Dr. John Hagelin undertook a two-month study of the hypothesis that the level of HRA crime (homicide, rape and assault) in Washington D.C. would drop if a large group participated in Transcendental Meditation®. Prior to the study, five years worth of FBI data was analyzed so that variables other than group size could be factored out. These included weather (crime usually spikes during the warm D.C. summers), changes in crime fighting techniques, and numbers of police officers on the force.

The results revealed a huge decrease in HRA crimes (solid line) associated with increases in group size (dotted line). The maximum decrease of 23% occurred during the final week of the project when the size of the group was largest at 3,800. Initially, with group size below 1,000, the drop

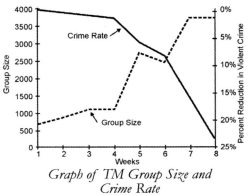

Graph of TM Group Size and Crime Rate

was only 1% compared with the same week for the previous five years, but once the group size reached an apparent critical mass of just over 1,000 in week 4, the crime rate began falling, first at 6%, then 8% and so on. (The probability of this happening by chance was computed at less than 1 in 500 million.) Study members calculated that 4,000 people continuing the practice indefinitely would have resulted in a 48% fewer HRA crimes compared with the previous five years.

Given the grave human and financial costs of violent crime, researchers urged policy makers to look at applying this approach on a large scale. Considering the reduced levels of fear in the community, and avoidance of trauma and bodily pain, TM seems to be a great investment, especially when it costs the community up to $50,000 to prosecute offenders and $20,000 a year to incarcerate them.

How does it work? Researchers attribute the drop in HRA crime to increased community coherence and reduced stress levels. Of course, cynics came crawling out of the woodwork but, finding the results unassailable, they could only mount personal attacks on researchers. Once again, the debunkers were debunked.

Another field study was reported by Dr. John Davies, co-director of Partners in Conflict and Peacebuilding at the University of Maryland, in *The Journal of Conflict Resolution*, 1988. In 1983, great tension existed between Israel and Lebanon, and 200 experienced meditators assembled in Jerusalem. They meditated together for seven periods between 1983 – 1985, during which the daily death toll from the conflict fell from 12 to 2, a 70 percent drop, and rose back to 12 after each period. Based on police records, violent crime also fell during those periods, as did traffic fatalities and other accidental deaths.

Also during one of the periods, the Lebanese government and opposition parties were able to forge a cease-fire and security plan, which Syria and Israel also ratified. However, when the period ended and the group disbanded, all the peace accords fell apart.

So what was going on? Maharishi Yogi said that if only one percent of a population meditated regularly, that was enough to create critical mass, and if they actually assembled together, you only need the square root of that number because body, mind and heart are all aligned. Unlike ordinary light, laser light can be beamed as far as the moon because it's *coherent*, i.e., the photons/waves are all aligned with each other, and don't cancel each other out. The same thing is true of the minds of people who meditate together—they form a coherent, harmonious field that exists independent of space, which influences everyone in the culture.

Group Coherence

The above TM-induced reduction in the crime rates involves *non-focus*, in that TM is about emptying the mind and radiating calm, peaceful energy. But what happens when two or more people get 'on the same wavelength'? Does a kind of group-think emerge that is greater than the sum of its parts? Anecdotally, we know that's true but a group at Princeton proved it scientifically.

A random number generator (RNG) is a box of electronics that randomly generates a 1 or a 0. The RNG they used does this 200 times a second, and over a minute, say, should produce 6,000 1's and 6,000 0's. Researchers use it to test whether individuals can entrain the RNG to deliver more 1's or 0's by focusing on that outcome, but here, they used it in a totally different way to see what would happen if a group came into coherence.

The researchers took their RNG to a group of people working on a joint project and set it going, while psychologists observed the group. While the group was in conflict over the project, the RNG results were pretty much 50/50, but when the group snapped into coherence and seemed to go into a 'mental lock-step,' thinking as one rather than as individuals, the group-think also blasted the RNG and it went two standard deviations from chance. (Whether it produced more 1's or more 0's didn't matter; what *did* matter was that it went way out of balance.) And the effect was non-local in that they affected the machine even when it was moved to another building.

When the results were revealed to the group, many members were excited to learn that something they had sensed intuitively was physically measurable, and productivity increased in subsequent group activity.

So the study proved three things:

1. Group coherence is a real phenomenon.
2. It is consistent and verifiable, in that whenever it happens, the RNG behaves the same way each time.
3. Even through group-mind happens spontaneously and cannot be scheduled, the RNG can signal to the group that the phenomenon is occurring.

Item #3 is interesting. What are the implications of a machine signaling the group that they are in harmony? How could a project manager use this information to direct the group? Or what if public speakers could know whether their audience with 'with them' and adjust their presentation accordingly? Or politicians informed that the crowd was for or against them? The mind boggles.

The researchers also found that groups of all women come into coherence faster than all-male groups because of what they call 'posturing' on the part of men. Mixed groups fall in the middle because members must establish a comfort zone with each other. Also, women seem more sensitive to coherence as it happens.

What are the implications for us? We now have proof of the power of group focus, such as prayer, meditation and visualization; the power is real, and not just some New Age woo-woo. So when two or more are gathered for a single purpose, they can *know* that the mental entity they are forming has the power to change the physical plane and influence events.

Group coherence actually has an interesting story. Under Princeton University's emeritus researcher Dr. Roger Nelson, the Global Consciousness Project aims to detect whether humanity shares a single subconscious mind that we all tap into without realizing. It is based on the pioneering work of Prof. Jahn, one of the first scientists to take seriously such paranormal phenomena as telepathy, telekinesis and ESP. At the heart of this effort lies a small black box, about the size of a calculator, that endlessly cranks out a stream of 1's and 0's at random. In any given second, this Random Event Generator (REG) should generate 100 of each, resulting in a flat line.

Prof. Jahn was the first to ask groups to concentrate their minds on his number generator and make it produce more 1's than 0's. The results were stunning and proved that people could influence the machine. The known laws of science say it's impossible, but it happened … and kept on happening.

Next, his colleague, Dr. Nelson, installed 40 REGs worldwide, linked by the Internet. The hub computer combines the 40 inputs to produce what is usually a typical flat line, as the numbers of 1's equal the number of 0's. However, on the morning of Saturday, September 6, 1997, the flat line went berserk just as one billion people around the globe tuned their TVs to the funeral of Princess Diana. Nelson was at a loss to explain how the massive outpouring of grief could affect his equipment in that way, but early in the morning of September 11, 2001, that flat line again became disturbed. It appeared that mass consciousness had had a premonition that something 'big' was in the works and had impacted the global REG output. Just four hours later came the attacks on the World Trade Center. And it happened again on December 25, 2004, 24 hours before the Asian tsunami that killed over a quarter million people.

Today, a total of 65 REGs in 41 countries monitor mass consciousness, with startling results. They have sensed every major world event, such as the NATO bombing of Yugoslavia, the loss of the Russian submarine *Kursk*, and global celebrations such as New Year's Eve. What really puzzles researchers is the *prediction* of the WTC events by four hours, and the S.E. Asia tsunami by 24 hours. By showing up hours ahead of time, such mass premonitions go way beyond simultaneous response to events as they happen. Unfortunately, the REG network can warn us that something is imminent but can't tell us exactly what. But what they *do* tell us is that we're all *far more connected* than we realize.

Can we use this innate human ability to moderate severe weather? If enough of us joined out telepathic forced, could we, say, 'steer' a hurricane along a harmless northerly path instead of west into Florida?

Merging Science and the Esoteric

From the inception of Earth Changes TV, my goal has been to give a balanced view of current science and ancient text. This would include what many call metaphysical or spiritual issues. As most of you know, I have had the top scientists in their field on my show—seismologists, paleontologists, astrophysicists, climatologists, geo-scientists, and the list goes on. I have also had disciplines in the more esoteric fields such as those who study the power of prayer, biblical history, Mayan and Aztec Calendars, Hopi Indians, Sumerians, the Dogon tribe, the Dead Sea Scrolls, and again the list goes on.

As I have said so many times before, never has the gap between science and spirit been so narrow. I believe we are close to hearing public announcements by the mainstream scientific community, acknowledging fully the credibility of ancient texts. It may go something like this: "We must know the past to understand the present, which tells us of the future."

The announcements and articles presented on ECTV, which have been the forerunner for so many news agencies, has been able to maintain the credibility and honor of presenting factual information using current science and personal research material, and connecting such directly to ancient texts. Earth Changes TV has now been acknowledged as one of the front runners for the study of solar activity and its relation to earth weather and human behavior.

I am humbled and grateful to announce that our website receives over ten million hits per day. The increase in hits coming from .gov., .mil, .edu addresses are a sure sign that many of our more conservative mainstream news sources and researchers are taking a keen interest in our material. Thank you for helping us become the 'new kid on the block,' and becoming a true and valued investigative source for the times we are in, and the significant changes ahead.

Edgar Cayce on Earth Changes

Edgar Cayce was possibly the best known clairvoyant of the 20th century. Dubbed "The Sleeping Prophet" because of his practice of going into trance to do readings, he forecast that the years between 1958 and 1998 would indeed be a period of great global transformation, with such events as the rising of Atlantis. However, these changes would not lead to TEOTWAWKI (The End of the World as We Know It) but to the dawning of a New Age of hope for humanity.

The groups predicting major cataclysms are failing to see that change is all about us—floods, earthquakes, tsunamis, famines, and strife based on politics, race, gender, culture, and religion divide and/or kill us. Yet many still await the Big One, be it a killer asteroid or other apocalyptic evidence of Earth Changes.

"But," Cayce said, "changes are happening *right now*. Our world, our civilization, and our individual lives are all undergoing dramatic personal and collective change, but because the changes are slow and incremental, it's hard for us to see them." Cayce predicted not so much about killer earthquakes but about the birth of a new world.

Of course, there will always be earthquakes, hurricanes and floods, but Cayce stressed the importance of us coming together as one global community to bring in the dawn of the New Age. From his perspective, the future offers not doom and disaster, but transformation, hope and community for mankind. Looked at from outer space, we are one global family living on an 8,000-mile-diameter ball of rock. Our collective destiny is to become spiritual beings living in harmony with the Earth

Cayce once gave a specific reading regarding sunspots, in which he said:

Sunspots, as well as earth changes, are reflections of our own state of consciousness, a result of our own actions, the boomerang of divine law. Sunspots are reflection of the 'turmoil and strife' that we ourselves have created, and our own mind is 'the builder.' Think about what you have built: *As what does thy soul appear? A spot, a blot up the Sun? Or as that which giveth light unto those who sit in darkness, to those who cry aloud for hope?* [Reading #5757-1]

The responsibility for earth changes lies squarely on our shoulders, and how we conduct our relationships with others has everything to do with the changing face of the earth. Earth changes are 'adjustments' that have to be made because something is out of align-ment. Just as we create chaotic conditions by our own out-of-align-ment behavior, so we can create positive transformation by our loving attitudes and actions.

In his book, *Edgar Cayce on the Millennium*, author Jess Stearn wrote: "In the final sequence of his life, the great prophet saw the relationship of man to his Creator as more tangible and consequential than any El Niño or eruption of the earth."

And in Hugh Lynn Cayce's *Earth Changes Update*, Cayce is reported as saying, "We are not ruled by the world, our environment or even planetary influences, but by our own free will. When we disregard di-vine law, we bring chaos and destructive forces into our life; when we are in harmony with the Divine, we create order out of chaos."

Final Words of Wisdom from the Lakota

We are all relations. The Sacred Mother (Earth) is screaming for life. Go to where the eagles fly, to where the wolf roams, to where the bear lives. Here you will find life because they will always go to where the water is pure and the air can be breathed. Live where the trees, the lungs of this earth, purify the air. There is a time coming, beyond the weather. The veil between the physical and the spiritual world is thinning.

It is time for the Great Purification. We are at a point of no return. The two-legged are about to bring destruction to life on Earth. It's happened before, and it's about to happen again. The Sacred Hoop shows how all things go in a circle. The old becomes new; the new becomes old. Everything repeats. Culture is having roots in the Earth. People without culture don't exist very long because Nature is God. Without a connection to Nature, the people drift, grow negative, de-stroy themselves. In the beginning, we had one mind, and it was posi-tive, a thing of beauty, seeing beauty everywhere.

The Last Word from Chief Seattle

In the 1800s, the chief of the Suquamish allegedly wrote this letter to the American Government:

The President in Washington sends word that he wishes to buy our land. But how can you buy or sell the sky? the land? The idea is strange to us. If we do not own the freshness of the air and the sparkle of the water, how can you buy them?

Every part of the earth is sacred to my people. Every shining pine needle, every sandy shore, every mist in the dark woods, every meadow, every humming insect. All are holy in the memory and experience of my people.

We know the sap which courses through the trees as we know the blood that courses through our veins. We are part of the earth and it is part of us. The perfumed flowers are our sisters. The bear, the deer, the great eagle, these are our brothers. The rocky crests, the dew in the meadow, the body heat of the pony, and man all belong to the same family.

The shining water that moves in the streams and rivers is not just water, but the blood of our ancestors. If we sell you our land, you must remember that it is sacred. Each glossy reflection in the clear waters of the lakes tells of events and memories in the life of my people. The water's murmur is the voice of my father's father.

The rivers are our brothers. They quench our thirst. They carry our canoes and feed our children. So you must give the rivers the kindness that you would give any brother.

If we sell you our land, remember that the air is precious to us, that the air shares its spirit with all the life that it supports. The wind that gave our grandfather his first breath also received his last sigh. The wind also gives our children the spirit of life. So if we sell our land, you must keep it apart and sacred, as a place where man can go to taste the wind that is sweetened by the meadow flowers.

Will you teach your children what we have taught our children? That the earth is our mother? What befalls the earth befalls all the sons of the earth.

This we know: the earth does not belong to man, man belongs to the earth. All things are connected like the blood that unites us all. Man did not weave the web of life, he is merely a strand in it. Whatever he does to the web, he does to himself.

Chapter 6

Earth Changes Escalate –
New Records Made!

Unlike Chapter 4, which talked about climatic cycles, this chapter is about the weather—events measured in minutes as with a brief twister, to weeks as when a tropical depression spawns off the coast of Africa and over the next several days, deepens to become a named hurricane that barrels west towards the U.S. But more specifically, this chapter is about *record-breaking* weather. It seems nowadays that records are being broken at ever-faster rates; in fact, we may even see records being broken for the most records broken in a month. Is it just that weather monitoring is getting better, or is some other phenomenon at work here?

Since 2000, I do not believe there has been one single month that did not make 'new records.' Earth changes are escalating, and never before in our recent history is it more important to 'be aware and prepare.' Chapter 15 (Preparing for Earth Changes) will offer information to improve our personal and national survival, but this chapter sets the scene for a *time to be aware and prepare.*

On December 31, 2000, Reuters put out a piece titled **Natural Disasters Reported at Record Level in 2000** in which they reported that the world was hit by a record number of natural disasters in 2000 and predicted that this would only get worse due to a rising population, according to Munich Re, the world's largest reinsurer. Apparently, what they consider to be natural disasters rose in number by more than 100 to 850 in 2000, although the number of deaths (10,000) was much lower than in 1999 (75,000) because less populated areas were involved. Material damage in 2000 was estimated at more than $30 billion.

Storms were clearly at the top of the list of disasters, accounting for 73 percent of all insured losses, while floods accounted for 23 percent of insured losses, hitting Mozambique in February worse, making half a million people homeless.

Devastating forest fires in the U.S. was the other major cause of losses—more than $1 billion, despite the fact that relatively less property was damaged.

How true is it that things seem to be getting worse? Yes, we see more disasters on the TV, as was noticeable in December 2004 when the TV news was saturated by footage about the tsunamis. But perhaps the presence of all those tourist camcorders played a role in intensifying the emotional impact on viewers. Without downplaying the tragedy that ripped so many people's lives apart and killed over a quarter million, we *saw* more of this disaster.

Winter 2000/2001 was quite a roller-coaster. On March, 16, 2001, ABC News reported that the winter just past had been 'abnormally cold.' Meteorologists at the National Climactic Data Center were reporting that for the lower 48, we'd just gone through the coldest winter in five years. Oddly, Alaskans had enjoyed the warmest winter on record since records began in 1918.

Such severe weather is one in the eye for the many scientists who attribute global warming to higher levels of greenhouse gases, including carbon dioxide.

"This winter was unusually cold," said Jay Lawrimore of the National Climactic Data Center. "But you have to consider that in the last 20 years, about three-quarters of the winters have been warmer than normal. This is just a novel season."

Kevin Trenberth, head of climate analysis at the National Center for Atmospheric Research, pointed out, "Europe and Western Russia—as well as Alaska—followed warming trends this past season. New studies suggest warming sea temperatures appear to be the main factor behind warmer winter seasons in these regions. The waves set up in a way so it was cold in the 48 states, but upstream and downstream it was exceptionally warm."

The National Climactic Data Center indicated that average U.S. temperatures have risen by almost one degree Fahrenheit in the past century. And data from the last 25 years reveal a more sudden change, suggesting that temperatures are rising at a rate of more than 3 degrees every one hundred years.

Lawrimore explained that this winter's main anomaly was the month of December, which was the seventh coldest on record for the 48 states and pushed winter averages below normal. February and March, meanwhile, featured more or less normal temperatures in the continental states. "Polar air funneled down from the Arctic and became the dominating weather factor for central U.S. and the Northeast. In Alaska, however, a warm maritime flow kept normally icy regions somewhat mild. In Fairbanks, temperatures registered 12 °F above normal while Anchorage was 9 °F warmer than usual.

The winter was not only cold, but also dry. During what was the 13th driest U.S. winter in the past 106 years, much of the Southeast and Northwest received far below their average levels of rain or snowfall. The dry conditions have already led to outbreaks of wildfires in Florida and Lawrimore says other states are now poised for burns. "Communities in the Northwest rely on melting snowpacks for water needs in the summer, so there is a concern of drought in those areas."

On October 30, 2002, I wrote the following article for ECTV with the same name as this chapter:

We have been witness to some of the harshest weather Europe has ever seen. I took special interest in quick temperature deviations, indicating as much as 10 °C variance within minutes. But even more significant were the so-called "freak storms" that are now a common term used to describe tornado-strength winds without the funnel. Parts of Europe clocked wind speeds in these straight-line storms in excess of 150 mph. Eyewitnesses often say, "The winds just seemed to come out of nowhere. It was frightening."

This type of event occurs when the jet stream dips from as high as 30,000 ft. down to almost ground level—often referred to as "hitting the deck." In winter and spring, when the tropopause (the thin layer of atmosphere between the troposphere and the stratosphere) drops to lower altitudes, the jet stream may make large bends under the influence of low- altitude pressure systems. These bends create significant weather changes. So what creates low-altitude pressure? You guessed it! The Sun. When the geomagnetic storms hit the magnetic field that surrounds the Earth, the magnetic field warps to absorb the blow. When this is done, pressure from the force of our defending magnetic field shoves jet stream winds downward, so far downward at times that it literally "hits the deck." This sort of phenomenon is behind a new term in the English language—*freak weather*.

Today's (10/30/02) sunspot count is at 168 and we are currently experiencing an M-class flare. I expect a CME to follow sometime today. Over the last 5 days, we've had geomagnetic storms hitting us one after the other. They are so close together, we can hardly distinguish the end of one from the beginning of another.

We have seen rain and wind storms slam our central states. We were also witness to a late season hurricane sneak onto the East Coast. Watch for continued 'record breaking' weather to continue.

On January 21, 2000, under the title, **More Powerful Hurricanes Predicted**, I posted a BBC News Online report warning that U.S. hurricanes may get more powerful in the next few decades, and that their higher winds could wreak more damage. Dr Chris Landsea of NOAA's hurricane research division told the BBC program *Costing the Earth* that he no longer thought the fictitious ploy called 'global warming' was responsible, but that more frequent and intense hurricanes were due to a natural cycle.

Landsea said, "Our best estimates now are that the frequency of hurricanes won't change much, but the intensities may go up by five or ten percent. A ten percent increase in the strength of the strongest hurricanes might mean between 50–100 percent more damage. That's a magnitude that's worth worrying about."

This topic is not idle chatter. For example, in July 2002, South Carolinians were running out of drinking water. The million or so people living in the Pee Dee River basin rely on the water in several reservoirs along the Yadkin River in North Carolina, and without extensive rains, those reservoirs had only a few weeks of water left, and would run dry by mid-September. Then water levels along the Pee Dee could drop by 80 percent, closing down many manufacturing plants. In a region whose unemployment rate hovers around 8 percent, that would be a disaster, with up to 20,000 jobs being lost.

A severe drought had gripped the southeastern states for five years. Hardest hit were central Georgia, the Carolinas and central Virginia, with some areas 60 inches below normal rainfall totals. Farmers were getting by day-to-day, but the underground aquifers were depleted, wells were running dry, and mandatory water restrictions were in force. Depleted aquifers do not just fill up overnight after a good shower; getting back to normal can take a decade of above average rainfall. (Heavy rainfall doesn't do much good, however. When a massive storm dropped up to 15 inches of rain in the Dallas/Fort Worth area, three days later, well levels were lower than before the storm. Most of the rain simply ran off because the ground was unable to absorb it.)

Statistically, the 1950s drought was more serious, but population had doubled in the past four decades, increasing water needs for drinking and industry. But in 2002, several businesses along the Pee Dee River temporarily shut down, with water-intensive industries such as textile and paper manufacturers planning to relocate, costing the area at least 2,500 jobs. In Georgetown County, water plant workers had to close their intakes during high tide, because there was not enough river water to keep seawater at bay. With streams and wells going dry, farmers were forced to sell livestock at lower prices, and many lost their farms. So real lives were impacted in very real ways.

Long range forecasts through the fall of 2002 were not optimistic. Less than normal rainfall was predicted, although some looked to the expected El Niño effect in the winter, when the region could receive above normal rainfall, as in the winter of 1998.

Record-Breakers from February 2004

Record-breaking temperatures in England

The Central England Temperature (CET) series is one of the most reliable and longest standing records of temperature in the world. The Met Office's Hadley Centre for Climate Prediction and Research, based in Exeter, has today released figures showing that recent warm weather has swept away previous records.

The overnight CET minimum temperature for February 3 – 4, 2004 was 52 °F (11 °C), beating the previous February figure of 50 °F (10 °C), dating back to 1878. The mean February 4 CET was 55 °F (13 °C), beating the previous February record of 54 °F (12 °C) from 1960, making it the warmest February 4 since recordkeeping began in 1772.

Generally, temperatures across central and southern parts of the UK were around 15 °F (8 °C) above normal on February 4, 2004.

The main reason for this exceptionally warm weather across southern Britain was the tropical source of the air—across the Atlantic Ocean, which is unusually warm for February. Sea-surface temperatures were around 3.5–5.5 °F (2–3 °C) above normal.

Record-Breaking Cold Bites Florida, Nips Southeast

Freezing temperatures reached south to Melbourne on Florida's east coast. A hard freeze dropped temperatures into the mid-20s for up to 8 hours. Tallahassee set a record low of 18 °F (-7 °C). The previous record for Feb. 28 of 24 °F (-4 °C) was set in 1935. Apalachicola also set a record low of 26 °F (-3 °C), sinking below the 27 °F recorded in 1935. Jacksonville and Gainesville both broke their record lows with 25 °F, a degree lower than records set in 1943 and 1935, respectively. The Florida Panhandle city of Crestview, sometimes called the icebox of the state, recorded Florida's lowest temperature of 14 °F (-10 °C).

It was the coldest air of the winter and only the second time an outbreak of Arctic air reached the state of Florida. The USA had been enjoying a benign winter, but that changed when frigid air, bottled up in northern Canada, Alaska and Siberia, began spilling south. Temperatures in Alaska warmed up some 30 to 40 degrees as the chill drained, while temperatures in much of the USA dropped by similar amounts as the Arctic front passed through.

The story of cold was repeated across the South and even parts of the mid-Atlantic, with up to 50 new low temperature records being set from Texas to W. Virginia. The previous day, 60 records were toppled in the cold across the southern Plains. For example, Austin's morning temperature dipped to 24 °F (-4 °C), breaking the previous record low for Feb. 28 of 28 °F (-2 °C) set in 1962. Houston beat its 1935 record low of 29 °F by one degree.

New Orleans also set a new record with 32 °F (0 °C) eclipsing the old record of 35 °F (1 °C) set in 1948. At Cape Canaveral, the launch of the shuttle Columbia was delayed a day due to the cold temperature of 38 °F (3 °C).

Records Fall as Northeast Temperatures Plummet

Temperatures also dropped well below zero across the Northeast, making it the coldest day in a decade for some cities and keeping all but the hardiest people indoors.

The lowest low was at St. Johnsbury, Vt., with -27 °F (-32 °C), the National Weather Service said. At Saranac Lake, New York, the unofficial low was -34 °F (-36 °C). Logan International Airport recorded a low of -3 °F (-19 °C), two degrees chillier than the previous record for January 10, set in 1875.

The wind chill dropped the perceived cold by 15–25 °F (8–14 °C) in parts of Massachusetts. At the NFL playoff game in Foxboro between the Tennessee Titans and New England Patriots, the kickoff temperature was 4 °F (-15 °C), with a wind chill at -10 °F (-23 °C).

The lowest low was recorded at the top of New Hampshire's Mount Washington, elevation 6,288 feet at a bone-chilling -38 °F (-38 °C).

Record Breaking January Warmth in Chicago! Flood Watch

Thunderstorms threatened up to 1½ inches of additional rainfall as Chicago's January temperatures soared into the 60s, coming close to the previous record high for the date (January 12) of 62 °F (16 °C) set back in 1890.

Storm-generated downpours and the record warmth quickly melted the snow cover over southern Chicago, making for run-off problems. Thunderstorms created hail and rain downpours, and record numbers of lightning strikes, with continued heavy rainfall and the runoff from melting snow threatened to produce extensive river flooding.

2005: Already a Year of Broken Records

January

As we've just seen, 2005 began with record-breaking snowfall in New England. Boston's January total was 43.1 inches, more snow than in any month since the National Weather Service began keeping records in 1892. Elsewhere in the world:

- Two feet of snow fell in Des Plaines, Il., tying long-standing records.
- Chaotic weather plagued Australia, with Victoria recording its coldest day in history at 32 °F (9 °C). (Remember that this is their summer.) Victoria also suffered the worst dust storm in a decade. Melbourne recorded its heaviest rainfall since records began in 1856.
- In Japan, the heaviest snowfall in 20 years killed three people. Afghanistan also suffered their worst snowfall ever.
- The worst snowstorm on record hit Moscow, closing airports, and snarling city traffic with 3-foot snowdrifts. This came after some of the mildest January temperatures on record, where the first 10 days were the warmest spell in over a century, the temperature approaching the record high of 42 °F (6 °C) degrees set in 1992.
- Areas of Utah received 149 percent of the normal precipitation, with 3.7 inches more water than normal. Provo Canyon got 7.7 inches more than normal—about 170 percent of the normal precipitation.
- Jammu, India received the first snow in recorded history.
- In Saudi Arabia, heavy rain and flash floods killed 29 people in Medina, the worst storm in 20 years.
- Seattle's January 19 high of 62 °F (16 °C) broke the previous high of 60 °F (15 °C) set in 1961.
- The Cape of South Africa suffered its worst drought since 1978.
- Portugal was also gripped by the nation's worst drought in more than two decades.

February

During February 2005, things got even wilder:

- Greenland's official record of 61 °F (16 °C) was the highest since record keeping began in 1958. An unprecedented and unexplained heat wave struck, melting off glaciers at record speeds. The warm air originated in the Caribbean, and rolled north along the frontal edge of the jet stream.

- Singapore was gripped by the worst drought in 29 years.
- Kashmir was blanketed under the worst snowfall in 20 years, with up to 15 feet in areas, with almost 40 people dying in avalanches and over 60 reported missing since Saturday.
- England was paralyzed by the heaviest snowfall in decades, with more blizzards expected.
- The LA Basin was drenched by the heaviest rainfall in 22 years.
- A mega-cyclone hit American Samoa's Manu'a Islands, reportedly the worst in memory.
- Bad weather in Australia continued, breaking about 100 records, including highest daily rainfall ever, wettest February ever, first sub-zero maximum temperature ever in Australia in February, and coldest February day ever.
- Heavy rains and snow lashed a vast region of Pakistan. The Islamabad area was hit with 12 feet (4m) of snow in five weeks, the most in 10 years. Rainfall in Baluchistan was the heaviest in 15 years.
- Areas of India received their heaviest snowfall in 25 years, plus record cold temperatures.
- Iran suffered its coldest winters in decades, with record snowfalls that paralyzed air and road travel, and closed schools and government offices.
- Afghanistan's snowfall continued to break records.
- Bulgaria was under one of its gravest winters in decades, blanketed by six feet of snow due to a rare Mediterranean cyclone packing winds of 45 mph. More than 140 villages were left without electricity and 72 continue to be deprived of water because of the damages incurred by the storm. Temperatures dropped to 0 °F (-18 °C).
- Thick winter smog blanketed southeastern Quebec, prompting the first ever smog alert in a February.
- Snowpack reached record lows in the Northwest U.S., with Montana enjoying an unseasonably warm spell. Snowpack in the Black Hills of South Dakota tied the lowest in 62 years. Washington state's January snowpack was the lowest in 28 years.

March

The year didn't let up anywhere around the globe, but Europe was hit particularly hard:

- Snow and fog triggered huge pile-ups and the cancellation of air and train traffic throughout Europe today as temperatures fell to a 100-year low in Germany, where even fur was not enough to keep the lions warm. Heaters had to be taken to zoos.

- Temperatures also plunged to record levels as the continent experienced one of its worst cold snaps in years.

- At least 25 people were injured in Germany in two pile-ups on an autobahn engulfed in thick fog. Rescuers worked to cut people free from the wreckage while the autobahn from Munich to Lindau in southern Germany was blocked in both directions following the crashes involving at least 100 vehicles. A 30-car pile-up also cut off Scotland's main highway linking Glasgow to Edinburgh, but no one was injured.

- In Spain, air traffic was disrupted out of Madrid and Barcelona by snow, with 180 flights grounded in Barcelona's El Prat airport alone. Trains were forced to return to stations in Spain's Grenada and Almeria, while frozen tracks led to the cancellation of dozens of trains in Switzerland.

- Ferries were also cancelled between Spain and Morocco due to strong winds in the Strait of Gibraltar, and port authorities in the Spanish enclave of Cueta on the Moroccan coast said winds had damaged several boats, including some police patrol boats.

- Records were broken across the continent. the Swiss capital Bern registered 4 °F (-16 °C), its coldest at this time of the year since data began to be collected in 1901. Croatia had its coldest night since 1963, with -6 °F (-21 °C) in the central parts of the country.

- France beat records set in 1971. It was coldest in the village of Saugues in the western region of Haute-Loire where thermometers registered -21 °F (-30 °C) overnight.

- Worst hit though was the Berchtesgaden region near Germany's border with Austria, with temperatures of -47 °F (-44 °C), close to the -51 °F (-46 °C) record set in 2001.

- At Stuttgart airport, the mercury dropped to -2 °F (-19 °C)—the lowest temperature in March in 105 years.
- The cold wave also cost millions of euros. Authorities in the southern Spanish city of Huelva said the cold snap has so far caused 80 million euros ($134 million) worth of crop damage in the region, including 26 million tonnes of strawberries.

It's Not Your Imagination ...

On Sunday May 22, 2005, I wrote a piece for the ECTV website under the above title in response to some pretty wild weather around that time:

> If you thought the weather lately is 'out of whack,, you are absolutely correct. Others may go further to say, "People have been acting different lately." This too, may not be off base. The weather is extreme and unusual, and as you will see from the articles below, the words "freak storm" and "record breaking" are used quite often.
>
> Why? Well you know this, but certainly worth mentioning again. It's the Sun. Always has been throughout history. We are at the beginning of a sharp increase in unstable weather conditions. And guess what? We are right on time. The Earth has seen this many times before and at much greater extremes. Most Earth scientists say we simply have been in a long period of stable conditions which is really more the exception rather than the rule.

How accurate was that prediction? Lets take a look at what occurred in just the next 72 hours:

Record Heat to Continue on Sunday

The National Weather Service reported that an unseasonable strong upper level high pressure system centered over West Texas would bring record heat to North Texas. High temperatures reached the upper 90s across North Texas with heat index values approaching 105 degrees. These forecasted temperatures broke the daily records for both Dallas/Fort Worth and Waco. Because this is the first episode of hot weather this year, residents were encouraged to reduce outdoor activities, drink lots of water or other non-alcoholic beverages, wear light colored-light weight clothing, and if possible spend more time in air conditioned or well ventilated areas.

15,000 Flee as Freak Tide Hits

Australia Broadcast Corporation reported that in southern India, upwards of 15,000 villagers were forced to flee their homes, following a freak wave. Small fishing hamlets in Kerala State were flooded by seawater, prompting fears of a tsunami. Sixteen makeshift camps were established to house the evacuees and fishermen were warned not to take their boats out to sea. It was unclear what triggered the freak high tides.

Freak Storm Shocks Forecasters

Reuters said the first and most severe of two storm cells developed in about 10 minutes about 5.30pm (AEST) yesterday, leaving no time for the Bureau of Meteorology to issue a severe weather warning.

The temperature in Brisbane *dropped by five degrees in a matter of minutes* and up to 50mm of rain fell in some suburbs. More storms were forecast for the Brisbane area later today, due to the mid-level cold air pool, he said. "Most of the havoc was from the large amount of small hail but pea-sized hail doesn't fit our warning criteria because it doesn't do any damage." Some of the hail covered the ground early today in some inner-western suburbs.

Rescue Planes Brave Freak Weather Conditions to Search for 26 Missing

In Chile, the 17th Infantry Battalion was trapped by a "tsunami of snow" as the soldiers made the 25 km journey from a camp in Los Barros to another known as Las Cortinas. When extreme weather occurred, order broke down and it was every man for himself as the *weather changed from minute to minute.*

NOAA: Busy Hurricane Season Ahead

NOAA forecasters expressed concern that the 2005 Atlantic hurricane season will be worse than average along the East and Gulf coasts — with up to five major hurricanes forecast. NOAA predicted up to 15 tropical storms, with as many as nine developing into hurricanes.

The Southwest Gets Soaked

The winter of 2004/5 was wet and wild for Southern California. According to NOAA, total rainfall for the rainy season (July 1 –June 30) in downtown Los Angeles was 37.25", making it the second wettest rainy season on record since 1877, and San Diego's Lindbergh Airport was 22.47", making it the third wettest rain season on record since 1850

Some other rainfall totals from southern California were LAX Airport – 26.51", Burbank Airport – 35.48", Santa Barbara Airport – 31.17" and Santa Ana Airport – 25.18".

Impacts on southern California included mudslides in which the hillside above La Conchita in Ventura County gave way, burying over a dozen homes under feet of mud and taking ten lives. All told, Southern California had the wettest winter in 120 years, courtesy of a weak El Niño system that brought warmer water to some parts of the Pacific, by pulling the jet stream farther south. Even Death Valley, which sometimes gets no rain, received four inches, leaving the normally parched badlands thick with wildflowers.

Combine all that rain with long periods of summer-like temperatures, and the state had 16 twisters, compared with the normal four or five statewide in a year. For example, on March 20, 2005, a tornado ripped through a 3-mile stretch of South San Francisco, damaging 54 homes and six commercial buildings, causing about $1 million in property damage.

So are weather events becoming either more numerous and/or more violent over time. Let's take a look at some statistics for floods and hurricanes (cyclones in the southern hemisphere)

Floods

On average, floods cause more deaths each year than any other natural disaster, and the Galveston hurricane-induced flood of September 8, 1900 was by far the deadliest flood in United States history, taking between 6,000–12,000 lives. (This is because it was actually a hurricane-driven storm surge, and came without warning.) Because the highest point of the island is only about eight feet above sea-level, with a 20-foot storm surge, residents didn't stand a chance because there *was* no higher ground to escape to.

In 1927, the lower Mississippi flooded, inundating around 27,000 square miles and killing hundreds of people - more than 1,000 by some estimates. The great Midwest flood of 1993 was the costliest flood in U.S. history, with estimated damages of $20 billion; however, only around 50 lives were lost.

Flood losses in other parts of the world dwarf U.S. losses of life, however. For example, in November 1970, Bangladesh lost 500,000 people and more than 138,000 in April 1991, due to flooding following a cyclone. And a staggering 3,000,000 died during massive flooding of the Yangtze River in China in 1931. (These numbers are the equivalent of the U.S. 'losing' a city the size of Houston or Phoenix.)

Let's take a look at the planet's worst floods in recent times (those taking 10,000 or more lives) to get an idea of whether things are getting more or less violent on the planet:

- 1911, China: 100,000
- 1931, China: 1,000,000–3,700,000
- 1931, China: 142,000
- 1935, China: 145,000
- 1954, Iran: 10,000
- 1954, China: 30,000
- 1971, North Vietnam: 100,000
- 1999, Venezuela: 15,000

This list suggests that loss of life was greater earlier in the 20th century, but there are many variables other than the weather. Foremost in reducing death tolls is improved flood control, such as China's massive Three-Rivers project, arguably the largest civil engineering project in history. Also, improvements in communication give better warning, so that people can move to high ground. So in terms of the human toll, things don't seem to be getting worse, but according to the rate at which records are getting broken, our environment is getting more intense. However, modern technology allows us to better predict disasters, modern communication allows us to tell those in harm's way about them, and modern medicine allows us to patch victims up better.

Hurricanes

Let's look at hurricanes/cyclones:
- 1900, Galveston: 6,000–12,000
- 1906, Hong Kong: 10,000

- 1912, China: 50,000
- 1922, China: 60,000
- 1942, India: 40,000
- 1963, Pakistan: 22,000
- 1965, Bangladesh: 30,000
- 1965, Bangladesh: 17,000
- 1965, Pakistan: 10,000
- 1970, Bangladesh: 500,000
- 1977, India: 20,000
- 1991, Bangladesh: 138,000
- 1998, Cental America, 11,000
- 1999, India:10,000

Hurricanes present no discernible evidence that weather events are getting more violent but major events do seem to be getting more numerous. Again, building improvements, early warning systems and evacuation planning reduce death tolls (see Chapter 15). However, the National Hurricane Center's hurricane tracking map for the 2004 season looks more like a diagram of the New York or London subway system.

Solar Activity and the Restless Earth

NASA scientists track solar activity in terms of flares, sunspots, and CMEs, and we know these bursts of high energy particles impact the earth and human beings in various ways But is there a link between solar maxima and natural disasters? Maybe. Seventy percent of the most powerful earthquakes in the 20th century occurred in the 40 years following 1960, which coincides with a warming trend, compared with only 30% in the 60 years before.

Has there been an increase in volcanic and seismic activity over the past half century? Many scientists claim that such activity is nothing out of the ordinary, so let's take a look. With a few exceptions, such as the 1906 San Francisco earthquake, the first half of the 20th century saw few volcanic eruptions and major earthquakes, but the last few decades have seen a jump in the number of earthquakes, volcanic eruptions and severe storms.

Let's start with Solar Cycle 21 (peaked 1979–1982):

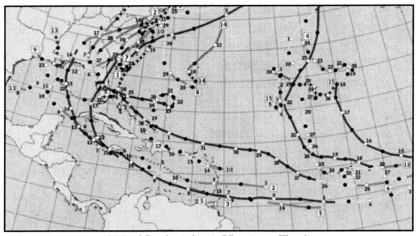

2004 North Atlantic Hurricane Tracks

- 1980: Mt. St. Helens
- 1982: El Chicon

For Solar Cycle 22 (peaked 1989–1991):
- 1989: Loma Prieta earthquake (N. California)
- 1990: Iranian earthquake kills 40,000
- 1991: Mount Pinatubo, Mt. Aetna
For Solar Cycle 23 (peaked 2000—2002)
- 1999: Taiwan earthquake devastates island
- 2000: Mt. Popocatpetyl, Mt Colima, Mt. Aetna
- 2001: Earthquakes in El Salvador, Seattle

Hey, Mitch, we need a wrap-up paragraph for this chapter. Any ideas?

Chapter 7

Solar Flares, CMEs
and 'The Equation'

The previous chapter discussed the accelerating rate at which weather-related records are being broken: highest rainfall in a 24-hour period, coldest day on record, deepest snowpack in history, etc. This chapter explains how and why this is happening.

Although only an average star, the Sun's visible surface has a temperature of nearly 10,000 °F, and the temperature of its outer atmosphere, or corona, reaches 1.8 million °F. Every second, it pumps out enough energy to power the U.S. for about 9 million years. It does this in three main ways:

1. Solar wind, emitted from coronal holes
2. Solar flares, emitted from sunspots, although they can erupt anywhere
3. Coronal mass ejections, also from sunspots.

Fortunately, most solar emissions storm career harmlessly into space, but some emanating from the equatorial region intersect with

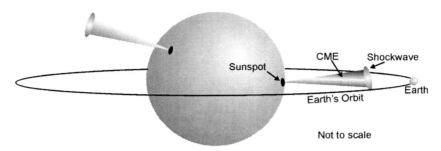

CMEs Erupting on the Sun's Surface

Earth's orbit just when Earth happens to be in the way. When this happens, even though it's only a minuscule fraction of the Sun's energy, it can have a devastating impact on our planet. For example, a modest solar storm in January 1997 poured 1,400 gigawatts of power into our planet's atmosphere over a two-day period—about twice the power-generating capacity of the United States.

Solar Wind is a stream of ionized particles that flows out from the Sun at a fairly steady rate of about one million tons per second, increasing when coronal holes form.

Solar flares are massive emissions of energy in many bands of the electromagnetic spectrum. Their precise cause is a mystery, but they often form near sunspots, relatively cool areas that appear as dark marks on the Sun's surface, which exist for several days to several weeks. At these locations, the lines of force of the Sun's magnetic field have become twisted and collapse. Somehow, this triggers a solar flare, a massive release of an enormous burst of energy, equivalent to maybe 40 billion Hiroshima-size atomic bombs. Since the 1960s, solar flares were blamed for auroral displays and geomagnetic events, but we now know this is not so.

A Coronal Mass Ejection (CME) is a huge bubble of coronal plasma, with a mass as large at 10 billion tons, forming its own intense magnetic field. During the Solar Minimum, CMEs can occur every few days, but two or three times a day during a Solar Maximum. Moving at enormous speeds, CMEs push the solar wind before them, creating a shockwave that hurtles through space, wreaking havoc on our planet's magnetic field and weather systems.

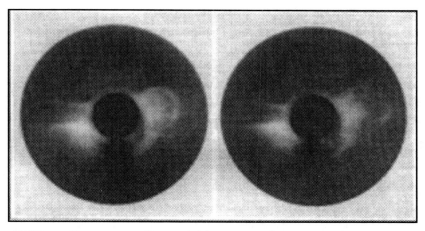

CMEs could not seen until a special instrument, the coronagraph, was put into space aboard Skylab in 1970. Two snapshots of a CME observed above the west limb of the Sun with the white light coronagraph on Skylab, August 10, 1973. The field of view of the photographs is 6 solar diameters, and the images are separated in time by 24 minutes. As is common in many of these events, this CME was not associated with a solar flare.

CMEs move outward from the Sun into interplanetary space with speeds as low as 100,000 mph, and as high as 2.5 million mph. Slower CMEs do not seriously disturb the Earth's magnetosphere or ionosphere, but faster CMEs cause major disturbances in the solar wind, because their huge mass generates a shock wave ahead of them and strong magnetic fields behind the leading edge. When the shockwave hits Earth's magnetosphere, we experience geomagnetic storms and spectacular auroral displays. CMEs are also our chief weather-makers.

Extreme Weather

Let's examine the various forms of extreme weather, and the linkage between the frequency and intensity of those forms: hurricanes, straight-line winds, and precipitation (non-hurricane).

Hurricanes

A hurricane is a tropical cyclone—a large, rotating area of clouds circulating around an area of low pressure. It is driven by the release of heat as water vapor rises and gives up its heat of condensation. Rising air creates low pressure below, which pulls in more warm, moist air. In order to start and sustain itself, it must form and remain over warm water, which provides the atmospheric moisture needed. In the northern hemisphere, hurricane activity peaks in late summer when water temperatures are warmest. For example, in the Atlantic Basin, water surface temperature must at least 80 °F.

Five things must happen for a hurricane to form:
1. Sea surface temperatures above 80 °F to a depth of 150 feet.
2. Upper level air temperatures must drop quickly with height, with moist air to about 20,000 feet.
3. A local weather disturbance, such as a thunderstorm off the coast.
4. Within about 10 degrees of the equator. This maximizes the Coriolis Effect (see below).
5. Lack of vertical wind shear, which would otherwise destabilize the rotational structure.

Coriolis Effect

Air heated at the equator rises and is replaced by cooler air drawn from the poles towards the equator, where the circumference is about 25,000 miles, which means that the planet is spinning to the east at just over 1,000 mph. However, the incoming air is not brought up to the easterly velocity necessary to match the Earth's velocity, so it 'falls backwards' compared with the Earth's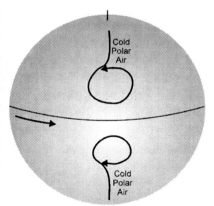
surface. A spin is thus introduced in the incoming flow of air, clockwise in the southern hemisphere and counterclockwise in the north. The circular motion prevents the air that has risen at the equator from returning to the poles, so it remains locked in the spinning formation.

The easterly movement of the Earth also forces an overall westerly movement on the large, twisting formation. In the north Atlantic, hurricanes forming off the coast of Africa drift west at 5 – 25 mph. Hurricanes play an essential role in maintaining global heat balance by moving warm, moist tropical air north or south to the mid-latitudes and poles.

Hurricane Frequency and Intensity

The main factor governing frequency and intensity is surface seawater temperature. The more this rises above 80 °F, the more hurricanes will form in a season, and the more powerful the heat engine effect will be, as more warm air rises faster, pulling in more cool air faster to replace it. The more the ocean heats up the incoming air, the faster the formation spins around the eye, hence producing more devastating winds. The higher the wind, the larger the storm surge it pushes before it, and the greater the property damage. Once the formation makes landfall, the heat engine effect ceases, but the larger the formation, the more rain it has to dump on land, and the greater the probability that the spinning motion will spawn tornadoes.

Hurricanes and Solar Activity

The big question is whether solar activity will increase or decrease vertical wind shear. If the shockwave generated by a CME causes a disturbance in the stratosphere, and pushes the tropopause down into the troposphere, that could disrupt the upper atmosphere and deny a tropical depression the stability it needs to deepen into a hurricane.

As the chart shows, when the 11-year sunspot activity (dotted line) is superimposed on hurricane activity (solid line), there is no discernable correlation. Any correlation would come when a specfic CME hit Earth while a hurricane was forming.

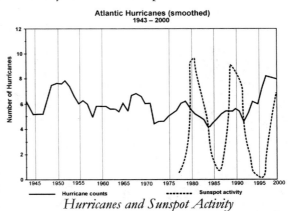

Hurricanes and Sunspot Activity

Straight-line Winds

The polar jet streams are fast air currents, between 60–250 mph, just below the tropopause, at an altitude of about 8 miles, or about 40,000 feet. They form at the boundary of cold polar air and warmer air, and constantly snake around, both horizontally and vertically, in the higher latitudes usually between 30°N and 70°N. As the two huge air masses meet, high speed winds develop in the upper atmosphere due to rising air. The greater the contrast in temperatures, the stronger the jet stream. This is why the jet stream is stronger in winter. The strongest winds form a ribbon about 60 miles wide and about 1 mile deep. The stream is about 3,000 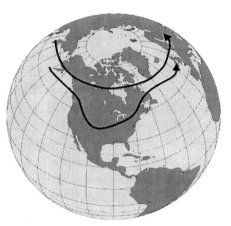 miles in length and because the Earth rotates east-to-west, the wind flows west to east. Jet wind speed usually weakens in summer as polar air warms and the temperature gradient falls. In addition to the polar jet streams are subtropical jets between latitude 20°N and 50°N.

The invaluable service provided by Live Weather Images [http://www.weatherimages.org] includes updated images of where the jet streams are currently flowing across the U.S. The source of the following maps for May 11–14, 2005 is http://www.weatherimages.org/data/imag192.html [courtesy of Live Weather Images].

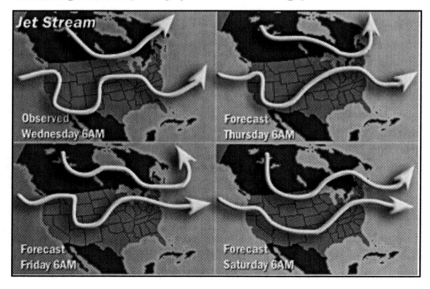

As geomagnetic storms rage and billions of tons of ejected solar material buffet the planet, they influence the jet streams both laterally and vertically:

- If the impact pushes the tropopause down from its 8-mile altitude, the surface could experience winds approaching full jet stream speeds of over 100 mph, as is often reported. Such an extreme wind would uproot trees, carry off houses, bring aircraft down, and sink ships. There could be little or no warning because straight-line winds do not exhibit the familiar storm cell's wall clouds or the twister's funnel cloud. In fact, victims report that "it came out of nowhere."

- If the impact pushes the jet stream laterally south, this allows polar air to spill further south, freed of its containment curtain. This would result in a dramatic drop in temperature of maybe 30 °F in just a few hours. If this happened over the U.S. and warm, moist air was flowing north from the Gulf of Mexico, the Venturi effect would suck that air in even more quickly and drop its temperature in minutes, resulting in unpredictable freak precipitation, such as damaging hail and snowstorms in August.

Straight-line winds are also caused by massive downdrafts in large thunder systems. Extremely cold air often descends within such a system at speeds of 100 mph, and fan out when they hit the

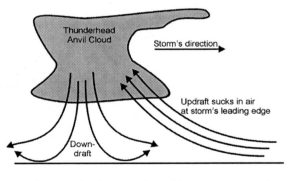

ground, often with tornado-sized winds only without the twisting motion. But they have the same destructive effect.

A third cause of straight-line winds commonly occurs east of the Rocky Mountains when a high-pressure system to the north pushes the jet stream south. This produces what's called a 'cut-off low,' a vortex that pulls in cold air. When this happens on the eastern side of

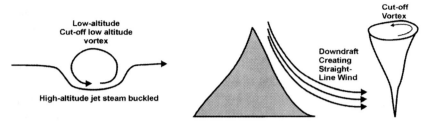

Formation of Straight-line Wind East of the Rocky Mountains

the Rockies, cold air streams down from the Continental Divide at speeds of up to 115 mph, demolishing everything in its path. Because this happens on a huge scale (unlike a tornado), the winds appear to be blowing in a straight line.

Precipitation

We all know the cycle:

Phase 1: Warm oceans evaporate and water vapor rises. In the U.S., the tropical air over the warm waters of the tropics and Gulf of Mexico absorbs moisture and rises.

Phase 2: At the higher altitudes, the air cools and cannot hold as much vapor, so it condenses around nuclei such as dust particles, to form clouds. The continued updraft keeps the clouds at their altitude, and the northerly airflow transports the warm, moist air and clouds into the United States:

- Cirrus clouds are wispy, and are typically found above 20,000 feet. They are composed of ice crystals that originate from the freezing of supercooled water drop- 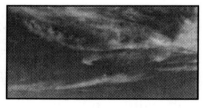 lets. Cirrus generally occurs in fair weather and point in the direction of air movement at their elevation.

- The bases of mid-level clouds (center) are typically between 6,000–20,000 feet, and are composed primarily of water droplets. However,

when temperatures are cold enough, they can also be composed of ice crystals.

- Cumulus clouds (right) are generated most commonly through either convection or frontal lifting. They can grow to 40,000 feet, and release incredible amounts of heat energy if the water vapor within the cloud itself condenses.

Phase 3: Cooler upper atmospheric air increases the size of water droplets until they can no longer be kept aloft by the updraft, and they obey gravity, falling as rain. If they encounter an updraft in the turbulent air of a thunderstorm, for example, they freeze to form snowflakes. As the snowflakes fall, liquid water freezes onto them to form ice pellets that will continue to grow as more and more droplets are accumulated. Upon reaching the bottom of the cloud, some of the ice pellets are carried by the updraft back up to the top of the storm. After several repeated cycles of falling/updraft, they can be as large as baseballs, and cause great damage when they plummet to Earth at their terminal velocity of 120 mph.

Rain can also begin as ice crystals that collect each other to form large snowflakes. As the falling snow passes through the freezing level into warmer air, the flakes melt and collapse into rain drops. Otherwise, it continues to the surface as snow.

Freezing rain consists of supercooled droplets freezing on impact. Ice storms result from the accumulation of freezing rain, which is rain that becomes supercooled and freezes upon impact with cold surfaces. Freezing rain is most commonly found in a narrow band on the cold side of a warm front, where surface temperatures are at or just below freezing.

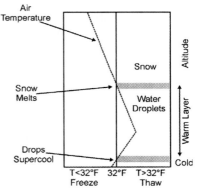

The diagram shows a typical temperature profile for freezing rain with the diagonal line indicating the atmosphere's temperature at any given altitude. The vertical line in the center of the diagram is the freezing line. To the left, temperatures are below freezing, while temperatures to the right are above freezing. Freezing rain develops as falling snow encounters a layer of warm air deep enough for the snow to completely melt and become rain. As the rain continues to fall, it passes through a thin layer of cold air just above the surface and cools to a temperature below freezing. However, the drops themselves do not freeze—a phenomenon called supercooling. When the supercooled drops strike the frozen ground (power lines, or tree branches), they instantly freeze, forming a thin film of ice, hence freezing rain (the phenomenon we saw in Chapter 1).

The Equation

Picture this. An aircraft carrier displacing over 100,000 tons, home to over 5,000 men, hurtling through the water at not her usual 30 knots, but at over 100 mph. Then picture 10 of them side-by-side sailing together. Now picture 10,000 of these enor-

mous craft, going not 100 mph but 1,000,000 mph. Can you picture the bow wave they would be pushing ahead of them? Assuming the engines were powerful enough, it would be hundreds of feet high and miles out ahead. Now picture that bow wave approaching an object that itself is careening through the ocean at 66,000 mph, while spinning on its axis at 1,000 mph. It doesn't take a rocket scientist to know that *something* pretty intense is about to happen, but it *does* take a rocket scientist with a very powerful computer to figure out what that something will be.

This analogy is exactly what happens when a CME aproaches Earth. Billions of tons of coronal plasma is blasted out of the corona and accelerated to over 1,000,000 mph. Two days later, it may approach the orbit of Earth, which itself is in orbit around the Sun, traveling

584 million miles in a year, or 66,000 mph. It's also spinning, so that a point on the equator travels 25,100 miles a day, or just over 1,000 mph.

The Solar Wind Shockwave of charged ions hits the thermosphere, then the stratosphere, and then the troposphere, followed by millions of tons of coronal plasma. At the same time, the intense magnetic field of the

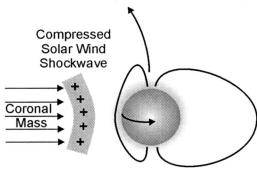

CME begins to distort Earth's magnetic field. As the shockwave washes over Earth, engulfing it, the planet itself is spinning and orbiting, so complex interactions disturb the layers of the atmosphere, soon reaching the troposphere, where our weather systems play out.

Depending on angles and speeds of impact, the jet stream could be displaced vertically and/or horizontally. If vertically, freak straight-line winds of over 100 mph could swoop down to the surface; if laterally, a blast of Arctic air could bulge down into the U.S., freezing orange groves in Florida. Or atmospheric instability could blow apart a young hurricane formation, causing it to collapse. Or cold (-50 °F) stratospheric air could be pushed down into the troposphere, supercooling water droplets in an 8-mile-high thunderhead cloud, resulting in huge hailstones that crash to the surface, where they could bring down aircraft, wreck trains, and cause huge traffic pile-ups. Whatever happens, it *will* be extreme.

All these possibilities have led me to come up with "The Equation":
Sunspots => Solar Flares => Magnetic Shift => Shifting Ocean and Jet Stream Currents => Extreme Weather

Chapter 8

The Super-duper Doppler Weatherman

On the evening of September 8, 1900, a category 4 hurricane swept in from the Gulf of Mexico and took dead aim at the island city of Galveston. The system's 125 mph winds pushed a high tide and storm surge of 20 feet across the island, maximum elevation eight feet, claiming between 6,000 and 12,000 lives. What makes this event remarkable is the complete lack of warning that would have allowed residents to evacuate the island.

Galveston had grown from a small settlement on the Texas coast into one of the wealthiest cities in the country. A natural deepwater

Photo credit: Texas State Library

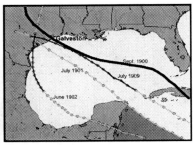

A House Is Swept of Its Foundation   *The Hurricane's Track*

channel made it the most important seaport in Texas, and trains carried cargo to and from the port. More than 70 percent of the country's cotton crop passed through the port of Galveston, visited by about 1,000 ships annually. Home to about 37,000 people, it was also a popular tourist destination because of the warm waters of the Gulf of Mexico.

The storm surge began earlier in the day, but caused no alarm because no one knew what it meant. By evening, however winds between 130 – 140 miles per hour were driving the extreme storm surge of over 15 feet, on top of a high tide.

As the storm surge rolled over the island from gulf to bay, it swept houses away, using each block as a battering ram to demolish the next block, finally forming a wall of debris two-stories high that was pushed across the island. At one point, a railroad trestle bridge broke from its foundations and scoured the island flat.

The tragedy was that this was all totally avoidable. At the time, the U.S. was having a political spat with Cuba, and the normal cordial telegraph relations that weathermen of both nations enjoyed were severed on orders from Washington. The hurricane had crossed over Cuba about two weeks earlier, and normally the Cuban weather agency would have warned their U.S. counterparts, but not this time. As it happened, no ships in the Gulf spotted the hurricane, so no warning reached Galveston.

Isaac Cline was the chief of the U.S. Weather Service bureau in Galveston in 1900, but due to ignorance and arrogance, he refused to raise the hurricane flag over his office until the Category 4 was on top of the island, leaving residents no opportunity to leave.

Without communication with Cuba, weather buoys in the Caribbean, radio links with ships, and satellite imagery, poor Isaac was effectively blind, unlike today's Super-duper Doppler weatherman.

(For more information, see www.1900storm.com)

The Tri-State Tornado of 1925

The deadliest tornado in U.S. history struck the Mid-West on March 18,1925. The so-called Tri-State Tornado took almost 700 hundred lives across three states, and traveled 220 miles over 3½ hours (whereas the duration of most twisters is measured in minutes). And because of poor communication back in 1925, and the complete lack of forecasting and early warning systems, the death toll was *far* higher than it could have been.

Around 1:00 p.m. just northwest of Ellington, Missouri, the twister formed and killed a farmer. From there, it raced northeast, killing two people and leveling 90 percent of Annapolis and the mining town of Leadanna. Leaving the Ozarks, it crossed Bollinger County, injuring 32 children in two county schools. By the time it had reached the Mississippi River, eleven Missourians had perished.

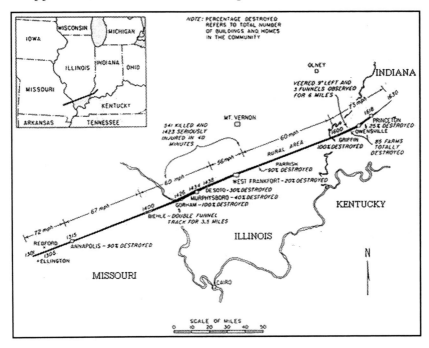

In southern Illinois, the entire town of Gorham was demolished around 2:30 p.m., killing 34 people. During the next 40 minutes, 541 people were killed and 1,423 were seriously injured as the one-mile-wide tornado obliterated the towns of Murphysboro (40%), De Soto (30%), Hurst-Bush, and West Frankfort. In eastern Franklin County, the town of Parrish was literally erased from the map, killing 22. Next it rolled across rural farmland of Hamilton and White Counties, where the death toll reached 65.

After taking the lives of more than 600 Illinoisans, the storm surged across the Wabash River into Indiana, demolishing 100% of Griffin. It veered left slightly and increased its lateral speed to 73 mph as it put down a *triple-funnel* that devastated 85 farms northwest of Owensville. Next it destroyed half the town of Princeton, with damage estimated at $1.8 million. At 4.30, it dissipated about ten miles northeast of town, having taken a total of 695 lives and inflicted property damage of $16.5 million (equivalent today to $185 million).

This monster traveled at speeds of between 60–70 mph, packing winds of 200 mph, tossing entire railroad trains around like a child's train set. And because communication wasn't as good as today, and there was no early warning system, residents had no idea that the town to the right had been destroyed and that theirs was about to be obliterated next, them with it.

Possibly driving this mother of all tornadoes was solar Cycle 16, which had peaked two years earlier, in 1923.

[Source: http://www.crh.noaa.gov/pah/1925/tt_frame.html]

Having seen two examples of the tragedies that can befall if we have no forecasting, communication, or early warning, let's turn to the weatherman of the future—the Super-Duper Doppler weatherman. On January 21, 2000, NOAA issued this press release:

Supercomputers for Meteorologists

One of the world's most powerful supercomputers is now generating faster and more precise predictions of the atmosphere, resulting in more accurate forecasts for every city in the nation. This new supercomputer is five times—and eventually will be 28 times—faster than its predecessor, which allows NOAA's National Weather Service to improve the accuracy of local and national forecasts and warning lead times for potentially dangerous severe weather.

"This new supercomputer puts us closer to reaching our goal of becoming America's no surprise weather service," said National Weather Service Director John J. Kelly Jr. "This gives our forecasters more sophisticated models of the atmosphere and oceans, which act as blueprints for upcoming weather patterns. On a daily basis, we should see a 10 percent improvement in predicting temperatures, humidity and pinpointing when, where and how much rainfall will occur."

The new supercomputer, known as a 786 processor IBM System Parallel, replaces a Cray C-90 that served the National Weather Service since 1994. Currently, the IBM SP processes data at a speed of 690 billion instructions per second. When upgraded in September with even more advanced technology and additional processors, the supercomputer will process weather data at a speed of 2.5 trillion instructions per second. This final upgrade will make the IBM SP supercomputer 28 times faster than the Cray C-90 and provide higher-resolution weather forecast models.

For more on the Super-Duper Doppler Weatherman's tools of the trade, here are a couple of excerpts from articles I posted on the ECTV website in 2000 and 2002.

June 22, 2000: Chaos Hot Spots: New Key To Better Weather Forecasts? NASA: Better Space Storm Warnings

Scientists have developed a new method for estimating when Coronal Mass Ejections (CMEs) from the Sun will reach the Earth.

The arrival from the Sun of billion-ton electrified-gas clouds that cause severe space storms can now be predicted to within a half-day, a great improvement over the best previous estimates of two to five days.

Scientists at the Catholic University of America and NASA's Goddard Space Flight Center have created a model that reliably predicts how much time it takes for CMEs to traverse the gulf between the Sun and the Earth, based on their initial ejection speed from the Sun and their interaction with the solar wind.

Earth-directed CMEs cause space storms by interacting with the Earth's magnetic field, distorting its shape and accelerating electrically charged particles (electrons and atomic nuclei) trapped within. Severe solar weather is often heralded by dramatic auroral displays, but space storms are occasionally harmful, by disrupting satellite orbits, radio communications and power systems.

October 30, 2002: Mapping Electric Power Flowing Into Upper Atmosphere

Researchers at The Johns Hopkins University Applied Physics Laboratory, Laurel, Md., (APL) are now able to simultaneously measure the magnetic and electrical fields over large areas of the ionosphere above the Earth's polar regions, providing the first continuous monitoring of electric currents between space and the upper atmosphere, and generating the first maps of electric power flowing into the polar upper atmosphere.

These advances will allow greatly improved understanding and forecasting of global space weather and help prevent disruption of communication and power systems when electromagnetic storms strike the nation.

Scientists at JHU/APL have developed techniques to extract the signatures of electrical currents flowing between the atmosphere and space from the magnetic field readings. Maps of the electric current in space are then constructed in much the same way that normal weather maps are made from weather station readings.

At the same time, SuperDARN—the Super Dual Auroral Radar Network, a multinational network of a dozen radars spread around the poles to study the ionosphere, sponsored by NSF and NASA and led by APL scientist Dr. Raymond A. Greenwald—is bouncing radar signals off the same regions to measure the electric field and its minute-by-minute variations.

"We're able for the first time to continuously map the powerful currents flowing between space and the Earth's upper atmosphere," says Brian J. Anderson, who leads APL's research effort. "This is a major achievement because monitoring this environment is extremely difficult due to its enormous volume, which can vary by a factor of 10 in one hour."

The maps of electrical current show dramatic shifts due to changes in the solar wind. These results will allow scientists to test computer models of Earth's space environment far more accurately and exhaustively than ever before. Preliminary maps of the power flow have revealed "hot spots" of energy flowing into the atmosphere at high altitudes, creating pockets of hot air that rise and create drag on spacecraft flying through them at altitudes below 300 miles.

"Timely, accurate space weather forecasts will give advance warning of electromagnetic storms that in the past have shown their ability to disrupt communications, degrade GPS accuracy, cripple electrical power grids, and menace astronauts, satellites and aircraft with dangerous levels of radiation," says Anderson.

Score Another One For The Super-duper Doppler Weatherman

On January 4, 2003, I commented on an article by Dermot McGrath of *Wired News*, that indicated just how close ECTV's prediction is coming into fruition. The article accurately depicted the very path I have seen unfolding and reporting on for over three years. Here's a taste of what he had to say:

Scientists are inching closer to unlocking one of meteorology's most intractable problems: how the Sun's activity affects the climate on earth. Thanks to a cooperative effort by space agencies and research laboratories around the world, a new type of weather forecast could soon be making its debut — the space-weather bulletin.

For example, solar events that can affect the weather on earth include coronal mass ejections, or CMEs, huge bubbles of electrified gas that travel at 1,000 times the speed of a Concorde airplane and contain more mass than Mount Everest.

"Coronal mass ejections are the hurricanes of space," said Nancy Crooker, an astronomy professor at Boston University's Center for Space Physics. "They have strong magnetic fields that link to the earth's field, thus breaching the shield that otherwise protects us from the onslaught of the solar wind."

Understanding and eventually predicting CMEs could help mitigate their potentially devastating effects on everything from spacecraft, astronauts and satellites in orbit to communications and power systems on earth.

Almost a year earlier, on May 1, 2002, I had written an article for the ECTV website titled *Scientists See Newscast Predicting Solar-Earth Weather in Future:*

I can hardly contain myself. Late yesterday, NASA released a public relations announcement that scientists are working feverously on implementing solar forecast on our local daily news and weather reports. Yes, just as predicted by ECTV last year, we will see our local weather personality showing charts, graphs, photos of solar events that are directly tied to Earth's weather.

For someone like myself who has been researching a direct Sun-Earth connection regards our weather, well - it just doesn't get much better than this. For the first time ever, our government agencies are confirming without hesitation The Equation.

In fact, a year earlier, I'd published a mock local weather forecast:

"Today, we see our Sun is really acting out. The sunspot count is up to 178. Watch for C-class or M-class flares to follow within 48 hours. It is likely to cause more 'record breaking' events. Now, with our new technology, our national weather center believes sudden wind shears will occur in the central part of the United States. Watch for record high winds to occur. We also see Southern India being hit by sudden cyclones. That's all from Channel 5 News."

I continued the theme on May 05, 2002 with an article titled under the title ***Center To Make Hurricane Forecasting Faster: Better Your Friendly Local Weathercast:***

Good morning everyone. I hope you're having a great day. Today's weather forecast indicates a strong possibility of more "record-break-ing" weather coming our way. Let's take a look at our Super-duper Doppler weather satellite. Thanks to NASA's latest equipment and their newfound discoveries of a Sun-Earth connection, we can now look deep into our skies to see what is in store for us.

Well, it looks like we have severe storms ahead. The Super-duper Doppler indicates a sunspot count of 271. Oh boy, this is going to be a big one. As a result of this unusually high sunspot count, we can expect X-class and M-class flares to follow within 48 hours.

Now let's take a look at our Super-duper Doppler and zoom-in. Oh my, it looks like the coronal holes are facing Earth. This means that the solar flares may be heading towards us. There may also be a CME to follow the large flares. I would say there is a good chance we will see freak storms, most likely in the way of tornadoes or what we now call "freak wind shears" to occur in our eastern plains.

Well, there you have it, folks. I wish I had better news for you, but you better pull out your raincoats, or warm winter gloves, or dress cool, depending on where you live. It sure looks like more "record-breaking" events are likely to occur. That's it for our weather forecast.

UV Index

I am convinced that the above will come to a TV news station near you in the not too distant future. Already forecasters include the UV Index in their forecasts. Developed by the National Weather Service and the EPA, the UV Index provides important information to help plan outdoor activities to prevent overexposure to the Sun's rays. Some exposure to sunlight is essential because that's how our bodies manufacture Vitamin D; however, overexposure to UV can cause immediate effects such as sunburn, plus long-term problems such as skin cancer and cataracts.

The UV Index provides a daily forecast of the expected risk of overexposure to the Sun. The Index predicts intensity on a scale of 1–11+. The NWS calculates next-day levels for every ZIP code, taking into account clouds and other local conditions. (If you enter your own ZIP code at the site: http://www.epa.gov/sunwise/uvindex.html, you will get the UV Index for your area. There is also a map of the U.S. showing the UV Index.)

The index levels are:

- *0–2: Low*—Wear sunglasses on bright days. In winter, reflection off snow can nearly double UV strength. If you burn easily, cover up and use sunscreen. Skin damage in 60 minutes of exposure.
- *3–5: Moderate*—Take precautions, such as covering up and using sunscreen, if you will be outside. Stay in shade near midday when the Sun is strongest. Skin damage in 46 minutes.
- *6–7: High*—Protection against sunburn is needed. Reduce time in the Sun between 11 a.m. and 4 p.m. Cover up, wear a hat and sunglasses, and use sunscreen. Skin damage in 30 minutes.
- *8–10: Very High*— Take extra precautions. Unprotected skin will be damaged and can burn quickly. Try to avoid the Sun between 11 a.m. and 4 p.m. Otherwise, seek shade, cover up,

wear a hat and sunglasses, and use sunscreen. Skin damage in 15 minutes.

- *11+: Extreme*— Take all precautions. Unprotected skin can burn in minutes. Beachgoers should know that white sand and other bright surfaces reflect UV and will increase UV exposure. Avoid the Sun between 11 a.m. and 4 p.m. Seek shade, cover up, wear a hat and sunglasses, and use sunscreen. Skin damage in less than 10 minutes.

We learned on November 29, 2000 that an ozone hole had formed over Europe. It began on November 17 over the UK, Denmark, Sweden, Finland and Russia. The level had dropped to under 225 Dobson Units. (On the Dobson Scale of 0–800, below 220 is officially an Ozone Hole.) Then on November 18, it spread to Poland, Finland and Estonia, with the level dropping to under 200 units. Next came the layer over parts of France and Spain. Since it's our main protection against much of the Sun's harmful UV rays, this had folks over there pretty worried.

Improved Super-duper Doppler Modeling the Sun-Earth Connection

The combination of satellite data capture and powerful computers allow us to create sophisticated 3-D models of what's going on in the atmosphere. For example, a NASA study, *Record Cold Winter May Increase Ozone Hole over North Europe,* used data from several NASA instruments and found that the late 2003 solar storms, which deposited huge quantities of energetic solar particles into Earth's atmosphere, had triggered the largest decline ever in upper stratospheric ozone over the Arctic and the northern areas of North America, Europe and Asia.

Using data from seven satellites, including NASA's Stratospheric Aerosol and Gas Experiment II and III instruments on the Earth Radiation Budget Satellite and the Halogen Occultation Experiment on NASA's Upper Atmospheric Research Satellite, the researchers concluded the record ozone declines were the result of a combination of unusual stratospheric weather conditions and energetic solar particles in the atmosphere resulting from the vigorous solar storm activity.

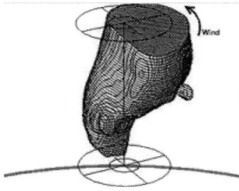

*ige: This 3-D image shows the
ndary of the Arctic stratospheric
ir vortex. Strong winds blowing in
direction of the arrow keep air con-
d in the vortex. In 2004, the up-
part of the vortex (top of image,
ut 32 miles above Earth) was un-
ally large and strong. This allowed
ogen gases that destroy ozone to
end into the stratosphere.*

The study's lead author, Dr. Cora Randall of the University of Colorado at Boulder's Laboratory for Atmospheric and Space Physics, said, "The phenomenon illustrates the difficulties in separating ozone-destroying atmospheric effects resulting from *natural* versus *human*-induced causes. These findings point out a critical need to better understand the processes occurring in the ozone layer, and demonstrate that scientists searching for signs of ozone recovery need to factor in the atmospheric effects of energetic particles, something they do not now do."

Natural chemicals in the stratosphere climbed to the highest levels in at least two decades in spring 2004 which was directly related to charge particles emitted from the Sun. Apparently the Sun's solar flux led to ozone reductions of up to 60 percent roughly 25 miles in altitude above Earth's high northern latitudes. The team of scientists from the United States, Canada and Europe looked at data from seven different satellites, concluding both the Sun and stratospheric weather were responsible for the ozone declines.

"Winds in the upper part of a massive winter low-pressure system that confines air over the Arctic region, known as the polar stratospheric vortex, sped up in February and March 2004 to become the strongest on record," Dr. Randall said. The spinning vortex allowed the nitrogen gases, believed by the team to have formed at least 20 miles above the stratosphere as a result of chemical reactions triggered by energetic particles from the Sun, to descend more easily into the stratosphere.

What Is a Space Weather Forecast?

Space weather forecasts are issued by the Space Environment Center, a division of the U.S. Commerce Department's National Oceanic and Atmospheric Administration, or NOAA, the government agency that operates the National Weather Service.

Sunspots are explosions on the Sun, and Space Weather forecasters keep the public informed about space weather with outlooks, watches and warnings like those ordinarily used for down-to-Earth weather. Some of these same techniques and the ability to interpret science's most advanced equipment are now being taught to your local weather meteorologist.

Even though we can't see space weather like we might see a tornado, hurricane or blizzard, our high-tech environment can be disrupted by the electromagnetic storms that race across the 93 million miles of space separating us from the Sun.

When a space storm hit arrives at Earth, satellites, cell phones and computers can be knocked out. There can be electrical power blackouts, as when a storm blacked out Quebec province in Canada in 1989 (see Chapter 1).

The storms also allow people on Earth to see the aurora borealis, or northern lights, as far south as the Gulf of Mexico.

The forecasters watch violent solar storms and alert the public and institutions that could be impacted by space weather. Reports are sent out by the National Weather Service on its Weather Wire service to broadcasters, private forecasters and other users across the United States. Space weather reports discuss current conditions and outlooks and describe general expectations for future conditions. As with events such as flash floods, space weather 'watches' indicate caution that severe space disturbances are expected, and space weather 'warnings' indicate that events are imminent.

Let's take a look at some of that sophisticated equipment that makes space weather monitoring possible.

Eyes in the Sky

The Super-duper Doppler Weatherman owes a lot to all that hi-tech gear flying around up there, which takes two main forms:

1. Geosynchronous satellites that look down on Earth, giving us instant images of our weather as it happens. They also measure ocean levels and temperatures.
2. Sun-watching satellites, monitoring the star right across the EM spectrum, and the interplanetary space between the Sun and Earth. SOHO is probably the most versatile so far.

GOES (Geostationary Operational Environmental Satellite)

GOES satellites provide continuous monitoring by orbiting the equator at a speed matching Earth's rotation, which they do by maintaining an orbit of 22,300 miles above the Earth. This is high enough to give them a full-disc view of the Earth. Because they stay above a fixed spot on the surface, they provide a constant vigil for the atmospheric "triggers"

Photo credit: NASA

East CONUS	West CONUS	Puerto Rico	Alaska	Hawaii
Infrared	Infrared	Infrared	Infrared	Infrared
Visible	Visible	Visible	Visible	Visible
Water Vapor	Water Vapor	Water Vapor	Water Vapor	Water Vapor

GOES Real-time Images of Earth from Space

for severe weather conditions such as tornadoes, flash floods, hail storms, and hurricanes. When these conditions develop, the GOES satellites are able to monitor storm development and track their movements.

GOES satellite imagery is also used to estimate rainfall during the thunderstorms and hurricanes to generate flash flood warnings, as well as estimates of snowfall accumulations and overall extent of snow cover. Such data help meteorologists issue winter storm warnings and spring snow melt advisories. Their sensors also detect ice fields and map the movements of sea and lake ice.

There are currently three GOES operational, each with 12 subsystems, and the program is managed by NASA's Global Hydrology and Climate Center. See: www.ghcc.msfc.nasa.gov/cgi-bin/post-goes

The port of entry to the site is: www.goes.noaa.gov, where various real-time images are displayed showing clouds by visible light, infrared, and water vapor. The server also offers spectacular color images and animation loops of varying durations.

SOHO (Solar and Heliospheric Observatory)

SOHO has proved one of the best eyes in the sky we've had, delivering spectacular images, but it's also had us sitting on the edge of our seats from time to time.

This $1 billion joint project by NASA and the European Space Agency was launched December 2, 1995. Although designed for only a two-year lifetime, scientists hoped to extend that so it would still be operational during the Solar Maximum in 2001. The satellite mission was to study the Sun from an area known as the L-1 position, about 1 million miles from Earth, between the Earth and Sun. (This so-called Lagrange Point is the area in space where the gravitational fields of two bodies are balanced, so an object is pulled equally towards both bodies.)

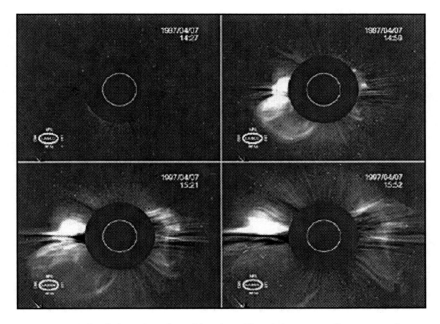

SOHO had already relayed back to Earth images of comets plunging into the Sun, huge solar flares and CMEs, and rivers of plasma when problems struck. Mission controllers lost contact with the satellite on June 24 but, using the huge radio telescope at Arecibo, Puerto Rico, NASA was able to locate the crippled satellite. On July 27, it was found spinning helplessly in space, probably due to software problems in its command and control computer system. Once out of alignment with the Sun, its solar panels could not longer supply electricity to the communications equipment, and its antennas were also no longer angled toward Earth.

Mission controllers tried to contact the satellite as it spun about 1 revolution a minute, still close to the L-1 point. On August 12, 1998, NASA was pleased when SOHO "answered the phone." It sent temperature and electronic data back to Earth in response to a request. "This is the best news I've heard since we lost contact with SOHO," Roger Bonnet, science director for the European Space Agency, said in a statement.

Somehow, its angle to the Sun had changed, allowing the solar panels to begin recharging its batteries, which allowed it to send information about its condition. "The team is working on the next series of procedures, which will try to thaw the on-board hydrazine fuel, currently at 0 °C (32 °F)," said a statement by the SOHO recovery team at Goddard Space Flight Center. "Thawing the fuel will allow controllers to re-establish control of the spacecraft. The thawing will be attempted later this week after both batteries are fully charged."

This set of four images of a CME event is typical of SOHO's observations, Taken on April 7, 1997, they span about 90 minutes as a huge CME belches billions of tons of plasma into space.

Then again on May 4, 2003, SOHO began to experience communication problems with the antenna it uses for high-speed communication with Earth.

NASA engineers explained that the High-Gain Antenna (HGA) can no longer move in a particular direction, possibly because a motor or gear assembly may be malfunctioning. The HGA must be maneuverable so that the data-stream beam stays centered on Earth as the planet rotates on its annual orbit. So for 18 days every three months, Earth will be out of the beam. (SOHO's Low-Gain Antenna (LGA) is not directional, and is used to monitor the satellite's status.

The site: www.nascom.nasa.gov provides the real-time image of the Sun sent back by the satellite, along with the estimated Kp Index, and the speed and density of the solar wind.

Earth Changes TV Website

Anyone familiar with the website knows about the two live NOAA links in the top left corner marked:

- *Solar Rays*, which had 'Active' setting on June 16, 2005.
- *Geomagnetic Field*, which had a 'Storm' setting on June 16, 2005.

Clicking on either of these takes you directly to the NOAA Space Weather site, where you are presented with a summary screen of the 6 major indicators (for readability, ithe black and whie have been inverted. It looks much better in color):

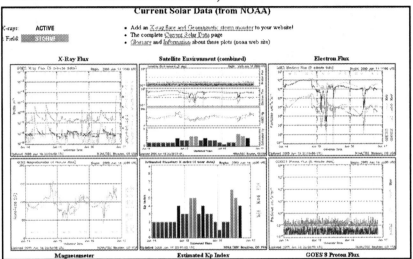

This tells us a tremendous amount of information about the weather in space, such as:
- The X-ray Flux and Electron Flux as measured by the three GOES satellites have just spiked because of an M-class flare
- The Kp Index peaked a few hours ago at 6 (out of a possible 9) and is now back down to level 4. Anything about 4 is a cause for concern.
- The readings of the GOES magnetometers are all over the place, revealing dramatic magnetic storms
- Proton flux is pretty active, another sign of something big happening up there.

The above Current Solar Data screen is a portal to even more screens, that show dozens of images of the Sun, such as the Solar Data Analysis unit within the Goddard Space Flight Center, and their Active Region Monitor page that displays current solar events:

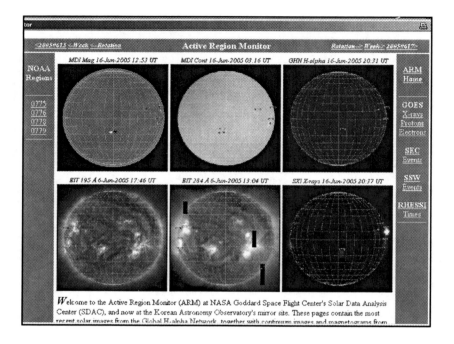

The site also offers a 'weather report':

BBSO Solar Activity Report 15-JUN-2005 15:37:13 UT

Sunny and warm. Solar activity has increased slightly with two good size level C-class events from NOAA 0775 yesterday. There has been no major changes in the regions on the disk so expect solar activity to remain about the same with possible C-class events. NOAA 0775, N09W68. Beta-gamma region. Region has slightly decayed since ysterday. Region produced two C-class events yesterday. C-class events possible. NOAA 0776, S06W57. Beta-gamma with some minor mixing. Region has been quiet. C-class events possible. Positions are for June 15, 2004 at 15:15 UT.

The above Current Solar Data screen offers access to information about space weather we could only dream about until recently, and probably enough tutorials and explanations to allow you to earn your PhD in space weather. You can easily get lost in the labyrinth of data and forget all about the passage of time in the outside world. Try it some time.

Chapter 9

El Niño, La Niña, and La Cucaracha

On July 5, 2004, under the title, *NASA Inches Closer To Full Endorsement for ECTV Equation,* I reported that NASA was saying, "Complex and distorted magnetic fields travel with the CME cloud and *sometimes interact with the Earth's own magnetic field to pour tremendous amounts of energy into the space near Earth."* [emphasis mine]

This insight on their part was many years in the coming. My interest in the Sun-Earth Connection began during the 1997/98 El Niño season. It seemed every single news report was talking about how "El Niño" was causing all this "unusual" weather. So I asked, "If that's true, then what causes an El Niño year rather than the 'normal' La Niña year?"

I distinctly remember how our local weather personality would come on month after month telling us, "El Niño will end 'this month,'" but it never did. It became so silly the local meteorologist would say, "Okay, folks, El Niño will end February." But of course it didn't. So they would come back on the next month and say, "Did I say February? I meant March." March would come and go, and yes, they would say the same thing. "Did I say March? I meant April."

Finally, they became so embarrassed, instead of changing the date, they changed the name. So instead of changing the date, we heard live on our television stations, "Hi, folks, well this nasty weather is still with us. Remember that El Niño I was telling you about? Well I meant to say it is 'La Niña.' Yeah, that's it, La Niña."

It was hysterical, but it fueled my interest even more. I just knew they were going to change the name again, so I added my own dialog. "Hi folks, this is your local weather forecaster. Remember that La Niña I told you about causing all this weird weather? Well, I meant to say it is the new 'La Cucaracha.'"

This humorous method of research has actually been a blessing. It brought me to the understanding of what was driving El Niño, La Niña, and of course La Cucaracha. After switching from my studies of NOAA, I could clearly see an undeniable interface with NASA. This is to say, where NOAA leaves off, NASA picks up. So what *is* driving the ocean currents to shift, which is what we know as Southern Oscillation . Simply put—*shifting ocean currents.*

Okay, now I have an understanding of what drives El Niño, La Niña, and La Cucaracha. It is the ocean currents that have somehow been manipulated to shift in unusual ways. But what causes the shifting of ocean currents?

Now we venture into NASA and their studies of the Sun. It was at this venture in my research that for the first time, I began to understand the Sun – Earth Connection. It was one of those 'hiding in plain sight' experiences. Soon I quickly turned my attention to the Sun. I wanted to know how the Sun was causing the ocean currents to shift. Turns out it's the Sun's impact on the Earth's *magnetic field* that has a causal effect on the Earth's ocean currents. So could this be the driving force behind shifting ocean currents? Why yes, but how?

As you can see, my pattern of research quickly became a form of "reverse engineering." I began with the end result, and worked my way back to the ultimate cause. So what is it that causes the ocean currents to shift? Well, it appears to be winds. Solar winds to be exact. What I have found is when the Earth's magnetic field shifts, it simultaneously causes a shift in ocean and jet streams. In turn, this causal effect drives El Niño, La Niña, and La Cucaracha.

But what causes the Earth's magnetic field to shift? This is where NASA comes in with significant theory and well-placed satellites to help answer this question. It didn't take me long to see an immediate cause-and-effect relationship between solar activity and its play on Earth's magnetic field. Yes, what I found is the Sun itself is the direct cause of the Earth's magnetic field shifting. And when the magnetic field shifts, the ocean and jet stream currents are sure to follow. And when the ocean and jet stream currents shift, we see the effects we call El Niño, La Niña, and of course, La Cucaracha. What I am saying is the previous names are just cute mythical identifiers our ancient fisherman ancestors gave to what scientifically is known as Southern Oscillation which simply means shifting ocean and jet stream currents.

The effect could have only been one source—the Sun. It didn't take long to log solar activity—CMEs, Solar Flares, Coronal Holes, and Geomagnetic Storms—to see that the ultimate cause of Earth's 'extreme weather' is Sol, the god of life.

Before we get more deeply into The Equation, let's get a handle on our kids, El Niño and La Niña.

What Is "El Niño"?

An El Niño occurs about every two to seven years, but since the early 1980s, they have become more frequent and more severe. A typical El Niño lasts about 18 months and is often followed by an opposite pattern called *La Niña*. The change back and forth between the presence and absence of El Niño conditions is known as the *Southern Oscillation*.

The term *El Niño* originally referred to a current of warm water that flows south down the coasts of Ecuador and Peru every winter. It was called El Niño because it usually occurs near Christmas, and is Spanish for *the boy*, referring to the Christ child. About every two to seven years, the warm current is exceptionally strong and long-lasting, and wind and precipitation patterns change across the entire tropical Pacific region. But before we look at him, let's look at his more normal sister.

Climate during a non-El Niño (La Niña) Year.

In a year with no El Niño effect, we see a huge convective loop operating, with cool air sinking in the eastern Pacific, fueling sea-level westerly trade winds that blow the water along too, warm air rising over S.E. Asia, and returning as high-level easterly winds:

1. The ocean water on the eastern side of the Pacific is 15 °F cooler than in the west.

2. Cooler water in the east cools the air, which makes it denser, so it sinks, increasing air pressure. The warmer waters in the tropics on the western side of the Pacific, near Indonesia, heat the air, which rises, so air pressure over those waters is low.

3. The resulting pressure gradient drives westerly trade winds along the equator, which blows surface water from east to west, resulting in sea-level in S.E. Asia being 1½ feet higher than near S. America. (In the old sailing ship days, this wind and current give the Pacific the nickname of 'the one-way ocean.')

4. Displacement of surface water pulls up deeper cold water to the surface, which is abundant in the nutrients that feed tiny organisms drifting at and near the surface. In turn, these organisms support a larger population of fish, making the waters off Ecuador and Peru more abundant areas for commercial fishing. The colder water also perpetuates the cycle.

5. In the west, the ocean-heated air produces clouds that provide monsoonal precipitation to the western Pacific.

6. The air over S.E. Asia returns to the east at high altitude to complete the cycle. For complex reasons, this pattern brings warmer, drier conditions to the Southeastern U.S., and colder, wetter weather to rest of the country.

After two to five years of La Niña weather, the little brother pops up.

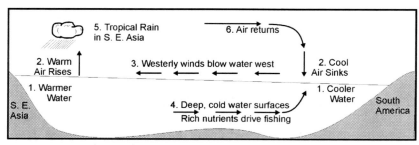

Ocean Currents and Winds in a La Niña Year

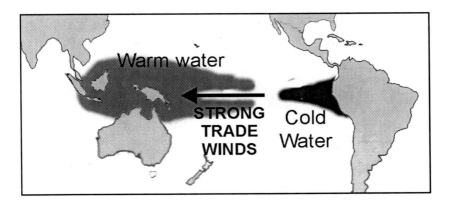

Climate during an El Niño Year

1. During an El Niño, air pressure is higher than normal in the west and abnormally low in the east.
2. The lack of pressure gradient weakens the westerly trade winds, and may even reverse them.
3. The waters off Ecuador and Peru remain abnormally warm. Nutrient-rich cold water does not rise to the surface there, and so the plankton and fish populations decline sharply.
4. Clouds and heavy rainfall occur mainly over the warmer water in the eastern Pacific. Consequently, the coast of South America becomes wetter than normal, often causing flooding in Peru.
5. To the west, by contrast, the climate in Indonesia and other nations of Southeast Asia is unusually dry. Lack of monsoonal rains mean droughts may occur.

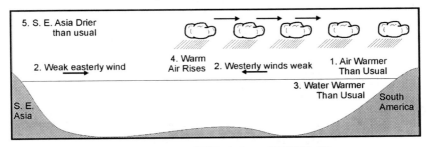

Ocean Currents and Winds in an El Niño Year

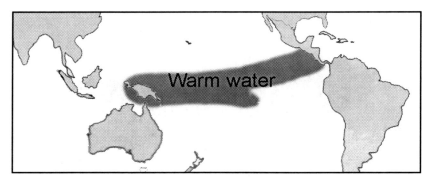

Climatologists call this changing pattern of winds and clouds the Southern Oscillation, or El Niño-Southern Oscillation (ENSO). The key change in ENSO is the lack of cooler eastern water, and the mid-ocean location of the pool of warm water and the convection cell it creates.

El Niños occurred in 1986-1987, 1991-1994 and 1997-1998. A strong La Niña occurred in 1988-1989, whereas 1995-1996 was a weaker La Niña year. It is unusual for ENSO to flip-flop as rapidly as it did during the decade 1988-1998, and for El Niño years to outnumber the others. All this has climatologists wondering what's going on.

What actually happens world-wide during an El Niño year?

1997-1998 El Niño Impacts

The El Niño of 1997-1998 was a mega-event, and caused disasters world-wide. Here are just a few examples:

- *October 1997:* Waves devour Rio's famous Copacabana beach (Rio's beaches shrank by 30-50 m over a few months). Killer storm hits Mexico, leaving 122 dead. Hurricane Pauline devastates Acapulco, with experts blaming El Niño for the severity of the storm.
- *February 1998:* El Niño-related storm system spawns 12 tornadoes in central Florida, killing at least 38 people. One tornado packs winds in excess of 350 mph. El Niño-driven rain destroys dozens of houses on the Californian coast. New Zealand's power grid collapses under the load created by use of air-conditioners, resulting in a chain failure of all four high-voltage underground cables. Flooding in the Chinese oil fields. Bangladesh families live on roof tops to escape floods.

Then ENSO flipped back in August 1998 and heavy monsoons struck Asia, and China suffered extreme flooding on the Yangtze delta partly as a result of excessive deforestation of the interior. Bangladesh was hit with the worst flooding ever, causing production losses of about $8 billion, and the US and Central America were hit with devastating hurricanes.

Climatologists had given plenty of warning about this. For example, on August 26, 1997, chief meteorologist Joseph D'Aleo warned:

The current El Niño event in the eastern Pacific is on its way to becoming one of the strongest ever recorded. Ocean temperatures are running better than 9 °F above normal in parts of the eastern tropical Pacific. This rivals the Great El Niño of 1982/83 which was blamed for major worldwide weather disasters including floods, droughts and powerful wind storms which that winter cumulatively did over $8 billion dollars damage and caused many deaths.

The 1982/83 disasters sparked a flurry of sponsored research into this phenomena that has documented that the El Niño and the opposite phase of the Southern Oscillation, the La Niña have definite correlations with weather features and both temperatures and precipitation patterns worldwide. The climate researchers, buoyed by their success with the Southern Oscillation then turned their attention to other phenomena in the atmosphere, the oceans and on the Sun and to various combinations of these phenomena with some more successes. Today, forecasters have a bevy of new statistical tools that can be used to project likely weather regimes months or seasons in advance and to provide warnings in advance of potential weather trouble.

Those tools tell us the upcoming winter could be a very stormy one with the potential for more heavy snows in the east and powerful storms with strong winds and flooding rains throughout the south.

SOUTHERN OSCILLATION

This is an oscillation of the relative strength of pressure features in the tropical Pacific. The variations in the pressure patterns affects the strength of the trade winds which in turn influences the ocean temperatures. We normally find cool water off the west coast of South America due to an ocean current called the Humboldt. The winds normally blow from the south along the west coast of South

America which causes the surface ocean water to move away from the land. Cool deep water rises to the surface, a phenomenon known as upwelling. This oxygen and plankton rich water makes this an ideal place for fish to feed and for fishing boats to catch fish. When the winds weaken, the current weakens and the upwelling is reduced. Ocean surface temperatures warm. This affects the fisheries locally and as the research has shown also the weather both locally (producing unusually warm and wet weather in the normally dry coastal regions of Peru) and globally.

In the U.S., El Niño years produce wet and relatively cool weather in the southeast and in most years in the southwest including California. In El Niño years, warmer and drier than normal weather is likely in the northwest and north central states.

In the opposite phase of the Southern Oscillation, which we call the La Niña, the normal tropical pressure features and the resulting winds grow stronger than normal. This causes enhanced upwelling which produces cooler than normal surface water in the eastern tropical Pacific. This too influences the weather globally. In the United states, La Niña brings warmer and drier than normal conditions to the southeast and colder, wetter weather to the northwest and north central states.

The 2000 La Niña was a doozy also. On March 11, 2000, CNN reported that the warm, dry weather associated with La Niña brought the warmest winter in U.S. history, and could bring a record-breaking fire season to the Southeast U.S. ... which it did.

The National Climatic Data Center reported all-time record high average temperatures for the December 1999 – February 2000 throughout the United States. The 50-state average temperature during the three-month period was 38.4 °F, 0.6 °F higher than the previous record set a year earlier. The NCDC also said it was the 16th driest U.S. winter in 105 years of record-keeping, except for areas of the northern Rockies and Midwest.

Sun-Earth Connection

The Solar Cycle

Since before 1700, astronomers worldwide have observed and documented sunspots on the solar surface. As we've already seen, the number of sunspots varies over time in a number of cycles, most notably an 11-year cycle. An active Sun with a high number of sunspots has been shown to be a slightly warmer Sun (a few tenths of a percent more energy emitted). Increased solar activity also leads to increased geomagnetic storms and ionospheric disturbances which influence communications and electrical transmissions on the earth and have also been shown also to have some influence of the position and strength of certain weather features.

As early as 1801, astronomer William Herschall noted a relationship between sunspots and the price of wheat. He saw that the more sunspots there were, the better the crop yield, so the lower the price of wheat. In years with fewer sunspots, the lower the yield, so the higher the price.

The suggestion was that Earth's weather depends on the Sun's natural variability - and 200 years later, scientists are still debating this effect.

Today, we argue over how important is human contribution to the made-up name 'global warming', and most researchers recklessly underestimate the Sun's main roles:

1. Driver of air and ocean currents via Earth's magnetosphere.
2. Shield to protect the solar system from the full brunt of cosmic rays, which would otherwise be sources of cloud nuclei in the upper atmosphere

Let's take a closer look at these roles.

The Sun as a Shield

One theory currently being offered by Professor Henrik Svensmark, of the Danish Space Research Institute (DSRI), is that variation in solar activity acts on climate by preventing cosmic rays hitting the Earth as they journey across our galaxy. "I knew that people had been seeing correlations between solar activity and the climate on Earth, and I knew that people dismissed it as being entirely accidental. However when I looked at the correlations at that time, I saw that there was too much to be really accidental."

Professor Svensmark's theory is that when solar activity is high, the Earth gets better shielding from cosmic rays because the magnetic fields carried in the solar wind make it harder for the rays to get to Earth. Conversely, when solar activity declines, more cosmic rays reach Earth, increasing the number of ionized particles to act as nuclei, so more clouds form, and therefore the cooler the climate.

The theory depends on the ability of cosmic rays to seed cloud formation. Do cosmic rays trigger cloud formation. First, cosmic rays are not really rays at all. They are particles, mainly high-energy protons, typically released when a star explodes at the end of its life. Professor Svensmark explains, "They are important in this context because they ionize the atmosphere. When these particles collide with the gas molecules that make up the atmosphere, the molecules are given either a positive or negative charge. These particles then become the nuclei of tiny droplets of water that go on to form clouds."

Svensmark's theory has gained support from the Europe's particle physics research centre (Cern) in Geneva. Jasper Kirkby, a physicist at Cern, says, "If you actually increase the amount of aerosol—these cloud condensation nuclei—then you don't increase the amount of water vapor in the sky, but you do distribute it over more droplets and smaller droplets. The amount of water is the same, but it's spread out over more droplets. The net effect is that the cloud actually lives longer, because it doesn't 'rain out' so easily. It's also brighter and very much more reflective, which affects the radiative energy balance on Earth."

So far, the necessary funding for a bigger, more conclusive experiment - to be conducted either in Geneva or at Stanford University in the US - has not been made available.

Clean lines

Other scientists try to quantify variations in the energy we receive from the Sun, and how those changes impact our weather.

Dr. Thejll of the Danish Meteorological Institute says, "After the effects of greenhouse gases, El Niño and volcanic activity are subtracted, a strong, clear solar signal in that data emerges. Temperature, atmospheric pressure, winds and circulation system change in behavior in time with the solar cycle. To us, it's a sign that it's caused by the solar cycle. The climate is complex, meaning all the parts interconnect. That's why so many results from statistical research into the climate produce confusing results. One person will say, 'Look, we can show it gets warmer in Bristol,' and another says 'No, it gets colder in Berlin. But wait a minute - they might both be the same phenomenon.'"

Sunspots and ENSO

No one knows why there is an above significant ENSO-sunspot correlation, or why variations in ENSO are modified or enhanced by an energy flux from the Sun during high sunspot counts. Since 1991, when Friis-Christensen and Lassen provided strong circumstantial evidence of a link between sunspots and temperature-mediated climate changes, scientists have tried to ascertain its nature.

I am pleasantly surprised by how many scientists in the field of climate change have more recently affirmed the Sun-Earth Connection. One such scientist is Dr. Gary Sharp. Here is an excerpt from one of his recent studies of which includes other noted scientists in the field of climate and weather:

Dr. Theodor Landscheidt, of Schroeter Institute for Research in Cycles of Solar Activity, in Nova Scotia, Canada has shown that the ENSO variation reflects solar activity, and allows proper forecasts for these phenomena, several seasons in advance of the present climate and ocean models.

These observations, along with recent work done by H. Svensmark and Nigel Calder suggest that solar activity turns out to be the dominant factor in climate change. IPCC scientists can no longer uphold their contention that solar variability over the next 50 years will not induce a prolonged forcing significant in comparison with the effect of increasing carbon dioxide concentrations, and that the impact of the Sun's variability has been underestimated in a way that reverses the proportions of its contribution to warming and cooling of the Earth's atmosphere by the Global Climate Modeling community involved in the Intergovernmental Panel on Climate Change (IPCC) Reports, hence the abundant scientific skepticism regarding the IPCC Report Conclusions... [http://sharpgary.org/NatureisBig.html]

In the following chapter, we show clear evidence that climate change has been around since before man took his first step on this planet, and would (and is) continued today even if every single polluting industry were shut down. This fact doesn't bode well for IPCC claims.

Chapter 10

Cores, Rings and Fossils

This chapter explores Earth's tumultuous 4-billion-year history as told in the ancient records left by the planet itself in rocks, coral, tree rings, lakebed sediment, and so on, beginning with an extremely violent incident soon after the planet first formed.

Earth's Violent Genesis

Following the formation of the physical universe, called by many The Big Bang, a few hydrogen atoms began to clump together, and attracted more ... and more ... and more. Within a few billion years, this ball of hydrogen had accumulated enough matter to be our Sun. It was surrounded by a disk of space matter captured randomly by the

gravitational field of this young star, spanning out to the orbit of Pluto. Over eons, the laws of physics determined that atoms of certain weights should take up particular orbits in this disk, which accounts for why certain planets have higher concentrations of certain elements that simply do not occur on other planets.

Again, over eons, the laws of physics determined that distinct bands began to form, much like the rings of Saturn. Eventually, these bands began to aggregate together to form planets, one of which was Earth, solid in form by about 4.8 billion years ago. For almost a billion years, this huge blob of molten rock cooled down, possibly hosting primitive early lifeforms that arrived on incoming asteroids—a phenomenon known as *panspermia*.

Earth a Snowball Planet?

We know from studies of isotopes with very long half-lives that our planet has gone through several very different climatological scenarios, some of which involved the oceans freezing over, so from space, Earth would have looked like a giant snowball.

Penn State geoscientists believe that glaciers that formed on tropical land areas around 500 million years ago during 'Snowball Earth' episodes could only have formed after the Earth's oceans were entirely covered by thick sea ice.

"There is strong geologic evidence of tropical glaciation at sea level during those times," Dr. David Pollard, research associate, Penn State College of Earth and Mineral Sciences' Environmental Institute,

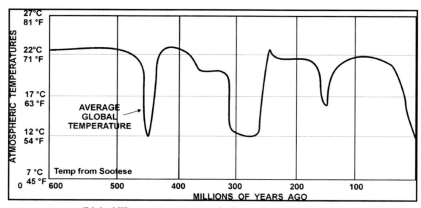

Global Temperatures over the Last One Billion Years

told attendees at the spring meeting of the American Geophysical Union on May 29, 2001. "We wanted to determine how tropical glaciers could have formed."

Pollard and James K. Kasting, professor of geosciences, first looked at the possibility that tropical ice sheets formed before the oceans completely froze into a snowball Earth, when equatorial oceans were still ice-free and could supply enough moisture for substantial snowfall.

During the several million-year lead-up to a Snowball Earth episode, the amount of CO_2 in the Earth's atmosphere decreased, the Earth gradually cooled from a mean 71 °F to about 54 °F, and the oceans begin freezing. The high reflectivity of the snow and ice that formed reflected more and more of the Sun's heat, further accelerating the cooling.

"Once the oceans are frozen to about 30 °N or S, this is the coldest that the Earth can get before all the entire ocean surface freezes," Pollard said. "Beyond this, there is no stable point at say 20 or 10 ° latitude: instead, the ice-reflectivity feedback becomes unstable and the system collapses rapidly to a Snowball Earth condition, where all oceans are ice-covered."

The researchers concluded that it was unlikely that tropical sea level glacial deposits formed before the collapse into Snowball Earth. But it was also unlikely that glaciers formed after the oceans had frozen, because there would have been little precipitation. "However, in further simulations with the global climate model for full snowball conditions, snowfall did exceed evaporation of snow and ice in some land areas, allowing a slow build-up of tropical ice sheets that would eventually flow to the sea. It would have taken several thousand years to form big ice sheets this way, but since it takes several million years to reverse Snowball Earth, there would have been plenty of time for the ice to form."

The team estimated that for Earth to come out of a snowball condition would have required a buildup of CO_2 by volcanic activity of 300 times today's levels, which would have taken millions of years. Could life have survived a Snowball Earth scenario? Yes, say many researchers. Oceanic life could have survived a full snowball condition in the waters around volcanic islands, or in tropical oceans where the ice may have been only a few feet thick. And then there are the species that live only around underwater volcanic fumaroles—perfect places to weather out a 10-million-year Ice Age.

Impact Earth

Every day, tons of space dust strike the Earth and, because of their tiny size, the particles drift slowly to the surface. Every 30 seconds or so, larger but still tiny rocks burn up, appearing at night as shooting stars. Meteorites larger than about 1 inch strike the Earth less frequently, and may only partially vaporize, thus striking the surface. Statistically, objects about 3 feet in diameter strike once a year, causing localized damage if they hit a populated area. Objects several hundred feet in diameter are rarer, striking every 10,000 years and causing major damage by direct impact or generating a tsunami. And statistically, a 5-mile-wide object strikes every 100 million years or so, causing massive and cataclysmic extinctions.

With an asteroid impact, it's not the mass that's the problem but the speed. Large objects are not slowed down by the friction of passing through the atmosphere, so they impact the Earth with almost deep space velocity of maybe 33,500 mph. A 100-foot-wide asteroid weighs about 300,000 tons, and at that speed, would release the equivalent of about 20 million tons of TNT, or 1,300 Hiroshima-size bombs. When such an object struck at Meteor Crater, Arizona about 50,000 years ago, it left a crater 3,600 feet in diameter and over 600 feet deep.

The monster that struck the Yucatan Peninsula about 65 million years ago, killing the dinosaurs and many other species, created the 112-mile-diameter Chicxulub Crater, and released energy equivalent to about 100 million megatons of TNT, or 50 million Hiroshima-size bombs. In comparison, the energy equivalent of the world's *entire* nuclear arsenal is only about 60,000 megatons.

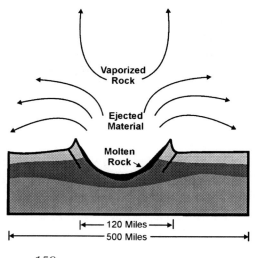

What actually happens during a large strike? As it first strikes the Earth, sheer momentum compresses several hundred feet of rock to form a hole and expel material into the atmosphere. Its continued motion plus an impact shock wave goes deeper and crushes the rock into fragments, some of which vaporize due to enormous pressure. The heat could also melt the rock at the site of the impact. The shock wave spreads out as a compression wave that eventually rebounds as an expansion wave. This lifts the floor of the crater and causes a rim around it.

The impact by a large object would likely be felt over the entire surface of the Earth. If impact occurred on land (25 percent probability), the pressure and heat waves would blow down and incinerate structures, trees, etc. Other effects include:

- Powerful earthquake, up to 12 on the Richter scale, and numerous large magnitude aftershocks felt for thousands of miles, causing incalculable death and damage.
- Millions of tons of dust ejected into the atmosphere that blocks the Sun's light for months, keeping Earth in perpetual darkness, and dropping temperatures by up to 20 °F, effectively ending photosynthesis, and wiping out that and maybe the next season's agriculture, resulting in widespread starvation.
- Wildfires generated by the heat wave throw up smoke that further blocks sunlight.
- Nitrogen and oxygen in the atmosphere combine to form nitrogen oxides, which combine with precipitation to form nitric acid that rains down on the surface, burning whatever it touches and polluting lakes and oceans.

If impact occurred in an ocean (75 percent probability):

- Intense heat creates a huge underwater steam cloud that erupts to the surface, pushing water aside to form a monster tsunami several thousand feet high. The water vapor remains in the atmosphere as a greenhouse gas that creates a warming effect for many years.
- The kinetic energy translates into mega-tsunamis estimated at up to two miles in height, which would wash over coastal ranges and flood miles inland, wiping out 90 percent of life on the planet.

Geological Ages and Extinction Events

Major extinction events have occurred several times in the life of our planet, notably:

- 505 m.y.a. (million years ago) (end of the Cambrian period)
- 438 m.y.a. (end of Ordovician)
- 360 m.y.a. (end of the Devonian)
- 245 m.y.a. (end of the Permian). This one almost wiped out *everything*.
- 208 m.y.a. (end of the Triassic). Paved the way for the ascent of the dinosaurs.
- 65 m.y. ago (end of the Cretaceous)
- 1.6 m.y.a. (end of the Tertiary)

Era	Period	Age
PALEOZOIC	Precambrian	570
	Cambrian	505
	Ordovician	438
	Silurian	408
	Devonian	360
	Mississippian	320
	Pennsylvanian	286
	Permian	245
MESOZOIC	Triassic	208
	Jurassic	144
	Cretaceous	65
CENOZOIC	Tertiary	1.6
	Quaternary	

All these events were probably caused by meteorites, whose impacts were so cataclysmic that they not only created great climate change but ushered in new geological eras.

Meteorite evidence from the event of 65 m.y.a includes a thin clay layer with an anomalously high concentration of the rare element Iridium. The widespread pattern of this layer is testimony to the enormous explosion. Clay layers at some localities also contain grains of quartz with a crystal structure impacted by a massive shock wave. Often present is a mineral named *stishovite*, which is not native to this planet, and *spherules*, or tiny beads of glass formed under intense heat and pressure.

What Happened 65 Million Years Ago?

Almost by accident, in the late 1980s, oil geologists in the Yucatan found they were drilling through a layer of impact-melted rock. Aerial surveys revealed a circular structure about 112 miles in diameter, and isotope dating showed it to have been formed about 65 million years

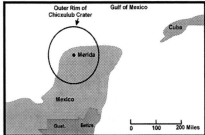

ago. Called the Chicxulub Crater, and centered on today's Merida, it was filled and buried by younger rocks. Surveyors also found deposits from a tsunami along the Gulf of Mexico coast, including Florida, and extending over much of Mexico's interior (solid black line). From the size of the crater, experts believe the meteorite was about 10 km in diameter.

What Happened 200 Million Years Ago?

Most scientists accept that a cataclysmic extinction event occurred 65 million years ago that wiped out Earth's large reptiles, but some scientists believe that a similar event occurred about 208 million years ago at the boundary of the Jurassic and Triassic. Did another impact wipe out 80 percent of all species about 200 m.y.a., scientists wonder.

The event proved to be the death knell for most species and helped crown the dinosaurs, which arose earlier in the Triassic, as the rulers of the Earth, according to Peter Ward, a University of Washington paleontologist who led a study whose results were published in *Science* magazine. "This calamity had tremendous similarities to two of the other five mass extinctions that have ravaged Earth over the past 500 million years. Like those, it appears this mass extinction was caused by a giant rock from space. We know now that asteroid impact can cause rapid extinction. It may not be an asteroid, but if it isn't, it acts like an asteroid."

At two remote sites in the Queen Charlotte Islands off Canada's British Columbia coast, Ward's team examined fossil samples that indicated a sudden collapse of the plankton population. They found an abrupt drop in the conversion rate of inorganic carbon into organic carbon by photosynthesis. Ward said, "The research indicated it took less than 10,000 years for the mass extinction to unfold. It could have taken place even more quickly — perhaps in an instant. This thing was real fast. At the time, most dinosaurs were relatively small, and they were locked in a survival-of-the-fittest battle with other well-adapted animals, including the mammal-like reptiles—the biggest of which were among the major herbivores of their day. These suckers were huge, hulking," Ward said. "But the mammal-like reptiles—whose earlier forms gave rise to the first true mammals—perished in the calamity. One of the great mysteries has been ... why would these creatures, which are seemingly better adapted for eating a variety of plant sources, die out and the dinosaurs not? And the answer is: Mass extinction doesn't give a hoot about your adaptations for everyday life. There's a lottery involved, for whatever reason."

Ward added, "There are ongoing studies to try to confirm an asteroid as the cause. We've found evidence of little carbon molecules called buckminsterfullerenes—buckyballs—that hint at a space rock as the culprit. A massive crater in Quebec called the Manicouagan structure, which measures 60 miles wide, could be the impact site. The crater has been dated to 214 million years ago, but that date may be too old. Alternative theories include an explosion of a nearby star that could have blown off the Earth atmosphere's ozone layer and sent temperatures soaring, or massive volcanic activity, possibly related to the breakup of the archaic supercontinent known as Pangaea."

What If It Happened Today?

Obviously the chilling questions are: What would happen if such an event occurred today? How much warning would we have, and what, if anything, could we do to prevent such a catastrophe?

First, what is the *risk* that such an impact could occur? Second, how can we *detect* such an impending event? Third, how can we *protect* ourselves from such an event?

Experts calculate the chances of dying from an asteroid impact in any given year are about 1 in 20,000. These are about the same odds of dying in an airplane crash, or a natural disaster such as a flood. To put this in perspective, the odds of dying in a motor vehicle accident are 1 in 100, of being murdered 1 in 300, or dying in a fire, 1 in 800. So I'm not going through my day with one eye on the sky.

Turning to detection, in March, 1989, a 1,650-foot-across aster-oid named 1989 FC passed within 435,000 miles of the Earth, and actually crossed Earth's orbit, so timing was critical here. How much notice did we have? None! It was not discovered until *after* it had passed through the orbit of the Earth. Such an impact is a 'once in a million years or so' event, and would have released energy equivalent to about 10,000 megatons of TNT (compared with the Chicxulub Crater event of 100 million megatons), but still enough to cause a nuclear winter. Now 435,000 miles seems like a long distance, but at the speed at which Earth moves along its orbit, it missed hitting us by only a few hours.

Then on March 19, 2004, a 100-foot diameter asteroid, named 2004 FH, passed within 26,500 miles of Earth, just outside the orbit of weather satellites, and well within the Moon's orbit of 225,000 miles. Admittedly, this one was small, but would have taken out a city the size of Dallas if it had hit. How much warning? Four days!

NASA's Torino Scale

To get a handle on this issue NASA has developed the Torino Scale that lays out the various levels of risk, impact, and response:

    0 — Code White / little consequence. The likelihood of a colli-sion is zero, or well below the chance that a random object of the same size will strike the Earth within the next few de-cades. This designation also applies to any small object that, in the event of a collision, is unlikely to reach the Earth's surface intact.

    1 — Code Green / little consequence. The chance of collision is extremely unlikely, about the same as a random object of the same size striking the Earth within the next few decades.

    2 — Code Yellow / concern. A somewhat close, but not unusual encounter. Collision is very unlikely.

    3 — Code Yellow / concern. A close encounter, with 1% or greater chance of a collision capable of causing localized destruc-tion.

    4 — Code Yellow / concern. A close encounter, with 1% or greater chance of a collision capable of causing regional devastation.

5 — Code Orange / threatening. A close encounter, with a significant threat of a collision capable of causing *regional* devastation.

6 — Code Orange / threatening. A close encounter, with a significant threat of a collision capable of causing a *global* catastrophe.

7 — Code Orange / threatening. A close encounter, with an *extremely* significant threat of a collision capable of causing a global catastrophe.

8 — Code Red / certain collision. A collision capable of causing *localized destruction*. Such events occur somewhere on Earth between 50 – 1,000 years.

9 — Code Red / certain collision. A collision capable of causing *regional devastation*. Such events occur between 1,000 – 100,000 years.

10 — Code Red / certain collision. A collision capable of causing a *global catastrophe*. Such events occur once per 100,000 years, or less often. In other words, a *really* bad hair day.

NASA estimates that over 90 percent of Near-Earth Objects (NEOs) have not yet been discovered. Due to their speed, our only warning might be an intense flash of light as the asteroid enters Earth's atmosphere. NASA scientists have proposed a Spaceguard Survey to find and track all large NEOs, which would give us years, even decades, to prepare for a catastrophic impact.

NASA's 1997 plan for the survey is to find 90% of the NEOs larger than 1 km in diameter within the next 10 years. However, at the current rate of funding (about $3 million per year), achieving that 90% objective will take over 100 years.

Friday 13, 2029: A Lucky Day … Hopefully

On Friday the 13th of 2029, the heavens will host a new pinpoint of light, at least temporarily, as asteroid 2004 MN4 passes within 18,600 miles of Earth—well within the orbit of our geostatic satellites. It's to be hoped that the calculations are correct, because at 1000 feet across, it could obliterate the state of Texas or cause mega-tsunamis.

According to Jon Giorgini of JPL:

"At closest approach, the asteroid will shine like a 3rd magnitude star, visible to the unaided eye from Africa, Europe and Asia—even through city lights. This is rare. Close approaches by objects as large as 2004 MN4 are currently thought to occur at 1000-year intervals, on average.

"The asteroid's trajectory will bend approximately 28 degrees during the encounter, a result of Earth's gravitational pull. Our ability to 'see' where 2004 MN4 will go (by extrapolating its orbit) is so blurred out by the 2029 Earth encounter, it can't even be said for certain what side of the sSun 2004 MN4 will be on in 2035. Talk of Earth encounters in 2035 is premature. More data are needed to forecast 2004 MN4's motion beyond 2029. The next good opportunities are in 2013 and 2021. The asteroid will be about 9 million miles from Earth, invisible to the naked eye, but close enough for radar studies. If we get radar ranging in 2013, we should be able to predict the location of 2004 MN4 out to at least 2070.

"The closest encounter of all, Friday 13, 2029, will be a spectacular opportunity to explore this asteroid via radar. During this encounter, radar could detect the distortion of 2004 MN4's shape and spin as it passes through Earth's gravity field. How the asteroid changes (or not) would provide information about its internal structure and material composition. Beautifully-detailed surface maps are possible, too."

Wow! No one in recorded history has ever seen an asteroid in space so bright, visible to the naked eye. Worth sticking around for, I'd say.

Turning to what we can do about an impact, we can either deflect the incoming object so that it passes harmlessly by, or we can destroy it. NASA believes that 10 years would be sufficient time to prepare a space mission to intercept the object and deflect it by detonating a nuclear device. And if we couldn't deflect or destroy it, at least we would have time to store food, water and supplies. Hopefully computer modeling would allow us to predict the impact site and, if on land, evacuate the surrounding area. If an ocean impact is foreseen, coastal populations could be evacuated. Psst, wanna buy a condo in Florida? Going cheap, I hear.

Deep Impact

On July 4, 2005, I wrote a piece titled: *NASA/JPL "Deep Impact" Mission Hits Bullseye*.

With less than one second off predicted time, the impact missile hit right on target. The space team exploded with excitement as they, along with all of us watching, viewed a spectacular display. The bright illumination that occurred appeared to be a surprise to all those watching, and I'm talking about the science team involved.

What we don't know yet are possible 'unintended consequences' that could occur at any time and for the next several days. One could argue we have already witnessed 'unexpected results' based on the reaction of the mission team. It was bigger, and brighter than most expected.

Oh yes, you can bet your bottom dollar all military 'need to know' personnel were right there watching every single movement. Part of this mission was to see what would happen when a missile hits an asteroid/comet. In the 'unlikely event' of an asteroid/comet heading our way, there are procedures to 'push' the bolide into an altered trajectory.

Here's NASA's press release on the subject:

Deep Impact Smashes Into Tempel 1

By NASA/JPL, July 4, 2005, 11:09

After 172 days and 431 million kilometers (268 million miles) of deep space stalking, Deep Impact successfully reached out and touched comet Tempel 1. The collision between the coffee table-sized impactor and city-sized comet occurred at 1:52 a.m. EDT.

"What a way to kick off America's Independence Day," said Deep Impact Project Manager Rick Grammier of NASA's Jet Propulsion Laboratory, Pasadena, Calif. "The challenges of this mission and teamwork that went into making it a success, should make all of us very proud."

Official word of the impact came 5 minutes after impact. At 1:57 a.m. EDT, an image from the spacecraft's medium resolution camera was downlinked to the computer screens of the mission's science team showed the tell-tale signs of a high-speed impact.

"The image clearly shows a spectacular impact," said Deep Impact principal investigator Dr. Michael A'Hearn of the University of

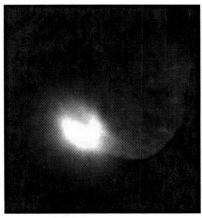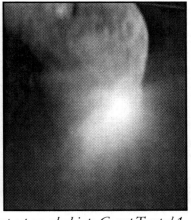

Two views of the moment that Deep Impact smashed into Comet Tempel 1

Maryland, College Park. "With this much data we have a long night ahead of us, but that is what we were hoping for. There is so much here it is difficult to know where to begin."

The celestial collision and ensuing data collection by the nearby Deep Impact mothership was the climax of a very active 24 hour period for the mission which began with impactor release at 2:07 a.m. EDT on July 3. Deep space maneuvers by the flyby, final check-out of both spacecraft and comet imaging took up most of the next 22 hours. Then, the impactor got down to its last two hours of life.

At the moment the impactor was vaporizing itself in its 6.3 miles per second (23,500 mph) collision with comet Tempel 1, the Deep Impact flyby spacecraft was monitoring events from nearby. For the following 14 minutes, the flyby collected and downlinked data as the comet loomed ever closer. Then, as expected at 2:05 a.m. EDT, the flyby stopped collecting data and entered a defensive posture called shield mode where its dust shields protect the spacecraft's vital components during its closest passage through the comet's inner coma. Shield mode ended at 2:32 a.m. EDT when mission control re-established the link with the flyby spacecraft.

The goal of the Deep Impact mission is to provide a glimpse beneath the surface of a comet, where material from the solar system's formation remains relatively unchanged. Mission scientists expect the project will answer basic questions about the formation of the solar system, by offering a better look at the nature and composition of the frozen celestial travelers known as comets.

Proxy Telltales of Ancient Earth

Many durable indicators exist on the planet that tell us by proxy what was happening to the climate millions of years ago—sedimentary deposits in lakes and oceans, coral reefs, fossils, and more recently, tree-rings. So let's take a look at some examples of what they're telling us and the people they're telling.

First is Paul Baker, professor of geology at Duke University's Nicolas School for the Environment and Earth Sciences in North Carolina, and Stanford geologist Robert B. Dunbar, who examined the sediments in Lake Titicaca in Bolivia and Peru. At 50-by-120 miles, Lake Titicaca is the world's largest body of fresh water and one of the best proxies of global climate.

According to Prof. Baker, whose study appeared in *Science* magazine, March 2001, "Lake Titicaca is a beautiful rain gauge. It's telling us some 25,000 years ago when glaciers from the last Ice Age covered most of the Earth, South America was quite wet, and not a dry region as many thought. While the planet went into a mini-Ice Age, the Andes were wet and temperate," claims Baker.

In addition to Dunbar and Baker, other co-authors of the *Science* study are Harold D. Rowe of Stanford; Geoffrey O. Seltzer of Syracuse University; Sherilyn C. Fritz and Pedro M. Tapia of the University of Nebraska; Matthew J. Grove of Duke University; and James P. Broda of the Woods Hole Oceanographic Institution. The study was titled: ***Lake Bottom Samples Indicate "Natural Cycles" Cause of Climate Change***, and probed what caused these thousand-year cycles of extreme wetness and aridity.

Since the last Ice Age, the North Atlantic has experienced periods of unusually cold surface temperature, often lasting 1,000 years or more and accompanied by centuries of intense precipitation. According to the authors, "These periods of plunging sea temperatures match the cycles of extreme wetness revealed in the Lake Titicaca core samples. The fact that alternating periods of dryness and wetness occur on a millennial time-scale or longer may be influenced, in part, by the behavior of the Earth as it orbits the sSun."

For example, the Earth's rotational axis gradually changes direction every 26,000 years — a process called precession. As a result, parts of the Earth that are relatively close to the sSun during summer today will be farther away during summer thousands of years from now.

So far, scientists do not have a complete explanation for the periodic climate changes in the Altiplano. For example, why did the water level of Lake Titicaca suddenly plunge to its lowest level 6,000 years ago?

"This drop occurred very suddenly in just two or three centuries," notes Dunbar, "suggesting that there can be rapid changes that occur in nature that we don't know much about. Natural variability can be enormous.

"The Altiplano is like a giant cup, and Titicaca is the deepest point in the vast plateau, so most of the precipitation in the Altiplano drains into the lake," says Dunbar. "Because very little water drains out of Titicaca, the lake serves as a reliable archive of rainfall patterns over many centuries—not just on the Altiplano, but in a large portion of tropical South America. Titicaca is the only large and deep freshwater lake in South America, and in deeper portions of the lake, sediment has accumulated continuously for at least the past 25,000 years.

"About 15,000 years ago, the Altiplano underwent a significant change. A dry era was launched, which continued for the next 2,000 years, causing Lake Titicaca to drop significantly. Between 13,000 and 11,500 years ago, Titicaca began overflowing once again. This wet period was followed by 1,500 years of relative dryness, followed by another 2,500 years of heavy precipitation as the lake again rose to overflow levels.

"Then, about 8,500 years ago, the lake level fell sharply as the Altiplano again became dry. But heavy precipitation would return for another 1,000 years, only to be followed by an extremely dry period between 6,000 and 5,000 years ago, during which Titicaca fell some 250 feet below its present-day level—its lowest level in 25,000 years. Titicaca finally began rising again 4,500 years ago. Since then, the southern portion of the lake has overflowed its banks numerous times."

How do they know? They drilled core samples of the lake bottom, of up to 50 feet in length. Then they looked at the fossilized diatoms—a kind of algae—and the ratios of various oxygen isotopes. Baker says, "Based on this geological evidence, the results suggest that the South American tropics were wet during cold eras. The Lake Titicaca region was not only wet during the last Ice Age, which began some 25,000 years ago and lasted until some 15,000 years ago, but also during the last cold periods of the North Atlantic Ocean region.

Another core sample study, this time from the Indian and Atlantic Oceans, took us back to 4 – 6 m.y.a. and found that the oceans underwent an unprecedented surge in biological activity.

Prof. Robert M. Owen of the Department of Geological Sciences, University of Michigan, and graduate student Casey Hermoyian looked at the levels of phosphorus in marine sediment cores. Reporting their findings at the 2001 meeting of the American Geophysical Union, Owen explained, "The waxing and waning of biological productivity in ancient oceans offers insights into climate change. Biological productivity is a measure of the amount of biomass (total living matter) produced in a given time. In oceans, biomass is produced mainly by photosynthesis, whereby microscopic organisms (plankton) capture energy from the sSun and use it to convert carbon dioxide and dissolved nutrients such as phosphorus into biomass. In the process, oxygen is released into the atmosphere as a byproduct.

"By studying patterns of biological productivity, we can make inferences about climate, which is affected by changing levels of atmospheric gases. For example, a long period of high biological productivity could lead to a net loss in carbon dioxide from the atmosphere, which in turn could cause the Earth to cool—an anti-greenhouse effect.

"A basic paradigm of earth science is that the present is the key to the past. But, in fact, in many cases the past also is the key to the future. One of the ways in which we try to understand the present-day climate and especially the future climate is by going back in the geologic record to see if we can discern the causes and effects of what occurred. And the more insight we can get from the past, the better we know how processes are working today—and more important, how they're going to work in the future.

"The results show that biological productivity increased by two to 30 times above background levels throughout the world ocean during the late Miocene and early Pliocene. This is significant because it means that the biogenic bloom occurred on a global, rather than a regional scale, and that it was not linked to a shift of nutrients but instead to a worldwide, overall increase in nutrient supply."

Now they are trying to understand why this happened. They suspect that rapidly rising mountains played an important role. "We know that both the Himalayas and the Andes were rising dramatically during this time. When mountains get higher, they become barriers that force the winds higher. Wind that crosses oceans carries a lot of moisture with it, and when it goes up, it cools off, dries out, and it dumps its moisture. The resulting rainfall flushes soils and nutrients into rivers, which empty into oceans."

The third example of ocean-floor core samples led researchers in a very interesting direction—an anomaly in the Earth's orbit around the Sun. A team led by Prof. James Zachos, Earth Sciences, University of California at Santa Cruz, analyzed sediment cores drilled out of the ocean floor, looking at the fossilized shells of tiny marine organisms. Oxygen isotopes in the shells, for example, reflect ocean water temperatures and the amount of ice trapped in glaciers.

Their findings were published on April 13, 2001, in *Science* magazine, and show that the glaciation during a period from about 20 – 25.5 m.y.a. corresponds with variations in the Earth's orbit known as Milankovitch cycles.

The astrophysicist Milutin Milankovitch hypothesized that, over about 100,000 years, cyclical *eccentricity* in Earth's orbit around the Sun can cause major changes in Earth's climate. The main variables are eccentricity, obliquity, and precession. Apparently, the orbit changes shape from nearly circular to elliptical over this period. It's tied in with *obliquity*, or the angle at which Earth's axis is tilted with respect to the plane of its orbit, varying between 22.1 – 24.5 degrees over a 41,000-year cycle.

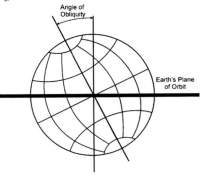

Zachos said, "Because there are several components of orbital variability, each with lower frequency components of amplitude modulation, there is the potential for unusual interactions between them on long timescales of tens of millions of years. We found at 23 million years ago a rare congruence of a low point in Earth's eccentricity and a period of minimal variation in obliquity. The result of this rare congruence was a period of about 200,000 years when there was unusually low variability in climate, with reduced extremes of seasonal warmth and coldness. Earth's orbit was nearly circular, so its distance from the Sun stayed about the same throughout the year. In addition, the tilt of Earth's axis, which gives rise to the seasons, varied less than usual. In other words, the tilt doesn't always vary between the same extremes in its 41,000-year cycles; the obliquity cycle itself varies in amplitude over a longer period of about 1.25 million years. Similarly, the eccentricity cycle peaks every 400,000 years. The combination would have caused only several degrees difference in summer temperatures at the poles, but it was probably enough to allow the Antarctic ice sheet to expand.

"I'm not sure everyone will be convinced that the orbital anomaly alone is responsible, but the congruence of those orbital cycles is a very rare event, and the fact that it exactly corresponds with this rare climatic event is compelling."

Turning next to tree rings, a fascinating article in *Nature* (6/12/01) told the story of how, about 50,000 years ago, a volcano in Chile buried a conifer forest. Thanks to an earthquake in 1960, the by now almost fossilized trees revealed details about Earth's ancient climate. Scientists from Chile and other countries examined the rings of 47 cross-sections and found a variety of decade-long and shorter climate cycles. They attributed the longer cycles to Solar Cycles, and wondered if the shorter ones—two to seven years—showed the influence of the El Niño cycle. The fact that modern trees exhibit the same variety suggests so, proving that change is the only constant.

For another proxy, we turn to a team at the Scripps Institution of Oceanography at the University of California, San Diego. Coral extracted from a reef of the remote Pacific island of Palmyra also reflects Solar Cycles during the 20th century. The record, which allowed the researchers to trace sea surface conditions over a 112-year-period, may hold implications for long-range climate forecasting and predictability due to the central tropical Pacific's key influence on climate conditions around the world (i.e., ENSO).

Reporting in the June 1, 2001 issue of *Geophysical Research Letters*, team members Kim Cobb and Christopher Charles found a 12- to 13-year cyclical pattern of temperatures in the Pacific, on top of a 2–3 year cycle. "This new, highly accurate coral record shows that there are processes that connect ocean basins on time scales longer than El Niño. We know from intensive monitoring of the El Niño that the ocean basins act in concert to a certain extent. But this record is showing without a doubt that there are processes, many of which are analogous to El Niño processes that are operating on 12–13-year cycles. So this shows that connections exist on much longer time scales, which is important for long-range forecasting and predictability."

Fossils, too, tell a story. William Zinsmeister, a Purdue University researcher, has developed a tool to unmask short-term events previously overlooked in the geologic record. "Stratigraphic plane analysis produces a multidimensional display of geologic data that can be used to analyze data from fossil records, archeological studies or any type of spatial geologic data," he says. "Early results using the technique reveal several short-term climatic events during the late Cretaceous period that may have played a significant role in mass extinctions at the end of that geologic era. The data coincide with findings from deep-sea core drillings that show short-lived fluctuations in the climate at that time," he reported in the March 2001 issue of the *Journal of Geology*.

"When you look at the history at the end of the Cretaceous, we know there was a long-term decline in temperature, and the climate was getting cooler and cooler. We often view it as a simplistic gradual decline, but if you look at a modern weather pattern, you see variations from year to year, so we know that weather does not have a smooth flow. Until now, scientists have not been able to see those perturbations in the geologic record. Using this technique we now can detect these short-term events."

Scientists know that the Cretaceous period saw massive extinction of many life forms, including dinosaurs and primitive birds. "How things became extinct near the end of the Cretaceous is just as important as the extinction itself, because the patterns tell us something about what actually happened," Zinsmeister says. "For 150 years, paleontologists have been developing range charts that plot fossils through the dimension of time. Though this method works well in many instances, it falls short of answering our questions when looking at how life forms change over short periods of time. The real problem is, when you look at the data set using conventional methods, you're looking at only one dimension – time. These data were collected over a large geographic area, but when we view the data in one dimension, the geographic component within the data set is obscured.

"By doing this on the computer, I can look at an enormous amount of data and see how these fossils were distributed in space and time. When you see that, all of a sudden the world looks a lot different."

Zinsmeister shows how a giant form of mollusk, known as an ammonite, occurs at only one point in time. "Looking at the data with traditional techniques, one wouldn't distinguish this giant ammonite occurrence from the others. But when you see it graphically, you can see that the giant ammonites line up along a single horizon. This begs the question, what's going on here? In this case, the sudden occurrence of this big ammonite may represent a drop in the sea level at that time.

"The data may help scientists better understand historical events and may even help put the controversy about the demise of the dinosaurs to rest. Here, we're able to see what the real world looked like. We have this long-term decline in climate, but superimposed upon it, we have these perturbations – where you have short-term warming events or the rise and fall of sea levels – and this adds to the distress on the marine animals at that time. Taking this into account, the mass extinction would most reasonably be viewed as a conjunction of events."

Chapter 11

NASA, NOAA
and a Thing Called 'Peer Review'

The story began on February 5, 2000, when a NASA press release warned of an M-class flare. Then, two days later, they said, "Oops, it's actually an X-class flare," but didn't tell anyone. That prompted me to ask in a February 7 ECTV article:

Is it possible there is indeed a struggle deep within NASA's walls? Is it possible there are some high up with enough influence to change NASA's direction of public relations? Or, is there recent independent data ready to be disclosed?"

NASA has issued a statement that suggests their acknowledgment of a sunspot/solar flare connection. NASA seems to be puzzled by the enormous X-Class flare which occurred during a high, but lower than expected sunspot count of 138. Today's sunspot count has already risen to 174. I am expecting double the count of the predicted "apex" of 150 by late next month. As I wrote yesterday, expect extreme or even recorded breaking weather within 48 hours.

On February 12, I wrote *A Large CME Has Just Hit Our Magnetic Field:*

NOAA has just notified us of a strong geomagnetic storm in progress. This occurred due to a large CME (coronal mass ejection) that occurred on February 9. Again, I am unclear as to why NOAA/NASA waits three days to notify us. With SOHO on watch, we know at the time it occurs and what direction the CME is heading.

On the next day (February 13, 2000) NASA issued another press release:

The prolific active region 8858 produced another M-class solar flare today — Geomagnetic Storm Alert - The Space Environment Center reports that disturbances in Earth's magnetic field reached severe storm levels in some places on Feb. 12. This activity is thought to be the result of a coronal mass ejection that left the Sun on February 9. Activity could continue at a somewhat lower level for the next 24 to 48 hours. Observers at high latitudes should be on the lookout for aurora. There is a 40 - 50% probability that minor geomagnetic storm activity could reach mid-latitudes.

On February 29, I posted a new article: *A Sign NASA Has Changed Public Relations Policy* that read:

Just hours after Earth Changes TV posted our article on the two CMEs and ten days of M-class flares, I received an email from NASA asking me to look at their web site: Spaceweather.com. Sure enough, NASA had just posted the occurrence of the two CMEs mentioned in my report. So we *do* make a difference!

I believe this to be a sign. NASA is listening to those of us who have been suggesting a new method of Public Relations. In my humble estimate, the article below is further indication NASA may be willing to share information BEFORE an event, as opposed to their apparent policy of admittance days after an occurrence (or sometimes not at all). I am very hopeful this new line of communication will continue as events "heat up." I am convinced it is far better to prepare people over a period of time so we will not be shocked by the events to come. I am thinking NASA may now feel the same way.

NASA directed me to a website, and this is the article I found there on February 29, 2000: *A Twisted Tale of Sunspots:*

Two large sunspots near the Sun's central meridian have developed complex magnetic fields. If solar flares erupt from these regions, Earth could be in for stormy space weather.

The NOAA Space Environment Center is forecasting a 70% chance of significant M-class solar flares from at least one of the two large sunspots currently visible on the solar disk. Because of their placement on the Sun, like a double-barreled ray gun, these two sunspot groups are likely to produce solar flares and coronal mass ejections (CMEs) aimed toward Earth. Stormy space weather could be on the way sometime during the next 72 hours.

Solar flares are the biggest explosions in the solar system. A typical eruption can release the same amount of energy as millions of 100-megaton hydrogen bombs all exploding at the same time. The energy source for solar flares is the Sun's magnetic field. Whenever the magnetic field around a sunspot group becomes twisted and sheared, like a stretched and twisted rubber band, an explosive release of energy could be just around the corner.

Space weather forecasters noticed on February 28, 2000, that both of the large active regions 8882 and 8891 had developed relatively complicated "beta-gamma" type magnetic fields. Most sunspots come in pairs with a magnetic field that looks somewhat like that of a bar magnet. Magnetic lines of force emerge from one spot (the north pole), loop overhead, and come back down to the other member of the pair (the south pole).

This is called a bipolar or "beta-type" field. "Beta-gammas" are bipolar sunspot groups that are so complex that no single, continuous line can be drawn between spots of opposite polarity. The energy stored in the twisted magnetic field lines serves as fuel for solar flares and CMEs. Eruptions occur when the fields rearrange to form a simpler, lower-energy configuration.

Intense M-class and X-class flares can overload electrical power grids and cause blackouts if operators do not take precautions. Satellites can be damaged or even destroyed when their electronics are saturated by charged particles from large flares. A large and famous space storm in 1989 induced electrical currents on the ground that caused a failure in the Hydro-Quebec electric power system. This prevented 6 million people in Canada and the US from having electricity for over 9 hours. The same storm caused the atmosphere to inflate and dragged the NASA's Long Duration Exposure Facility satellite to a lower orbit earlier than expected.

On March 14, 2000, I posted the following article on the ECTV site under the title, *You Do Make A Difference, NASA Responds.*

I received the following articles within hours of my post regarding NASA Survey. Just a coincidence? Perhaps, but I favor the idea we do indeed make a difference. Could this be NASA's way of saying, "Yes, we're listening"?

Although the articles below are not the magnitude of which the survey reflects, I remain hopeful NASA will adopt a Public Relations policy of "inclusion" rather than historical "exclusion."

You know, in some ways NASA is no different than many old corporate-style organizational managements with the old idea of control and manipulate your employees. A mind set of "do what I tell you and don't ask questions." As most of us know, this style is no longer effective. More and more corporate organizations have quickly moved to a enhanced open "inclusive" style of management with their employees and customers. Let's hope NASA catches up quickly. Remember, the Brookings Report is 40 years old. Let Us All Move On!

Space Weather Advisory … 03/14/00

Summary For March 6-12: Isolated Category R1 (minor) radio blackouts occurred on March 7, 8, 11, and 12. R1 radio blackouts are normally associated with minor degradation of HF communication signals and low-frequency navigation signals for brief intervals.

Outlook for March 15-21: Continued R1 (minor) radio blackouts are expected to continue. Isolated Category R3 (strong) and R2 (moderate) radio blackouts are possible. R3 radio blackouts are normally associated with a wide area blackout of HF communication signals with loss of radio contact for mariners and en route aviators for about an hour on the sunlit portion of Earth. In addition, R3 blackouts degrade low-frequency navigation signals for about an hour, affecting maritime and general aviation positioning.

Potential Major Solar Flare Warning...03/14/00

Astro Alert News / Sun-Earth Alert

Active sunspot region 8906 is a large sunspot complex now passing the south-central solar meridian. Recent analysis of the magnetic fields that make up this region suggest there is a distinct possibility of a major M- or X-class solar flare sometime over the next 3 to 5 days.

The trailer spot complex of this region contains a delta magnetic configuration where opposite polarity sunspot umbrae are encompassed by a single penumbra. Strong magnetic field gradients have been measured along the neutral line that separates these opposite magnetic polarities. The concern right now is that recent detailed magnetic analysis performed by Mees Solar Observatory in Hawaii (www.solar.ifa.hawaii.edu/mees.html) have revealed significant levels of magnetic shear along this same neutral line. These factors, when considered together, suggest that there may be significant levels of pent-up magnetic energy within this region.

The largest solar flare from Region 8906 observed thus far was an M-class 3.6/1B event late in the UTC day of 12 March (if x-rays reach the class M5.0 level, the flare becomes a major category event). Although there have been no major levels of activity from this region since its appearance on the eastern solar limb, recent data supports the idea that a major M- or X-class solar flare is very possible over the next several days. The overall pattern of the magnetic fields near this region is not unlike some in history which have produced major X-class flares.

Sunspot Region 8906 is large and complex enough to spawn a major proton producing solar flare. Such events can affect the health and stability of satellites in orbit around the Earth and can wipe-out ionospheric communications through the polar regions of the ionosphere. Although there has been no hard evidence yet to suggest that Region 8906 is capable of producing a proton flare, it is at least statistically large and complex enough to be capable of doing so.

Any major solar flares that occur will likely be associated with coronal mass ejections (CMEs) that should be well-directed toward the Earth over the next 72 hours. Thus far, there have been no significant observed Earth-directed CMEs from Region 8906. But this could change rapidly if this region spawns a major flare event.

Observers with hydrogen-alpha filters should pay close attention to the region around the trailer spot complex. White-light observers may want to pay close attention to sunspot group as well, for if a major X-class flare develops, there is a slight chance it may produce a brief white-light manifestation of the activity (known as a white-light flare). Although the odds of such an event occurring are extremely low, they are still worth considering.

On the same day (03/14/00) as the two NASA releases above, I posted the following article on the ECTV site: **It Is Not Your Imagination...**

Have you noticed NASA's reduction on all their websites of news regarding solar activity? No, it is not your imagination. A source close to the issue has reported there may indeed be an order to reduce news of escalation regarding solar flares, CMEs, gamma ray burst and other solar activity. This includes NOAA's "Space Weather Advisories."

Just when I have thoughts of NASA's Public Relations division having adopted a policy of "inclusion," I witness almost two weeks of omission. I continue to believe there is an internal struggle within NASA to capture the hearts and minds of the public. Having witnessed NOAA's report last Friday regarding the cause of our weather being related to solar activity, all may not be lost. I remain hopeful "inclusion" wins out.

As a mental health professional who specializes in PTSD (post traumatic stress disorder), I am convinced it is far better to include the public on unfolding and escalation events. Let people prepare in their unique way for events to come. Again, it will be the sudden shock of occurrences that will cause the most damage.

This is not Y2K. Events have already begun. It is not a question of *if* events are going to occur. It is a question of *how* and *when*. I would suggest to NASA's Public Relations that they look at the solar escalation more like a war than like weather. We are all aware of how a nation prepares for war. Public Relations begins a campaign that starts months in advance to prepare us for events ahead. At the same time, they try to win our support for what they would like to propose. NASA, this is exactly what you need and have indirectly expressed. Wake up!

On March 21, 2000, I posted an article about several aspects of life with "The Giant" where I included the first chapter of **Earth's Bio-**

logical Record from the website of Space Daily News, part of the Goddard Space Flight Center:

NASA has collected the first continuous global observations of the biological engine that drives life on Earth. Researchers expect this new detailed record of the countless forms of plant life that cover land and oceans may reveal as much about how our living planet functions today as fossil and geologic records reveal about Earth's past.

"This is a period of exploration for us," said lead author Michael Behrenfeld, an oceanographer at NASA's Goddard Space Flight Center, Greenbelt, MD. "We've never been able to see the Earth this way before."

The study, which appears this week in the journal *Science*, is based on the first three years of daily observations of ocean algae and land plants from the Sea-viewing Wide Field-of-View Sensor (SeaWiFS) mission, creating the most comprehensive global biological record ever assembled. Scientists will use the new record of the Earth's surface to study the fate of carbon in the atmosphere, the length of terrestrial growing seasons and the vitality of the ocean's food web.

"With this record we have more biological data today than has been collected by all previous field surveys and ship cruises," added Gene Carl Feldman, SeaWiFS project manager at Goddard. "It would take a ship steaming at 6 knots over 4,000 years to provide the same coverage as a single global SeaWiFS image."

The new study presents a global assessment of the fundamental work that plants perform to make life possible Ð producing food, fiber, and oxygen Ð and how their productivity changes from season to season and year to year in response to our changing environment.

The biological record from SeaWiFS indicates that global plant photosynthesis increased between September 1997 and August 2000. Photosynthesis by land plants and algae absorbs carbon dioxide from the atmosphere and ocean, which plays a critical role in regulating atmospheric carbon levels. The initial increase in carbon fixation was largely due to the response of marine plants to a strong El Niño to La Niña transition.

"With three years of observations we can see seasonal changes in plant and algae chlorophyll levels very well, but we don't yet have a long enough record to distinguish multi-year cycles like El Niño from fundamental long-term changes caused by such things as higher carbon dioxide levels in the atmosphere," Behrenfeld concluded.

More information about the SeaWiFs program is available on the Internet at: http://seawifs.gsfc.NASA.gov/seawifs.html.

[I encourage a visit to the site, as it's packed with great information and breathtaking views of our oceans from space – Mitch]

The Thing from Outer Space

On February 19, 2002, I posted a major article that questioned NASA's stance on secrecy:

Does NASA Have A Split Personality?

No it is not your imagination. You have been witness to an internal conflict within NASA. A unconfirmed source close to the situation has stated most within NASA are for disclosure of information regarding celestial objects such as asteroids and comets, as well as very unusual activity with our Sun. However, there is a more powerful minority who has intervened and rapidly closed the door of information to the public. It appears those in power decided the Brookings Report findings should stand, and vital information that affects us all will be acknowledged as "National Security." In other words ... secret.

Boo! It's Toutatis

On October 31, 2000, NASA released a report telling of a large asteroid named Toutatis. The article came one day after the event. Not only did NASA withhold pertinent information, but they also went one step further to placate the public as if we were all adolescents who did not know better. Then came word of a possible collision scenario for 2030. Here's the text of my response:

The world has recently been witness to a tug of war regarding the disclosure of asteroid 2000 SG344. First we were told there was a very dangerous possibility of collision on September 21, 2030. Then, all of a sudden, they stated a miscalculation had been made and moved the date ahead 41 years to September 16, 2071. It has been suggested by a source close to the case who is within NASA that they disclosed the original information of September 2030 knowingly to gauge the public's reaction. Reportedly, this was done as a result of an article written by this author, who challenged NASA to discontinue their current Public Relations policy, which has proven to be a dismal failure, treating the public with disrespect, negligence, and out of step with current general public awareness of factual data.

What NASA has not told you (according to a source close to the case, unconfirmed) was they believed the public's reaction to perhaps the true disclosure of a possible collision in 2030, was too disturbing and had caused an "uncomfortable rift in public awareness and fear of further civil unrest could ensue." Originally it was believed the announcement of a possible collision 30 years in the future would be far enough ahead to not cause undue concern. Apparently they received information telling of a less-than-comfortable reaction had taken place. The reports had come from Third World countries. The only one mentioned was Brazil. It was within 48 hours that NASA had moved its impact date 41 years ahead to September 16, 2071.

It has been suggested there are several (perhaps a majority) of those in and around NASA who believe their Public Relations policy is out of touch with today's society and its people. They would support a more seamless rapport of disclosure in an appropriate and responsible manner. The need of daily education is the key for a healthy interaction.

Unfortunately there is more to this story. For reasons unknown, NASA felt a need to go one step further and discount the possibility of a near-miss asteroid, and now is suggesting it is only "space junk."

On November 1 , 2000, I entered the Toutatis fray with the following ECTV article: *Asteroid Nearly Hits Earth, NASA Silent*

Late yesterday night, a large NEO (near-earth object) 600 meters in size came close enough to the Earth to be named a "near miss." NASA astronomers have named this asteroid Toutatis. It is one of the largest known "Potentially Hazardous Asteroids" (PHAs) and its orbit is inclined less than half-a-degree from Earth's.

Why was NASA silent on such a large event? Did they not know it was coming? The answer is a very suspicious NO. According to NASA's own article, they did know of its presence, and for some time. Why was the public not notified? It's not as if they have not been public of other NEOs. In the last month, I have seen no less than ten articles on Eros. So why the sudden surprise with this one? Is NASA so dense to think that suppressing information, then releasing it after the fact will only enhance suspicion and speculation. I believe this is not only self-defeating, but reckless, and irresponsible.

In 1997 or 1998, a press release was put out stating: "Toutatis was an unpredictable asteroid with unreliable trajectories."

Here is an example of how NASA minimizes, and in my opinion makes light of those such as myself, who take this very seriously. The title they gave to this story was: "Trick or Treat: It's Toutatis." If this was such a 'joke,' why not let us in on it from the time they were tracking? NASA could say: "Uh oh, here comes the scary monster now. Boo! Did I scare you?"

Folks, I have a feeling that behind the scenes, we might see those involved wiping the sweat from their brow. This may be an exaggeration, but my guess is that some were very much concerned. If NASA was not concerned, we would have heard about this weeks ago.

Just when I think NASA has come around in correcting their dismal Public Relations policy, which has been a total failure for years, we get placated, as if we are all adolescents who don't know better. "Now, now, children, go out and play. There is nothing to worry about."

In the same breath of placation as above, NASA will tell us, "Uhh, did I mention we are only tracking about 10% of potential NEOs. They are very dark and hard to pick up. Also, there is an urgent shortfall of eyes in the sky to see them."

How ironic this story comes just hours after my article written last night. Perhaps just another wake up call for this curious onlooker. The bottom line still holds true (even, and maybe mostly, when politics and events unfold as this one). Follow your inner wisdom, not mine. I have a feeling many more such articles will be coming forward. Stay grounded and focused, but awake and aware.

Two days later, on November 3, 2000, the plot thickened when NASA discovered something else lurking out there. The ECTV response was:

Asteroid Discovered Last Week, Much Closer Than Toutatis

This latest article by NASA could not stress my concern more pointedly. Yesterday another asteroid named 2000 UG11 came 10 times closer than Toutatis, which zipped by a day earlier. NASA now admits this new asteroid (2000 UG 11) was just found last week. Yes, that's right just discovered last week and *10 times closer.*

I hope some of you will better understand my sharp words and concern over NASA's attitude and Public Relations policy. If ancient texts hold true, there is no place for NASA's cutesy attitude, minimizing a certain and real danger.

As a Certified Trauma Resolution Therapist, I can tell you first hand, it will be the sudden shock of information or event that will cause much more damage than disclosing true information allowing people to be better informed and prepared. The only exception might be what is known as "a planet buster." Obviously there is no way to prepare for such an event. However, some would make a good argument that it would help families come together for a final gathering and spiritual preparedness. But this would never happen. All governments are trained to derail civil unrest and anarchy.

NASA is convinced the better way is to not tell the public what is happening in our universe. Their belief is based on an antiquated report released in 1960 known as the Brookings Report. The team of statisticians was ordered to gather demographics to find how people would act if information was released stating there is intelligent life outside of earth. Their findings was that of chaos, mass hysteria, anarchy. Basically a collapse of our basic fundamental belief system.

As a result, our government (and perhaps that of the world), decided any such information would be deemed "National Security," and therefore will remain undisclosed to the public. Although the Brookings Report was directed at intelligent life outside Earth's, I believe the same holds true for "earth-changing events."

So the question will remain, would you rather be informed as to unfolding events that affect us all, or would you rather not know until after the fact (total annihilation withstanding). Reminder, ancient text states life will end as we know it. This does not mean *all* life will end. It will simply be part of a bigger plan I call The Transition, a move into another place. Some may call it another dimension, or higher vibration, or the 5th world. Whatever the words, I believe the meaning to be the same.

The Object Known as 2000 SG344

The debate continued on November 8, 2000, in my ECTV article *Much Ado About 2000 SG344* that read:

> Last Saturday a syndicated sportswriter compared LA Lakers center Shaquille O'Neal to 2000 SG344, a newly-discovered near-Earth object (NEO). During Shaq's game the night before, O'Neal had barreled into the opposing center "like 2000 SG344 — that object hurtling

toward Earth." Fortunately for basketball fans, O'Neal is far more likely to score a free throw than 2000 SG344 is to crash land on our planet.

Although SG344 is nearby now, scientists say there is no appreciable chance of a

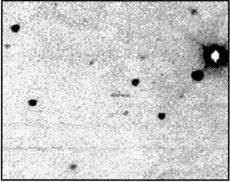

The dim streak in this negative image is 2000 SG344 moving against the background field of stars on Sept. 29, 2000.

collision for at least 70 years. (Shaq, on the other hand, should make plenty of baskets between now and then.)

2000 SG344 was discovered by asteroid-hunters on Sept. 29 as it was gliding by Earth approximately 20 times farther away than the Moon. Astronomers quickly realized that the faint object was unusual. Its 354-day orbit is very much like Earth's, so much so that 2000 SG344 might not be an asteroid at all, but rather a piece of manmade rocket debris.

Our planet and 2000 SG344 move through space like two runners racing along a track at nearly the same speed; it takes a long time for one to lap the other. The NEO, which is moving a bit faster than Earth, is slowly drifting away and won't return for 30 years.

As recently as last Friday, astronomers were concerned that the next encounter might be too close for comfort.

Close but no collision in 2030

Jan.
Feb.
Mar.
Apr.
May
June
July
Aug.
Sept.

orbit of Earth
orbit of 2000 SG344
close encounter ~Sept. 21, 2030

A panel convened by the International Astronomical Union (IAU) announced on Nov. 3 that 2000 SG344 might hit Earth in the year 2030. The chances of an impact were slim, they said, and new data to refine the object's orbit would likely rule out a collision altogether.

That's exactly what happened. Shortly after the IAU announcement, astronomer Carl Hergenrother found "pre-discovery" images of 2000 SG344 from May 1999 in archives from the Catalina Sky Survey.

"The pre-discovery images let us calculate a better orbit that absolutely rules out a collision in 2030," says Donald Yeomans, manager of NASA's Near Earth Object program at the Jet Propulsion Laboratory. "It won't come any closer to Earth than 11 lunar distances. However," he added, "the new orbit increases the chances of encounters in years after that. For example, there is a 1-in-1000 chance of a collision on Sept. 16, 2071."

Just as the possible 2030 encounter was excluded by better data, Yeomans anticipates the same will happen to the 2071 date. "Additional observations this year and in 2030 when SG344 comes back again will certainly alter our conclusions as we learn even more about its orbit."

If Earth and 2000 SG344 do cross paths in the future, what happens will depend on the nature of the near-Earth object. When the object was first discovered, it appeared to be a small asteroid, but another possibility is gaining favor among researchers. "The orbit of SG344 is so Earth-like, it makes you wonder if came from our own planet," mused Yeomans.

In 1971, the last time 2000 SG344 was in the vicinity of Earth, NASA's Apollo program was in full swing. 2000 SG344 may well be debris from an Apollo-era rocket masquerading as a space rock.

"Initially we thought it was too bright (and thus too large) to be a rocket fragment, but it's possible that this is the S-IVB stage from a big Saturn V," continued Yeomans. S-IVBs were booster rockets that propelled Apollo Command and Service Modules toward the Moon from their parking orbits around Earth. "Many of those boosters were targeted to hit the Moon, but the S-IVBs from Apollo 8 through 12 went into orbit."

If SG344 is a derelict rocket booster, it's probably no larger than 15 meters and wouldn't pose much of a threat even if it did strike Earth. An incoming S-IVB would burn up in the atmosphere as a dazzling but mostly-harmless fireball. Spectators in Texas and Oklahoma witnessed just such a display last month when the casing from a Russian Proton rocket disintegrated over North America.

2000 SG344 might be a leftover S-IVB booster from a Saturn V rocket launch.

On the other hand, if 2000 SG344 is a bona fide space rock, it's likely to be bigger and more dangerous. Typical near-Earth asteroids reflect about 3% − 20% of the sunlight that falls on them. The apparent brightness of 2000 SG344 corresponds to such an asteroid 30 − 70 meters across.

"Whatever it is, 2000 SG344 is certainly no dinosaur killer," Yeomans added, referring to a 10 km space rock that may have triggered mass extinctions when it hit Earth 65 million years ago. A 70-meter asteroid (the worst-case scenario for 2000 SG344) could obliterate a city if it landed on one, but it would not trigger a global catastrophe.

At the lower end of the scale, around 30 meters, 2000 SG344 might not even reach the ground. "It depends on what it's made of," says Yeomans. "A 30-meter slab of iron could make it through the atmosphere and do some local damage." On the other hand, a fragile carbonaceous chondrite like the widely-publicized Yukon fireball of January 2000 would mostly disintegrate high overhead.

The September discovery of 2000 SG344 by astronomers David Tholen (University of Hawaii) and Robert Whiteley (now with the Catalina Sky Survey) was no accident. Using the Canada-France-Hawaii telescope atop Mauna Kea, the pair was looking for unusual near-Earth asteroids in orbits whose greatest distance from the Sun coincides with the Earth's orbit. Such objects could hit our planet, but they would rarely be found by search programs that hunt for space rocks coming from the general direction of the main asteroid belt.

"We're not doing a full-fledged survey like LINEAR, Spacewatch, or LONEOS," says Tholen. "We observe only a few nights each year." Nonetheless, the pair has discovered ten near-Earth objects since they began their part-time hunt in 1996. Their most celebrated find, 2000 SG344, is technically classified as an Aten: an Earth-crossing object with an orbital semi-major axis smaller than one astronomical unit. Atens spend most of their time inside Earth's orbit, crossing over for brief intervals only.

But is 2000 SG344 an Aten asteroid or an Aten rocket shell? That's the 10-megaton question. Whatever it is, astronomers plan to track SG344 as it slowly recedes from Earth—more data will reduce the uncertainties about SG344's orbit and naturally answer many of the questions about this mysterious NEO.

But there's not much time. The orbit of 2000 SG344 is carrying it toward the blinding glare of the Sun. By mid-2001, the object will be dimmer than 25th magnitude as its solar elongation dips below 90 degrees. "That's a tough combination for observers," noted Yeomans. "We might find more pre-discovery images," he added hopefully. "Pictures from 1971 would really lock down the orbit and probably tell us whether SG344 is a rocket or an asteroid. We just have to keep looking."

Reminder, NASA (at least part of their split personality) has recently disclosed there are 700,000 NEOs (near-miss near-Earth objects) less than 1 kilometer in size, which are an ongoing potential hazard.

One may ask the question: "Are there more near-miss asteroids now than before?" I would say yes. One would certainly have to factor the reason we are seeing more is simply because we now have the technology to do so. But even with this given fact, my early research suggest we are in fact experiencing more celestial bodies coming into our orbit than in recent history. Extended history is still an unknown. Some would suggest ancient text speaks of what we see today, occurred in ancient times.

Question: "What would be the cause of this increase in celestial bodies?" My current (and early) research is pointing toward Magnetics. As the Earth's frequency increases, at the same time the magnetic field decreases, this could be the cause of pulling celestial bodies into a near orbit. Still too early to make firm suggestions. More coming soon ...

NASA and the Sun-Earth Connection

At least on the Sun-Earth Connection, NASA seems to be getting the message, for on May 29, 2002, I was able to post the following piece on the ECTV website: ***Sun - Earth Connection of Keen Interest to NASA.***

This breaking article will be of no surprise to many of you. NASA has just announced "a fleet of spacecraft were sent to observe our atmosphere's response to recent solar storms." One such spacecraft is called "TIMED" (Thermosphere, Ionosphere, Mesosphere, Energetics and Dynamics). This is NASA's way of measuring ECTV's "equation".

Sunspots => Solar Flares => Magnetic Shift => Shifting Ocean and Jet Stream Currents => Extreme Weather ... and Human Disruption

NASA states their shifting focus is providing important new information on the final link in the Sun-Earth Connection chain of physical processes that connect the Sun and Earth. In other words, the connection between solar activity and our weather.

As mentioned in an earlier chapter, I believe we are just months away from daily reports of the Sun-Earth connection viewed on our local weather forecast.

But maybe I spoke too soon, because on August 29, 2003, I had cause to post the following article: **NASA Confesses to "Destructive Culture**.

Folks, this could be a crack in the corporate infrastructure. NASA is no different than any other large corporation. They are an antiquated organization based on the old Industrial Revolution 'pyramid" where sh*t runs down hill. Only the most diabolical, back-stabbing, intimidating, control/power mongers make it to the top. It is a certain "character profile" that is attracted to administration. Anyone who has worked for a corporation knows what I am speaking of.

In many ways NASA is no different than Enron. They are both corrupt. And those who know how to "play the game" make the rules. It is the nature of the beast. This is the foundation of what all the press releases and talking heads are addressing when they say NASA "culture" is the cause.

Now let me say, I do not fit in the box of those who say NASA is all conspiracy, although, at times, this could in fact be the case. What I am addressing in the above paragraphs has more to do with "repression" of employee expression. NASA has gone on record as of yesterday, stating they have not been open to employee feedback. Employees have come forward stating it was dangerous (meaning losing their job or being blackballed) to express their true feelings or new research or insights.

I believe most of the scientists and instructors associated with NASA are second to none. Many of them are truly the best of the best. Unfortunately, their voice is too often repressed. I am hopeful more of them, as in the vein of Dr. Tom Van Flandren, will come forward. But let's not kid ourselves, progress and change of this nature can be very slow. But it is a great first step. As most of us know, those who are in power now, will most likely fight to the death to maintain their cooperate position. It's their nature. It's part of their unique make-up. It's what we call in the mental health field "character profile" or "personality profile."

So let's all keep an eye on this hopeful event. BTW, isn't it interesting that this "shift" occurred on the exact day (August 28, 2003) as mentioned in my interview with Dr. Buryl Payne. You may find our interview rather "prophetic" in light of today's news.

Still on the same theme, a few weeks later on September 17, 2003, I posted the following article: **NASA/NOAA Space Weather Center in Dire Straights ...**

Have you noticed fewer and less accurate reports coming from NASA's Spaceweather.com and NOAA'S Space Environment Center? To this day there are conflicting reports as to the status of SOHO. Most sunspot and solar activity reports have been coming from Boulder, Colorado's Space Environment Center using "ground-based telescopes." Gee, my not so good friend Dr. Tony Philips, coordinator of Spaceweather.com and Spacescience.com may be losing his job. What a shame, he was a true NASA company man and we had so much respect for each other. Hey Tony, send in your CV and three letters of recommendation, and I'll see what I can do. On second thoughts, I've seen your work. Never mind!

Okay, sarcasm aside, this truly is a blow to maintaining accurate data and current readings. If you have noticed a lack of space weather news, now you know why. I have been extremely skeptical of the accuracy of what has been distributed on NASA/NOAA sites. In my opinion, they can no longer be trusted. No, not because of some hidden conspiracy, although there may be flavors of such from time to time, but because there is no longer trusted integrity of data provided. It is no secret of my disdain for people like Tony Philips who reflect NASA's recently disclosed "Destructive Culture" which reeks of corporate corruption...Enron Style!

My comments on Tony Philips were the content of an August 18, 2003 ECTV article titled *Is This the "Smoking Gun" re: Blackout?*
Were you aware SOHO was off-line five hours prior to, during, and after, the August 14 blackout? It is impossible for anyone to have come forward to make an "absolute" statement that geomagnetic storms did not play a role. Even NASA's popular Spaceweather site did not completely rule out this possibility.

Here is Dr. Tony Phillips statement:
"Readers have asked if solar activity could be responsible for the widespread blackout in the eastern US and Canada. Not likely. There were no strong solar flares or geomagnetic activity yesterday to trigger the outage."

Not likely? Is that a yes or a no? Or does it mean ... possibly, but maybe not?

I have had heated disputes with Mr. Phillips in the past. I have found him to be nothing more than a "company man" willing to compromise his integrity for the good of the company. In this case, the company is none other than NASA. Mr. Phillips has a history of demoralizing reasonable dissent. He attacks those who are outside the company and is quick to pigeon-hole and belittle those who oppose him. As a result of Mr. Phillips' behavior and subsequent disingenuous cause-and-effect reflex, I no longer have confidence in the Spaceweather.com site and Mr. Phillips' display of "subjective" analogy. I have turned my attention, as with astronomy, to the thousands of amateur solar observers across the nation and the world.

As part of Earth Changes TV's zeal for truth and accuracy, I search and seek out, highly talented and credible "independent" sources when evaluating events, predictions, trends, and outcomes. I will go on record at this moment to state, I have reasonable doubt corporate officials and regulators have chosen the path of "disclosure." Information is coming forth that suggests those in corporate administration have been ordered, or have personally chosen, the road of "omission."

Disclosure vs. Omission

On May 22, 2002, I posted a piece titled **Fighting For Hearts and Minds Over Inclusion Policy,** wherein I wrote:

Recent disclosure by the FBI, CIA, and a half dozen other government agencies that chose to not disclose terrorist threat information has caused great concern with the American people. Some would make the case our president was part of the recent suppression of information that would affect us all.

Now, just today, New York City has been placed under an "extreme caution" terrorist threat level. Some would say that we have been under this threat for many days but the news is just emerging today. So what's going on? Is there an internal battle to win the hearts and minds of the American people so that certain hidden agendas can be fulfilled? I am afraid my answer will be unsettling to some. I would suggest the answer is YES!

I have brought this issue to surface on many occasions. My personal battle with NASA has always been with their "public relations policy." For years NASA has acted on the belief the general public simply could not absorb the truth regarding current asteroid threats, extreme solar conditions, and the speed of climate and weather changes. As many of you have witnessed, I have gone to battle with this particular government agency and, with a good deal of perseverance and a growing audience, we have begun to see change. NASA now freely acknowledges a direct connection between solar weather and climate change.

Back to New York. Here is the protagonists. In one corner, we have the strongest lobbying forces known to man, which will fight to the death to protect their investments. Yes, I am speaking to the dark side of our chosen democracy ... capitalism! The last thing this almighty force would want is for you to learn about their lack of control over economy and commerce. They truly believe the old slogan: "What the public doesn't know, won't hurt them."

In the other corner, we have a growing consortium of public service officials, i.e., congressman, senators, councilmen. They, too, have an agenda. This group truly believes the more informed the public is, the better we are able to absorb the shock of sudden change. Their motto might be: "To know is to learn. And to learn is to be empowered and prepared." However, theirs is not without a touch of greed as well. Perhaps their hope is you will rely on their opinion for direction. In other words, they may say, "Follow my truth, I am on your side. I will lead you to what you want." The problem here may be obvious and certainly counter to my affirmation that states: "Follow your truth, not mine or anyone else's. Seek and you shall find." Find what? *Your* truth!

What is unfolding in front of our eyes has been around for hundreds of years. It stems from old parliamentary procedures. On the one hand, there is the *right of participation*. On the other hand is the *right of decision*. These two principles were originally designed to work in harmony, simultaneously, and with a sense of unity. Boy, what happened to these ideals? The answer is one word—GREED. This goes back to the cave man days. Some would say we are simply "hardwired" to follow this innate drive as hunter-gathers for self preservation.

Is there no hope? I would say there is a great deal of hope. It may not come in a very comforting way, however. I believe the great equalizer will not come from man but in the form of natural forces. Yes, I am saying it will be through the tragedy of outside forces such as solar extremes, continued 'freak weather,' volcanoes, earthquakes, or even an asteroid hit. Is it just a coincidence most of our ancestors speak of "something coming from the sky" or "from the heavens"?

As events escalate in the way of weather and war, it is my belief that the *status quo* will be loosened. The power brokers may panic, errors will be made, and change will ensue. But this is the smaller portion of the equation. It will be the *external* forces that make the difference. As the Hopi say: "The world as we know it will end." This does not mean life will end. It is saying our way of knowingness will end. The Mayan Calendar suggests this very same notion with a given year of 2012. It is in this year the current Long Count—and, in effect, the calendar itself—ends. Nothing is known or predicted about another Long Count after that date. Most Mayan scholars suggest this, too, means life as we know it will shift, and so dramatically that we can know nothing about what that will look like.

What is my best guess of current events? The freedom fighters will make a grand push. We will have a sense of openness and inclusion of all matters concerning terrorism and even solar/weather/ asteroid events. Unfortunately, greed will win out and the *status quo* may resume. But wait! After this period of time, external forces will escalate to such a degree that we will be forced to once again rely on our neighbor. Community, family, togetherness will be essential for our survival.

Am I crouched under the table fearful to even go outside? Not even close. This is a very natural 'cycle of events.' The Earth has seen this many times before. Change is as essential for life as oxygen and water. It is how we cope with change that will make the difference. The disciplines of spirituality will indeed help many of us find our way. Our ancestors have told us this time and time again. In many ways 'spirituality' was indeed their 'science.'

The Demise of NOAA's Solar Environment Center?

On September 17, 2003, co-worker Joe Rao from the Solar Environment Center at NOAA's Boulder, Colo. facility had this to say: "I am very sorry to report that things are suddenly looking quite bleak for the Solar Environment Center in Colorado. Because of the short-sightedness of our elected officials in the House and Senate, the budget for SEC has been significantly slashed for fiscal year 2004. The direct result of this means the possibility that there could be no more space weather data and forecasts (for such things as solar flares and geomagnetic storms) in the coming weeks ahead. Full details are provided below in a message by Mr. Ernest Hildner, Director, Space Environment Center that was forwarded to me by Ms. Candice Curtiss of NOAA."

Here is today's press release from Ernest Hildner - Director, Space Environment Center:

U.S. Space Weather Service in Deep Trouble ... 9/17/03
Ernest Hildner - Director, Space Environment Center; Manager, NOAA Space Weather Program

For Fiscal Year 2004, starting October 1, 2003, the House Appropriations Bill for Commerce, Justice, and State continues Space Environment Centers funding at $5.2 M (a reduction of 40 % below the FY02 level). Worse, the FY04 Senate Appropriations Bill zeroes Space Environment Center and all space weather in NOAA, so services, data and observations, and archiving would all disappear if the final appropriation is at the Senate level. At the House funding level, starting October 1 SEC will rapidly lose about half its staff, negatively affecting its ability to serve the nation with operational products, data collection, and R&D. Unless the appropriation level for Space Environment Center is restored to the level of the President's FY04 Budget Request, $8.3 million, the nation's civilian space weather service is in trouble. At the president's requested funding level, Space Environment Center can almost return to FY02 level of services, data, and R&D.

In the omnibus appropriations Bill for FY 2003, the SEC received a severe cut to its budget of about 40%, with no explanation for the reduction. One-time funding additions have kept SEC afloat in FY2003. The president's budget request is $8.3 million for SEC in FY2004 (an amount consistent with its past budgetary levels), but the House Commerce-Justice-State Appropriations Committee provides only $5.2 million, or roughly 40% less than the amount necessary to maintain SEC at its current operational effectiveness. Again for FY04, no explanatory text was included in the Committee Report to explain this reduction, and it far exceeds the 18 % reduction below request meted out to NOAA Research overall and the 1% reduction to National Weather Services request. The Bill has not yet been acted upon by the full House.

Solar observation. The Atmospheric in NOAA does not extend to the astral. Absolutely no funds are provided for solar observation. Such activities are rightly the bailiwick of the National Aeronautics and Space Administration and the Air Force.

Needless to say, there is no evidence to suggest that NASA and the Air Force agree that one or the other, or both, should operate the nation's civilian space weather service.

Conclusion

Unless SECs appropriation level is increased in Conference, the best outlook is that Space Environment Center shrinks to less than half its capability, and the worst is that space weather will disappear from NOAA. In this case, the nation's space weather service will have to be reconstituted in some other agency, at greater cost and lesser capability, to meet the nation's needs.

As a result of this sad and harmful event, ECTV has stepped up its efforts to network with the thousands of independent amateur astronomers throughout the world. I will do everything I can to continue providing the most accurate solar activity news. I am proud to state that ECTV is now rated the number 1 provider of 'space weather' and 'earth science' in breaking news events. Thank you!

Spring 2005 saw a sudden upsurge in solar activity, to which NASA responded with: "All is well, so go back to bed, children." On May 7, 2005, I wrote the following piece for the ECTV website in response to that "all is well" report:

It seems every time NASA stumbles on their published predictions related to solar activity, they usher out Dr. David Hathaway, solar physicist who represents NASA Marshall Space Flight Center. The latest back-peddle is related to the recent sunspot activity and forthcoming solar flares and CMEs.

NASA suddenly tells us "there is a myth about solar cycles." Oh really? And what might that "myth" be? According to the latest news release, NASA representatives tell us the solar minimum is not a safe time at all, and that continued solar activity is likely. But wait just a minute. That's not what Dr. Hathaway told us just six months ago.

Let's take a closer look. On October 18, 2004, Dr. David Hathaway appears to tell a different story: "*Solar minimum is different. Sunspots are fewer—sometimes days or weeks go by without a spot. Solar flares subside. It's a safer time to travel through space, and a less interesting time to watch polar skies.*"

Well that's pretty interesting. It seems Hathaway's latest news release tells us 'not all is well' and caution should be adhered. Just days ago, Hathaway tells us: "*Astronauts traveling through the solar system, far from the protection of Earth's atmosphere and magnetic field, can't drop their guard—ever.*" Hathaway and colleague Bob Wilson, both working at NASA's Marshall Space Flight Center, believe they've found a simple way to predict the date of the next solar minimum. "We examined data from the last 8 solar cycles and discovered that Solar Min follows the first spotless day after Solar Max by 34 months," explains Hathaway.

Thank you, Dr. Hathaway, for giving us an exact month to observe. Now we can all witness the validity of your theory. Hathaway tells us the first spotless day was January 28, 2004. That would make the "official" Solar Minimum November 2006. This will help us maintain an accurate measure to your current and previous "news release(s)" and for any mention of "unusual" or "misrepresented" myths" as it relates to possible future changes.

Well, folks, this is getting really quite interesting. As you might expect, I believe this gives sustenance to my "mega-cycle" hypothesis. I expect the scientific and world community to witness a "mega-cycle," which is to suggest a cycle outside of a cycle. I predict we will see continued announcements or "news releases" from NASA telling us of new so-called "myths" or "unusual" events to unfold. As always … time will tell.

After posting the above article, I went back and read it again (after getting past all my misspellings and grammar, for which I am famous. Really hard to stay on top of this when getting the article out fast and first is most important), I began to wonder who this Hathaway guy really is. I've never met him, spoken to him, or communicated by email, but what came to mind is this guy could be no different than me. One could certainly say it's just as possible my hypothesis could be as far off the mark as I believe his is.

Accordingly, on May 8, I posted the following:

Some reflection on yesterday's article

It seems I may have this knee-jerk defensive posture when so-called "authorities" publish their data and it presents as an unquestionable "inner peer" fact. I know you have certainly seen this come out when I talk about the environment (the Z-word). You see what happens is this … I too used to take our "expert's" words as factual data which was not to be questioned. But when I began my own research into the Sun-Earth connection, I quickly found that what "any" expert has to say is in many ways nothing more than their "personal, subjective conjecture". And guess what … so is mine. Now it is true that theirs as well as my own is certainly based in factual data, but it is the "outcome" which is uncertain.

Hathaway says he has it all figured out by reviewing the past eight solar cycles. He tells us that 34 months after the date of the first zero sunspot count will come the Solar Minimum. As stated, that would make NASA's "official" Cycle 23 minimum November 2006. I say Hathaway is wrong, and what we will see is continued "unusual" solar activity that will not reflect previous cycles. I call this a "mega-cycle".

As we all now know regarding cycle 23, the sunspot count was more than double the so-called maximum of 150. In fact on more than a few occasions it went to well over 400. I think the largest number was 438, but maybe higher, but I know it did not quite reach 500. As for the so-called quieting down slope suggesting we would see minimal if any activity, now almost three years after the so-called maximum it remains very active. In fact, just four months ago on January 11, 2005, a new sunspot region

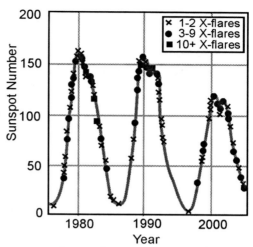

appeared which quickly grew to almost the size planet Jupiter unleashing two X-Class flares. And of course as of today, two more M-Class flares fire off.

[The chart wasn't in the article. I inserted it for the book to show that in 2005, Cycle 23 is still alive and well, generating X-class flares, sometimes as many as nine a month.]

So when NASA rolls out Dr. Hathaway to make some "authoritative," unquestionable notion, something comes over me that wants to remind everyone: "Hey, this guy is guessing just as much as anyone else." The problem with that kind of statement is it suggests that I have the answers. Well, I don't, and neither does anyone else.

Armed with the knowledge that I have gained while doing my research (not to mention interviewing the absolute top scientists in the world on this subject), it is difficult to not take such authoritarians to task. But I will have to learn how to do this without sounding superior myself. One method I am now employing is to involve you. Yes, I am currently doing an outcome study, and presenting the data "in real time." I am hopeful to perhaps set a trend. This can now be done with our current technology which was unavailable in Hathaway's time. The good news is everybody gets to see events unfold as they proceed. The bad news (for some), is that Hathaway and those like him will not be able to play the "bait and switch" as outlined above. From where I view this, it's 'good-good news'. But I think other traditionalists may not think so.

I've been a non-conformist rebel my whole life, I doubt seriously I will stop now. But I do wish to be most effective in presenting my data. But when organizations such as the 'global warming' cult plays their deceitful, manipulative, but highly effective game, I just go berserk. Seems I heard this in a movie somewhere. I think maybe it was the 1970's movie *Billy Jack*. It doesn't matter; I think you know what I mean.

Interview with Dr. Brekke

We end this chapter with an account of a recent ECTV show where I had as my guest Dr. Paal Brekke, Deputy Director of the SOHO Project stationed at NASA Goddard Space Center, and a noted Global Warming myth-buster, but before we get into the detail of the interview, we must introduce a key concept called 'The Hockey Stick Theory,' pioneered in 1998 by Michael Mann, environmental science professor at the University of Virginia.

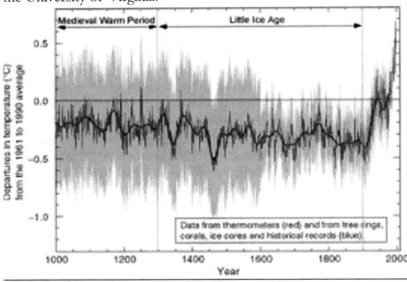

This theory is at the heart of the current global warming hysteria—the argument that the last 10 years are the hottest in the last thousand, and that there was no such thing as the "Little Ice Age" or the "Medieval Warm Period." The graph presented to the UN IPCC shows a slight cooling trend for 900 years, from 1000 – 1900, and then a sudden, rapid 100-year warming trend. Because its shape resembles a hockey stick, the name has stuck.

Mann's theory gained strong support in the IPCC, but a growing number of climate experts are questioning it. However, it led to the Kyoto Protocol, aimed at curbing greenhouse gases, and most nations have ratified it. Canada, for example has committed $10 billion to implementing it.

The demise of the Hockey Stick began in January 2005, when a University of Guelph economics professor, Ross McKitrick, and a Toronto mineral exploration consultant, Stephen McIntyre, published an article in the journal, *Geophysical Research Letters*. The article's main findings were:

- Many teams have tried to independently replicate the above chart, but none has succeeded, yet the IPCC inexplicably accepted the theory as scientific fact.
- McIntyre asked Mann for his original data and was told, "We've forgotten where we put it." And amazingly the IPCC never actually verified the data.
- Mann has been vague and evasive on which "proxies," such as tree rings, he used. Initially it was 112, but then in 2003, Mann suddenly increased the number to 159.
- When asked, Mann refused to provide the original computer code for his model, but McIntyre found evidence that Mann had worked backwards from the hockey stick graph to determine which tree rings to select.
- Climatologists know *for a fact* that the weather in the 15th century was actually warmer than in the 20th century, but Mann's model completely ignores it.

So, Watson, the game is afoot, and there's no telling how it's going to turn out. Time will tell, however.

The interview with Dr. Brekke flat out endorsed my "Equation." Having taken the risk to ask Dr. Brekke directly and without hesitation what he thought of my premise suggesting there was a short-term causal effect between solar events and Earth's weather, if you could have seen the look on my face when he concurred. Well let's just say, I was giving high fives to thin air, but it felt like a thunderclap. You may ask why such excitement? Because, as with all peer reviews, you never know the reaction of prominent scientists who are at the top of their field. In short, in a two minute period last night, I had put my entire reputation on the line. Yes, it was one of those moments when you feel as if you're standing in front of the classroom in your underwear.

But it got even better. I spent another five minutes making my case that many scientists have published highly regarded data showing a distinct Sun-Earth connection as it relates to climate (meaning decades, centuries, and millennia), and Dr. Brekke quickly agreed. Then I suggested to him that my research goes beyond climate, and laid out my theory of a Sun-Earth Connection related to *weather*, meaning a causal effect measured in hours, days, and weeks.

At first there was a pause, my chest tightened, my legs became tense, my back straightened stiff, then the answer came. "Yes, Mitch, I would agree with you. There are many scientists who are looking into this more immediate reaction. They are now studying the Northern Pacific Oscillation." [Northern or Southern Pacific Oscillation, better known as NPO or SPO, simply means "shifting ocean and jet stream currents."]

So Dr. Brekke had just confirmed the second portion of my Equation:

Sunspots => Solar Flares (CMEs) => Earth's Magnetic Field Shift => Shifting Ocean and Jet Stream Currents.

Dr. Brekke then took a few minutes to discuss a recent event. Two weeks earlier, a consortium of scientists from the University of Colorado had made a stunning announcement. According to research associate Cora Randall of CU-Boulder's Laboratory for Atmospheric and Space Physics. "Nitrogen oxide and nitrogen dioxide gases in the upper stratosphere climbed to the highest levels in at least two decades in spring 2004. The increases led to ozone reductions of up to 60 percent, at roughly 25 miles in altitude, over Earth's high northern latitudes," said Randall. *"This decline was completely unexpected, and was caused as a result of chemical reactions triggered by energetic particles from the Sun."*

Dr. Brekke's response surprised me: "The original 'hockey stick' which all this global warming was based as brought forward by Michael

Mann, is bad data. Whole climate time periods were left out. They erased entire centuries of climate related to the Medieval Mini-Ice Age. *It is now safe to say this so-called 'hockey stick' is broken.*" We quickly agreed that the "climate always changes," and has done so for the life of this planet, with or without humans.

Dr. Brekke does acknowledge it is very difficult to distinguish what percentage is caused by the Sun and what percentage is cause by humans. According to him, it may be 70/30 caused by Sun/humans. But those are his assumptions. As for myself, not having a monolith such as NASA breathing down my neck, I can easily go out on a limb and say, "It's 3 – 12 percent of the current warming trend human-induced, with between 88 – 97 percent solar-induced."

The connection between "real" climate/weather science and so-called global warming pseudo-science is a lie. There *is* no connection. As I state in a many ECTV articles, we could shut down every massive polluter in the world, and the Earth would still go through its natural warming and cooling cycles. But we certainly would have cleaner air and water… and who would not be for that!

Then I laid out my thoughts about the environmental zealots and their propaganda of manipulation and lies. This was a great risk to myself, not having a clue how such an esteemed and highly placed scientist would react to my harsh statements and of course to be judged by hard line scientific facts.

This led to one area that Dr. Brekke and I more closely agree— that the IPCC is a "joke," filled with self-centered, self-seeking, agenda driven, cloaked lobbyists who have no vested interest in science. No, what drives this team of environmental zealots is simply *money.*

Chapter 12

The Sun and Human
and Animal Behavior

As an NADA certified acupuncturist, in March 2002, I attended our annual NADA Acupuncture Convention, held that year in Las Vegas, Nevada. I have been a practicing member of N.A.D.A. since 1995. At the 2002 convention I delivered a presentation on the Sun-Earth connection. As you will see later in this chapter, the discipline of acupuncture is probably the most ancient and fitting practice to demonstrate just how much a role magnetics play in human and animal behavior. As you have witnessed from my 1998 published Equation, I have long known of our symbiotic relationship with the Sun.

Equation:
Sunspots => Solar Flares => Magnetic Shift => Shifting Ocean and Jet Stream Currents => Extreme Weather and Human Disruption

An article published May 14, 2005 by AFP titled **Whale Strandings Linked to Solar Activity** brought world attention to a better understanding of just how much solar activity affects our home and ourselves. The article tells us:

"Surges of solar activity may cause whales to run aground, possibly by disrupting the creatures' internal compasses, according to German scientists." It has been hypothesized that humans also have an 'internal compass,' but perhaps not only to provide a sense of direction or whether it's 'day or night' or 'up or down,' but also as part of human intuition.

The whale article goes on to state: *"University of Kiel researchers Klaus Vaneslow and Klaus Ricklefs looked at sightings of sperm whales found beached in the North Sea between 1712 and 2003. They compared the record with another set of historical data - astronomers' observations of sunspots, an indicator of solar radiation. They found that more whale strandings occurred when the Sun's activity was high."*
In fact, they found that 90 percent of strandings happened when the length of the Solar Cycle was below average, which some scientists believe leads to a higher flux in solar radiation, and hence a greater distorting effect on Earth's magnetic field. So the important thing is not sunspot count, but intensity. Further, if the effect is indeed magnetic, then if you've read so far, you know that CME blasts are the real culprit.

Noting that homing pigeons and dolphins have an organ containing small crystals of magnetite that allows them to 'see' magnetic fields, the authors wonder, "It may be the same for whales. Sperm whales migrate long distances with very little visual clues as to where they are going. It would be unsurprising if they too had a magnetic sense."

Let's look at the science behind this. First, scientists are aware of a strain of bacteria called *magnetotactic bacteria* whose internal bodies contain lodestone (magnetite). R. Blakemore, a researcher at the University of New Hampshire, discovered that, within their single-celled bodies, they create about 20 cubical crystals of magnetite, oriented along the axis of their body. They appear to use this to navigate in straight lines rather than go round in circles. Since then, magnetite-bearing organs have been found in homing pigeons, tuna, honey bees, dolphins and whales.

R. Aidan Martin, of the ReefQuest Centre for Shark Research (www.elasmo-research.org) reports on their website that in 1988, Dr, Margaret Klinowska of the Research Group in Mammalian Ecology and Reproduction of Cambridge University compared records of mass cetacean strandings in Britain and the United States against geomagnetic maps (which plot variations in the intensity of magnetic fields at the Earth's surface caused by a variety of reasons, including differences in the underlying rock. On the maps, these magnetic variations appear as contour lines, with areas of high magnetism showing as 'hills' and areas of low magnetism as 'valleys.' Analysis revealed that most mass strandings occurred where the magnetic valleys were oriented perpendicular to the shore.

This discovery suggests that at least some whales navigate by following a magnetic map of the ocean floor in lieu of landmarks in the vast, dark ocean. There are regular magnetic variations in the oceans, and magnetic hills and valleys stretch for huge distances across the ocean floor. Possibly the whales use the magnetic contour lines in the same way we see roads on a map. These magnetic 'freeways' often follow continental shelves, but not always. Dr. Klinowska theorizes that whales may strand when they follow a magnetic road leading onto shore. She also suggests that solar activity can affect this pattern, possibly causing irregular fluctuations that 'move the road.' So whale mass strandings may be the magnetic equivalent of traffic accidents.

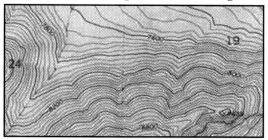

Topographical map analogy

Martin goes on to speculate how whales sense Earth's magnetic field. Studies in Germany suggest that cetacean retinas contain magnetite, making them sensitive to magnetic fields of an intensity consistent with geomagnetism, and may see the surrounding magnetic field superimposed on their field of view. It's possible that they 'see' a magnetic field analogously to contours on a topographical map.

Earth's magnetic field may provide several types of cues useful for navigation based on memories of previous migrations. This works well if things are stable from year-to-year, but things are not. Because of the displacement of magnetic poles from the rotational poles, there is a difference between true north and magnetic north. This variation slowly changes over time as the magnetic poles drift. In addition to these horizontal and vertical directional components, the geomagnetic intensity also increases with latitude, from about 0.3 gauss at the equator to about 0.7 gauss at the poles. (A few millennia ago, it was more like 5.0 gauss. For comparison, a typical therapeutic magnet has a field intensity of 10,000 gauss.)

Field intensity also decreases with distance from the Earth's surface. In addition to these global features are localized magnetic anomalies depending on such things as iron content of surrounding rocks. On top of that, we have the push-pull effect of magnetic disturbances associated with solar activity. If a pod of whales migrates based on memory of a field like a road map, a magnetic storm could 'move the roads around,' and they end up crashing on the beach.

Other researchers speculate that as the whale moves through the Earth's magnetic field, this movement generates tiny, micro-voltages in its body, which specialized organs detect.

As a NADA certified acupuncturist, I have some understanding of magnetics and the human/animal grid. It has been known for thousands of years that an energy runs through all living things. The Chinese call it chi or Qi; the Japanese call it ki; in India, it's called prana.

In the practice of acupuncture, we are taught early on of the magnetic grid that surrounds and permeates the body. When this energy field is disturbed and becomes out of balance, it manifests as illness (both physical and mental). The very basis of acupuncture is the study of the human grid or energy field and its connection to our anatomy. The largest part of an acupuncturist's study is identifying and defining the energy network through the human/animal body, made up *meridians*. Meridians are a network of bio-magnetic grids (energy points) that run through all living things. When the life force energy is out of balance, it manifest as illness. Depending on the ailment, an acupuncturist manipulates certain meridians to restore balance to the body and mind.

I believe it is the action of charged particles emitted from the Sun in the way of solar flares and CMEs, and interaction with the Earth's magnetic field are the causes of our extreme weather disruption. I also believe this very same interchange has a direct effect on human/animal behavior. Could it be true there is an epidemic of human "mood and personality disorders" such as depression, anxiety, phobias, and addictions that could be attributed to a changing environment directly related to the Sun?

A shocking statistic indicates the world's population has reached record-breaking consumption of pharmaceutical drugs, which tends to confirm this epidemic of mood and personality symptoms. Could magnetic shifts also be affecting humans as well?

Just as the Earth has its magnetic field, so do humans. It makes sense that what would certainly disrupt one would disrupt the other. Are we indeed connected to the Earth and universe in ways current science cannot explain?

Outside the U.S. (where the AMA, FDA, and big pharmaceutical companies can't limit healthcare options to expensive drugs and surgery), medical practitioners totally accept 'the magnetic human' concept, and use it extensively to control pain, and to heal. Every year in Europe and Asia, dozens of conferences and symposia present the latest findings in magnet therapy, as it's often called.

Studies have shown that magnets may be an effective therapy for the relief of discomfort. It is believed that applying magnetic fields to an injured area improves blood flow and oxygen to enhance the body's natural healing process. Magnets create a magnetic field believed to attract and repel charged particles in the blood, creating movement and heat. This causes the blood vessels to widen which is believed to accelerate the healing process by allowing more blood to pass through the capillary thus improving blood flow, which takes away the toxins in the system and brings in nutrient rich blood to the affected area. The improved blood flow and fluid exchange to the injured tissue helps reduce discomfort and inflammation. The magnetic field is also thought to stimulate the nervous system, triggering blockage of discomfort sensations.

John Zimmerman, Ph.D., is one of the leading authorities in America on the subject of magnets. He is president of the Bio-Electro-Magnetics Institute, an independent, nonprofit, educational, research organization dedicated to furthering our understanding of bio-electromagnetism. Dr. Zimmerman has published extensively and is currently conducting a double-blind, placebo-controlled study on the effectiveness of fixed magnets for low back pain. Another researcher,

Dr. Philpott, a member of the North American Academy of Magnetic Therapy, claims that the north pole of a magnet placed against the skin will relieve pain, reduce swelling, promote tissue alkalinization, promote sound, restful sleep, increase tissue oxygenation, calm the nervous system, and assist in relief of addictive tendencies.

Doctors in Russia and Eastern Europe make wide use of pulsed and alternating magnetic fields, and have developed an extensive body of knowledge on applications and treatment of specific conditions, all non-invasive and can even be done at home.

(To learn more about this fascinating topic, enter "magnet therapy" into Google, and it will list about 21,000 pages.)

Schumann Resonance Factor

The Schumann Resonances are quasi-standing electromagnetic waves that exist in the Earth's 'electromagnetic' cavity between the surface and the ionosphere, about 40 miles up. The waves are formed by electrical activity in the atmosphere, notably the 1,000 lightning storms occurring at any given moment worldwide. As lightning shows us, the atmosphere is actually a weak conductor and lightning 'rings' the cavity much like a striker rings a bell, creating electromagnetic waves with a set of resonant frequencies that is unique to the ionospheric cavity, i.e., the atmosphere has a unique 'tone,' just as no bells make exactly the same sound.

The cavity has several resonant frequencies, specifically 7.83, 14, 20, 26, 33, 39, 45 and 50 Hz. The reason these frequencies are called 'resonant' is that they have wavelengths such that, as the wave created by a lightning strike travels around the cavity, bouncing from the surface to the bottom of the ionosphere, it arrives back at the original lightning strike location just in time to reinforce itself. (Non-resonant wavelengths just die out.)

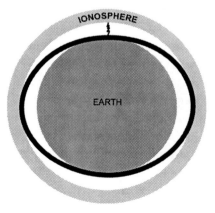

We can find the wavelength of the 7.83 Hz frequency by dividing that number into the speed of light (186,000 miles per second). The result is 23,754 miles, or the circumference of the Earth at the equator. The wavelength of the 50 Hz frequency is 3,728 miles, which would be a shorter path at a higher latitude.

The so-called Resonance Factor is the average of the frequencies in play at any one time, and for centuries was close to the lowest frequency of 7.83 Hz because its amplitude dwarfed all the others, having the most direct path around the planet. Historically, the Schumann Factor has been so reliable that many scientific instruments used to be calibrated to 7.83 Hz. However, scientists are puzzled by a recent increase in the predominance of the 14 Hz component, which is driving the 'average' upwards. This points to a mysterious change in either the ionosphere (possibly absorbing more lower frequency energy than before), or in the nature of the atmosphere itself.

The nature of the cavity also changes when the ionosphere becomes charged as during solar flare activity and, in 2001, we were at the Solar Maximum. And even though the official 'policy' of scientists is to deny the existence of a super-charged area of space, it is real, and we may be entering it. (Actually, Russian scientists are working with it publicly and are very concerned. Openly their American counterparts remain quiet but, behind the scenes, however, it's a different matter, as the military worries about the effect on weapons systems.) The effect of the area on the ionospheric cavity is unknown, but measurements show distinctly that the amplitude of the higher Schumann frequencies is increasing, which means the 'average' Schumann Resonance frequency is going up. But why is this important?

We humans evolved over millions of years in the Earth's resonant field and the human brain formed in its environment, and tends to entrain itself to environmental frequencies. (This is the basis of bio-feedback machines that play tones to synchronize the brain's hemisphere.)

Now the human brain can operate at frequencies between just above 0 Hz and about 50 Hz. For convenience, five frequency bands have been identified:

- *Delta* (0 – 4 Hz), occurring in deepest meditation and dreamless sleep. It brings profound feelings of peace and triggers the release of a growth hormone that helps healing and regeneration. Deep sleep is therefore restorative.

- *Theta* (4 – 7 Hz) also occurs during sleep, and during deep meditation, where we are awake but open to vivid mental imagery. This boosts creativity, learning, intuition and ESP, and reduces stress.
- *Alpha* (7 – 12 Hz) occurs during dreaming (REM sleep), relaxation and light meditation. The alpha state is the gateway into deeper states of consciousness. We depend on alpha brain activity for our overall mental and body/mind coordination, calmness, alertness, and learning. This is our 'mental resting state.'
- *Beta* (12 – 25 Hz) occurs during normal waking consciousness and outward attention. *Slow Beta* (12 – 17) is normal information processing and mental activity; *fast Beta* (17 – 25) is heightened alertness and flight-or-fight anxiety.
- *Gamma* (25 – 50 Hz) is a rare 'super-normal' waking state, that can occur when we are simultaneously processing information in both brain hemispheres, e.g., people of genius stature, and whales and dolphins.

An Australian engineer named Hainsworth concluded that the human brain states evolved in response to the Schumann frequencies (see diagram).

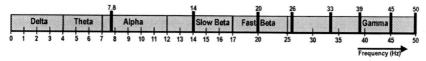

If Hainsworth's hypothesis is correct, our brains evolved around the 7.8 Hz frequency as the basis of our Alpha state. This is our 'resting state,' when we relax, daydream, or just take a break from thinking hard. As the mean Schumann Resonance rises from 7.8 Hz to slow Beta (14 Hz, say), our brain entrains to that frequency, and Alpha state relaxation becomes impossible. This higher frequency resting state can show up as mental disturbance, drug addiction, seizures and suicide, and as antisocial behavior such as road rage and plane rage. It could lead to panic attacks, anxiety disorders, ADHD, problems sleeping, obsessive-compulsive disorders, and countless other stress-related conditions.

Whether coincidence or not, in one week in February 2005, a disgruntled man shot the husband and mother of a Chicago judge (she too would have died if she'd been home), a convicted rapist shot an Atlanta judge and two enforcement officers, and a member of a Wisconsin church congregation shot seven other members and then himself. It seems that the pressures of life plus the changing energies are pushing more and more people over the edge into violent measures. Also, the local TV news seems to run a road-rage story every evening nowadays.

On a practical note, the Internet abounds with wave generators that emit certain frequencies. My co-writer is inseparable from his Bio-Shield generator, which has several preset frequencies, such as 7.83 Hz for an enjoyable state of well-being while resting, 12.3 Hz to enhance brain function, and 5.66 Hz for deep sleep.

This article is typical of one I could have written on a couple of days of any month, so the specific date doesn't really matter:

The Effect of Magnetics on the Human Body and Mind

We have just been witness to three X-Class flares in a row, with large CMEs and continued geo-magnetic storms. The latest report indicates no signs of letting up any time soon. This is all part of a very natural mega-cycle that the Earth has seen many times before. Some of the flares being released could generate a powerful geomagnetic storm capable of knocking out power grids, and produce one heck of a aurora show.

Today at work I had one patient who made an 'escape' when our unit was not locked down. Three other patients experienced severe anxiety attacks, and two got into a fist-fight, all before lunch. On my return from a quick lunch, I witnessed three staff members themselves in conflict. This came after I'd already initiated a 'high alert' as a result of several patients acting out.

Several cases of depression and some suicide attempts have also been reported. Feelings of disorientation, fatigue, anxiety and hyper-vigilance are also common occurrences I believe to be related to solar magnetic storms.

Have I seen this before? Yes. Was it during or around geomagnetic storms as a result of solar activity? Yes. Folks, I would like to suggest, in the same way many of us have accepted the idea that a full moon affects behavior, so too does magnetics. I have also noticed a spike in the number of missing pet reports in the newspaper. This goes along with people talking about how their pets have been acting strangely over the last few weeks. One cannot help but ask the question: "Is there a connection between solar activity, geomagnetic storms, and human/animal behavior?" My guess is Yes!

On August 23, 2004, I reported on the ECTV website what was happening in the field of mental health. The article was titled: ***Mental Health Field Turns Focus on New Energy Fields***:

I have just returned from my mental health symposium for continuing education credits. It was refreshing to note the mental health field appears to be making a turn for the better. I was taken back when the second speaker began by saying: "There are energy fields we are just beginning to explore which may affect the brain related to mood and personality disorders." I immediately sat straight up in my chair, giving my full attention. Needless to say my hand went up within minutes with my onslaught of questions and information interplay. Problem was, there were 53 other clinicians looking at us with a puzzled, but inquisitive look. I could tell immediately, they were not quite sure what the hell we were talking about.

So what *were* we batting back and forth? The new innovative study of energy fields that go beyond the known fields, such as gravity, magnetic field and plasma field? No, we were talking about unified field theory, collective consciousness fields, and electrical intuitive fields. You may remember the 1960s and early 1970s when we used the terms such as 'negative vibes.' Well, those 'negative vibes' could be an electric magnetic field that surrounds all humans, or better stated, all living things.

To many of us, this is really not all that new, but here, mainstream science is beginning to notice. Better yet, fully acknowledge. This means that funds have become available for further research into areas many of us have known about but could not quite wrap our brains or understanding around. (Of course, Chinese healers have known about all this for 5,000 years—that's where acupuncture came from.)

Of course we discussed neurotransmitters and receptor sites as to distribution of acetycholine, dopamine, norepinephrine, serotonin, GABA, endorphins and enkephalins as it relates to mood and personality disorders. But the new twist of the day is how to treat such symptomology with electro-magnetic stimulus, proteins, and 'empathetic cessation.' Again, nothing new to many of us, but I can't tell you of the expression on my face and the matching feeling inside as I witnessed a conservative, mainstream scientific body speak in such terms. We were on such a roll that I thought for just a moment that they might acknowledge the pineal gland* as the psychic or intuitive center of the body. But we didn't quite make that turn.

To summarize, what I witnessed over the three days of this symposium was an unconscious acknowledgment of what our ancestors have been telling us for centuries. Simply put, we are evolving into the spiritual beings we've perhaps always been, but just forgot about. Is this not in perfect alliance with what the Mayan Calendar has told us? "We are now in the time of escalated expanding consciousness. The time in which our heightened intuition is becoming fully developed and our intuitive nature is to be acknowledged and exercised."

But it is also a time of challenge, or testing. It will be important to remain in our integrity. To remain in truth is essential for a more smooth transition. Those who may be more attached to status quo are likely to experience high levels of stress and potential physical breakdown. Instead of going by the mantra of "the way things ought to be," giving the impression there is some rigid standard to abide as written by Rush Limbaugh, we may do much better going by the suggestion of, "we're all just kind of guessing." This suggests it is better to remain flexible, open-minded, and humble as our fast-changing paradigm is in the act of unfolding.

Back on November 7, 2002, I penned this piece titled **Earth Changes TV Focus on Change** for the ECTV website that ponders what's going on:

It doesn't take one of my guest's distinguished pedigrees to tell us something very significant is unfolding in and around our world. One only needs to look out their window to see the vast changes occurring with our weather. But there seems to be more at change than just the weather.

---

* The human pineal gland is a small cone-shaped organ in the brain and sits directly in the middle of the forehead just above the center point of the eyebrows.

207

I have noticed people themselves changing, me included—personality changes, mood swings, physical energy changes, relationship changes, and hopefully, and in a good way, spiritual changes. If I stepped of the world 20 years ago and then returned today, would I see 'obvious' change? I would think certainly weather-wise. Perhaps a noticeable personality change, most likely a mood change, but I believe most of all, I would notice a social or community change.

Growing up in the 1960s certainly was an influence, but I believe my parents and their generation were still attached to a social community. We knew our neighbors, we sat on the porch, we played in the street, and we knew our relatives. You could say we kept certain rituals and traditions—Thanksgiving with the whole extended family, Christmas tree hunting, decorating the tree and the yard, and my favorite, opening gifts at 6 in the morning. July 4th backyard picnic with lots of sloppy barbecue. Halloweens filled with spirit and surprise. Whole neighborhoods would decorate, dress up, and have outstanding theatrical displays that would indeed scare the hell out of me.

I lived in a typical neighborhood where I went to grade school, middle school, and high school, living in the same home. I grew up with people and friends who really knew me. Yes, the good, the bad and the very embarrassing. I remember going to my 20-year high school reunion. I was so excited because I missed my 10-year. I was very anxious to learn how my school mates would remember me—as a trouble maker, just another kid trying to be more, or the athlete I thought I was. Or worst of all, would anybody remember me at all?

Why this self-exploratory musing? Because I will never forget what my instructor taught me when training for the Red Cross Disaster Team: "Forget about our wonderful fire department, our expert police force, or specially trained rescue teams. When disaster strikes in the way we think it might in the near future, none of this will matter. The person you will depend on, and most likely to save your life, will be none other than … your neighbor."

Folks, this is what it's all about—community. If the earth changes keep their current pace, all our emergency services will be too overtaxed to come save you. We can see the Herculean effort that's made when a large earthquake hits a city. What would happen if two earthquakes hit in slightly different areas? What would happen if a large earthquake and a volcano erupted at the same time? Or a 9.0 earthquake and a tsunami an hour later? What happens when New York is hit, then LA?

It is my belief our ancestors have been trying to prepare us for such events. Yes, the Hopi, the Dogon, the Maya. I think we all know the list by now. What has their message been? "Life will change, then change again." Change will happen, things and life will be different, then things will change again."

Perhaps it is community that helps us along the way. As change comes, we will need to know our neighbor. I have noticed in my travels around the world that it is *spiritual practice* which appears to keep people together. Rights of passage, rituals, traditions, spiritual disciplines may have a place in our life after all.

Blessings to all.

P.S. It is good to see the media covering the accelerated weather phenomena that Earth Changes TV has been covering for almost a year. I knew early on there was no way this event could be missed. How do you hide "records" being broken weekly? This is a very different venue than coverage of space and planets so far away from all of us. When it's in our backyard, it's hard to ignore.

In hindsight, the above article really hits home. Following the S.E. Asia tsunamis, getting relief workers into the hardest hit sites took days, so those poor folks *had* to rely on each other for their survival, while still dealing with their grief.

We can talk all we want about the causes and nature of earth changes, but when they begin hitting us between the eyes, the only thing that will matter is: Can you count on your neighbors to drag your butt out of the rubble that once was your home? And have you prepared adequately so that you can go drag *their* butts of their pile of rubble? In other words, when the chips are down, will you be there for each other?

Chapter 13

Global Warming ...
or a Warming Globe?

This chapter examines the hysteria surrounding 'global warming' and recasts it simply as a 'warming globe,' something the Earth has been through thousands of times in its 4-billion-year lifetime. Our main problem is that we are far too close to the situation to see the big picture, as when you put a microscope to a photograph in your newspaper and see just a few dots of varying size. You would have no idea what the photograph actually portrays.

Let's start with a few headlines from the summer of 2001:
Global Warming Will Continue For The Next Century
Scientist: Ice Shelves Face Breakup
Skeptics Denounce Climate Science 'Lie'
Global Warming Much Worse Than Predicted, Say Scientists
Global Warming to Hit Poor States' Food Output
Glaciers All Over The World Are Shrinking
Global Warming Hits Species All Over World-Study
Sea Level Rises 'Underestimated'
New Climate Data Puzzles Scientists
Global Warming Said Devastating Aquatic Ecosystems

Warm and Getting Warmer...
Sun Alert as Skin Cancers Quadruple
Satellites Shed Light on a Warmer World

On the one hand, we have organizations such as the Tyndall Centre for Climate Change Research, based at the University of East Anglia, England reporting in the magazine *New Scientist:*

"Parts of central Asia, where temperatures already regularly exceed 40 °C (105 °F), can expect some of the biggest rises ahead. There will be increases of more than 5 °C (9 °F) in countries from Kazakhstan to Saudi Arabia, several of them affected this year by famine. Next in line are a number of countries in West Africa which are also prone to drought. Among countries expected to warm by between 4 – 5 °C are India, Egypt and the US. Earlier predictions that the Russian and Canadian Arctic should expect a rise of more than 6 °C by 2100 are confirmed. Those likely to warm least—3 °C or less—are the UK, Ireland, Argentina, Uruguay, Chile and New Zealand."

The researchers also divided each country's national wealth by its predicted temperature rise to assess the probable impact of warming on its population. By this criterion, the four most vulnerable countries in the world are Afghanistan, Ethiopia, Sierra Leone and Tanzania, because they have just $100 of their GNP for each citizen to spend on coping with every degree of warming. The least vulnerable country is Luxembourg, which can spend $8,800 per head.

The study also notes that the countries threatened most starkly by global warming produced the smallest amounts of the greenhouse gases believed to be causing it.

On the other hand, we have British researchers such as Jeremy Marlow of Newcastle University saying: "The world has become 10 degrees Celsius chillier in the last 3.2 million years. The cooling off is five times greater than previously believed, enough to bring about changes that have sent human evolution into overdrive."

In an article in the journal *Science*, Marlow said, "People have been looking for a climate event that could explain what is seen in the geological record. We postulate that this dramatic cooling could be it. Up to two million years ago, the vegetation across southern Africa was fairly rich and typical of a temperate climate where evolutionary pressures were not that great. Then you get this sudden cooling. There's less evaporation from the sea, less rain, and you start to see a build up of savannah appearing. Resources become limited; food is harder to get and there's less tree cover, increasing the danger from wild animals. The hominids around then would have been under greater pressure to survive, and they would have switched from gathering to hunting. This would have provided the spur needed to push human evolution forward."

The Newcastle team discovered tell-tale signs of the fall in temperature in the molecular fossils of microscopic marine algae. Examining the pattern of deposition of algae sediments revealed evidence of a climate change cycle spanning thousands or even millions of years. It showed that the Earth has been cooling for about five million years. During this time, threshold points were reached which saw sudden and pronounced temperature dips, surviving which spurred man's evolution.

Another volley was fired on September 2, 2003, in *"Earth Hits 2,000-Year Warming Peak,"* an AP story by Alex Kirby, a BBC News Online environment correspondent: "The Earth appears to have been warmer since 1980 than at any time in the last 18 centuries, scientists say. They reconstructed the global climate from data derived from ice cores, vegetation and other records. They believe their research provides unequivocal confirmation that humans are affecting the climate. But skeptics still insist that any human contribution is likely to be too small to explain what is happening."

According to Kirby, the scientists hitting the panic button are Professor Philip Jones, of the climatic research unit, University of East Anglia, UK, and Professor Michael Mann, of the University of Virginia, US. Their study, published in the journal *Geophysical Research Letters*, supports recent findings from the Intergovernmental Panel on Climate Change. After studying temperature data from up to 1,000 years ago, they said the late 20th century had been the warmest period on record.

"The Earth has warmed by at least 0.2 °C in the last 20 years or so. ... It just shows how dramatic the warming has been in recent years. You can't explain it in any other way. It's a response to a build-up of greenhouse gases in the atmosphere."

Kirby goes on: "Some scientists believe the recent temperature increases are explained by solar radiation, with emissions of carbon dioxide and other greenhouse gases too small to account for the changes observed. Others say the historical record proves the climate fluctuates naturally, with human influence irrelevant to global trends."

So What Is Global Warming?

It all started in 1988, when James Hansen, director of NASA's Goddard Institute of Space Studies, testified before the U.S. Senate that, based on computer models and temperature measurements: "I am 99 percent sure that the [human caused] greenhouse effect has been detected and is changing our climate now." The media took up the torch and the term 'global warming' entered the public's awareness.

Most of the scientific community believed that Hansen's announcement was premature at best and rash at worst, but critics of this apocalyptic vision were ignored. In the chart Hansen presented, the upper solid line models the temperature assuming scenario A, i.e., no action is taken to curb greenhouse gases. Curves B and C show more moderate growth in the gases due to curbs being put in place.

"Not so fast," retaliated Dr. Patrick Michaels of the University of Virginia, who also testified, calling Kyoto 'a useless appendage to an

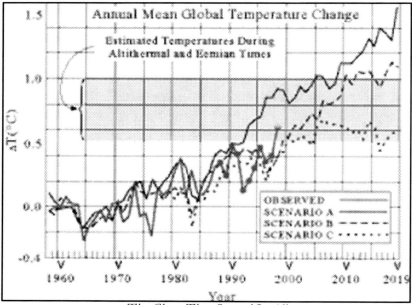

The Chart That Started It All

irrelevant treaty.' Scientist Richard Lindzen spearheaded Hansen's critics and attacked his data point-by-point:

- Hansen: global temperature has risen 0.5–0.7 °C in the last century. Lindzen: 0.1–0.3 °C
- Hansen: doubling CO_2 levels means up to a 3 °C increase. Lindzen: < 1 °C
- Hansen: global warming means more water vapor. Lindzen: less water vapor.
- Hansen: if all CO_2 were removed from the atmosphere, temperature would fall by 5–10 °C. Lindzen: removing CO_2 would still leave 98% of current greenhouse effect.

The global warming hypothesis relies on doing two things: building accurate climate models, and analyzing the models to project outcomes. Early models were full of flaws. For example, they used sea water temperatures instead of air temperatures for the atmosphere over oceans, which made an enormous difference in outcomes.

Bad conclusions drawn from bad models led to alarming statistics. For example, if no action were taken to curb greenhouse gases, especially CO_2 (scenario A in Hansen's 1990 model), we'd see up to a 6.0 °C increase in temperature by 2050, with melting glaciers causing widespread coastal flooding. However, an improved 1996 model suggested a maximum increase of only 3.5 °C by 2100, and a more recent survey came up with only a 2 °C maximum increase.

Better models predicting less warming, and over longer periods, have eroded the hypothesis, and it now has few proponents in the scientific community. For example, an article appeared in *Nature* (3/11/99) stating that global temperature has varied by only 1.5 °F over the last 11,000 years, while CO_2 levels jumped all over the place. An article in *Science* (3/12/99) stated that every time we come out of a mini-Ice Age, the temperature increases *before* CO_2 levels, not after. Most scientists therefore, have dropped off the global warming bandwagon, but changing public opinion and governmental policies is a bigger juggernaut to turn around. We need better data from better satellites, and better models on better computers, but it would be premature to commit huge sums of taxpayer dollars to solve a problem that may not even exist. And Hansen himself said, "The forces that drive long-term climate change are not known with sufficient accuracy to define future climate change." Strange from a man who in 1988 testified before Congress that: "I have 99 percent confidence in my projections of global warming trends."

Still on the same tack in April 28, 2005, *Science* published another Hansen article in which he says, "Global temperatures will rise by 1 °F this century even if greenhouse gasses were capped tomorrow. But if CO_2 and other heat-trapping emissions instead continue to grow as expected, things could spin out of our control, especially as ocean levels rise from melting Greenland and Antarctic ice sheets." The article mentioned a worst-case increase of 10 °F in mean temperature.

A network of improved instruments allowed Hansen's team to determine that the Earth receives almost one watt of energy per square meter more than it radiates back into space. "And that imbalance began at exactly the same time of the build-up of greenhouse gases," the team claimed. However, this is a common fallacy in logic, called *post hoc, ergo propter hoc*, meaning "after it, therefore because of it." This ignores the possibility that warming and CO_2 levels could both be the *result of* some as yet unknown cause. Gee, I wonder what that could be?

Having said that, yes, the globe is warming, and during our current interglacial warm period, has greatly altered humanity and our environment. For example, about 15,000 years ago, temperatures began to rise, ending and reversing glacial advance, and raising sea levels worldwide by 300 feet. By 8,000 years ago, this had submerged the Bering Strait land bridge, cutting off the migration from Russia to North America.

Actual temperatures are subject to many cycles within cycles, some of which we saw in Chapter 4:

- 11-year cycles of sunspot activity
- 78-year Gleissberg solar cycle
- 200-year solar cycle
- 21,000-year cycle of the Precession of the Equinoxes
- 41,000-year cycle due to wobble in Earth's orbit
- 100,000-year cycle of solar magnetic field variation
- Heat retention by water vapor, carbon dioxide, methane, and other gases—the so called "greenhouse effect"

- Solar reflectivity from white clouds, volcanic dust, and polar ice caps
- Landmass distribution causing changes in ocean currents
- Underwater volcanic activity heating up oceans.

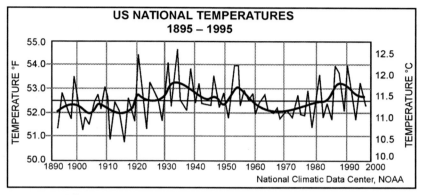

According to NOAA, the last 100 years have seen two cycles of warming and cooling in the U.S, but no overall warming trend. The following chart (U.S. National Temperatures) shows annual averages and a smoothed curve, but the century's mean temperature was consistent at 52.5 °F (11.4 °C).

The "record-breaking" news media headlines are based on *ground* temperature readings, which are misleading. The high-altitude temperatures recorded by orbiting satellites show no actual warming over the short period we've had satellites up there. However, over a period of several millennia, significant warming has occurred. But for reasons that are unclear, the period known as the *Holocene Maximum* has been the warmest period in human history. Proxies tell us that, 7,500 –

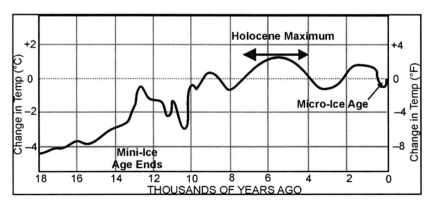

4,000 years ago, and long before human-generated pollution, temperatures were about 3 °F higher than today.

The Greenhouse Effect

Let's take a deeper look at this alleged phenomenon. Is this just talk by some Russian realtors who want to turn Siberia into a new Russian Riviera, or is there something to it? Not much, as it turns out. As we'll see, total human contributions to greenhouse gases account for less than 0.3 percent of the so-called "greenhouse effect."

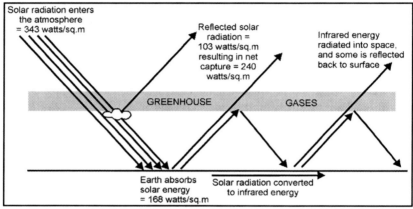

Any greenhouse effect 'expert' will tell you that the Sun's energy enters the atmosphere and some is reflected back into space. However, most gets through and is trapped either by the greenhouse gases themselves or beneath them, unable to escape. And when the planet tries to radiate energy, the gases also reflect it back to the surface. So, just as in an actual greenhouse, the net effect is a steadily rising temperature. The 'expert' will also tell you that since man has been burning fossil fuel since the Industrial Revolution, the temperature and levels of gases have been steadily climbing. Then the 'expert' will try to sell you a nuclear power plant as the solution to the problem. So let's put this in perspective.

Water vapor is actually Earth's most prevalent greenhouse gas, accounting for over 95% of the greenhouse effect—a fact conveniently forgotten by environmental activists—and this water vapor is purely natural in origin. Other atmospheric gases that make up the remaining 5 percent include carbon dioxide (CO_2), methane (CH_4), nitrous oxide (N_2O), and miscellaneous others such as fluorocarbons.

Human activities such as farming, manufacturing, power generation, and transportation contribute slightly to greenhouse gas concentrations. However, these emissions are less than one percent of emissions from natural sources, and have a neglible effect on global climate.

Therefore, **about 99.7 percent of the "greenhouse effect" is due to natural causes** — mostly water vapor and traces of other gases, which we can do nothing at all about. (Bovine flatulence is real, but cows will be cows.) Going back to the horse-and-buggy days would have zero impact on our climate. In fact, if graphs of temperature and solar wind flux are superimposed, they are identical, showing that Earth temperature is almost wholly dependent on the Sun.

Of course, this doesn't give us license to trash the environment. For example, coal-burning power stations belch tons of mercury into the air we breathe, and many believe mercury is the leading cause of autism in children. They also point to thimerosal in children's vaccines as a factor in the increase in autism, rising from 1 child in 2,500 two decades ago to 1 in 166 today. (By the time children reach first grade, they've had 22 vaccinations, most using thimerosal (or ethyl mercury) as a preservative. This has pumped 187 times the EPA maximum level for mercury, a proven neurotoxin, into their bodies.)

The Great Carbon Dioxide Myth

CO_2 in our atmosphere has been increasing steadily for the last 18,000 years – long before humans began burning fossil fuel. In fact, today's Earth temperature and CO_2 levels are similar to those during the previous interglacial cycle of 120,000 – 140,000 years ago, after which the planet entered a full-fledged mini-Ice Age. And today's CO_2 level is only a tiny fraction of what it once was, earlier in this planet's history. Ignoring this inconvenient little fact, global warming activists get hysterical over an alleged increase in atmospheric CO_2, blaming it for a so-called "runaway greenhouse effect."

Of the 186 billion tons of CO_2 entering Earth's atmosphere each year, only 6 billion tons are from human activity. About 90 billion tons come from biological activity in oceans and another 90 billion tons from land sources such as volcanoes and decaying land plants.

At today's level of 368 ppm, CO_2 is a minor constituent of Earth's atmosphere, i.e., 0.03%. This is only a fraction of what it was during

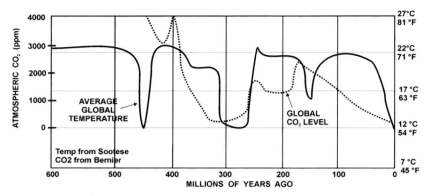

previous geological eras, and in fact the lowest it's ever been in Earth's history. In the early days of the planet, dozens of volcanoes were active at the same time, belching out huge volumes of gas. For example, in the Cambrian period, it was 7,000 ppm, or 0.5 %.

Plants absorb CO_2 and emit oxygen as a waste product, and humans and animals breathe oxygen and emit CO_2 as a waste product, so CO_2 is a much needed nutrient, not a pollutant. CO_2 is an essential ingredient for all life on earth, and when plant-growers want to stimulate plant growth, they introduce more carbon dioxide. Any CO_2 that goes into the atmosphere is continually recycled by terrestrial plant life and activity in the oceans.

The following delightfully outspoken article, titled **Correlation Between Temperatures and CO_2 (A Shot in the Foot for the IPCC and UNEP)** by Eduardo Ferreyra, President of the Argentinean Foundation for a Scientific Ecology, puts one more nail in the casket of global warming. It is reproduced as is, with the author's permission:

The website of the United Nations Environmental Program [www.grida.no/climate/vital/02.htm] is a perfect source (and example) of the misinformation plaguing the mainstream media. Take your time and pay it a visit. This site provides a series related to Global Warming, and one of the pages tell us about the close correlation between atmospheric CO_2 levels and temperature increase, clearly implying that manmade CO_2 emissions are responsible for the observed warming, urging the ratification of the Kyoto Protocol.

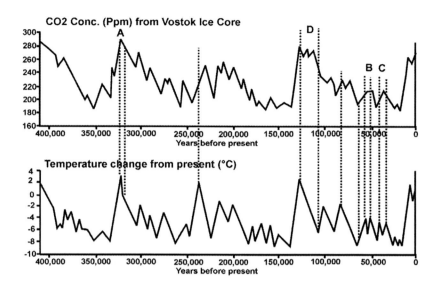

The UNEP provides us with a beautiful graph, with the simple addition of some vertical lines linking both CO_2 levels (upper) and temperature (lower) charts, in order to make my thesis more clear—that the increase in temperatures happened well in advance of the carbon dioxide increase, blaming temperature increase for CO_2 increase, contrary to the current IPCC global warming hype. Not that this is any news for people who work in paleoclimatology, but this side of the story is not well known by the general public. We use the same data provided by the UNEP and IPCC to support our theory - so they cannot say we use biased data. However, the sheer poor scientific quality of the graphs invalidates our theory, not to mention theirs! So, if you are disappointed because CO_2 increase will not warm the Earth, don't blame me. Blame the IPCC.

Following comes what the UNEP says - their wording is in *italics*.

Over the last 400,000 years the Earth's climate has been unstable, with very significant temperature changes, going from a warm climate to an ice age in as rapidly as a few decades. These rapid changes suggest that climate may be quite sensitive to internal or external climate forcings and feedbacks. As can be seen from the upper curve, tem-

221

peratures have been less variable during the last 10 000 years. Based on the incomplete evidence available, it is unlikely that global mean temperatures have varied by more than 1°C in a century during this period

I will be piously kind and will not shout at them *liars!* I will only say the last phrase is utter balderdash. They say climate can be highly sensitive to forcings and feedbacks but, if it became less variable in the last 10,000 years, this means the forcings either disappeared or the climate became less sensitive to the same forcings. Why? They don't say. I wonder if they know.

The most serious proxy studies performed by paleoclimatologists have shown that global mean temperatures around 1100 AD were 3.6 °F (2 °C) higher than today, and 6 °F (3.5 °C) higher than those during the *Double Maunder* of the Little Ice Age (circa 1640). In the Sargazo Sea, temperatures increased from 70 °F (21.5 °C) in 600 AD by 5.4 °F (3 °C) to 75.4 °F (24.5 °C) in the year 1200 AD, going down 5.4 °F (3 °C) again to 70 °F (21.5 °C) by the year 1450.

The information presented on this graph indicates a strong correlation between CO_2 content in the atmosphere and temperature. A possible scenario: anthropogenic emissions of greenhouse gases (GHGs) could bring the climate to a state where it reverts to the highly unstable climate of the pre-ice age period. Rather than a linear evolution, the climate follows a non-linear path with sudden and dramatic surprises when GHG levels reach an as-yet unknown trigger point.

These people have the boring habit of speaking always in the potential form: "may," "could be possible," or vague terms such as, "probably," "it suggests," "it is likely," and the horrible double negation, "wouldn't be unlikely." Then, after introducing the potential wedge into the argument, they continue as if everything had been shown to be a proven fact, with no room for further discussion. Tricks like this fool only those quite unaware, or those ignoring almost everything needed to be called literate. Really, the graph shows an apparently strong correlation between CO_2 levels and mean global temperatures – *only temperatures increased first, and then CO_2 levels followed.* Check for yourself, and will see how this people have been lying more than politicians on campaign. Please, don't ever vote for them!

Correlation between CO_2 and mean global temperatures. Which came first?

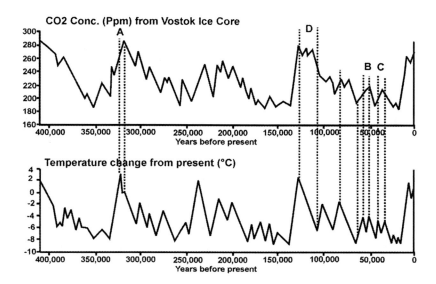

The issue of "correlation" can be of great visual help for an *"approximate correlation"* - when it comes to graphs - but in order to establish a true and *"precise correlation"* we need graphs with a wider scale. Each division on the graph shown above corresponds to *10,000 years.* Keeping this in mind, we can make a rough analysis of these alleged "correlations."

Many paleoclimatic studies, especially those related with very "modern" times, as the last 1,500 years, show that temperatures rose *before* CO_2 levels did and, generally, the rise in temperature anticipated by 200 – 400 years the rise of CO_2 levels - a period of time that would pass unperceived in the graph by the. Could this suggest that the rise in temperature provoked the rise in CO_2 levels? Maybe. There are much more possibilities of this being true, and not the contrary as claimed by the IPCC. Let us see the examples marked in the graph:

Under letter **A**, at left, in the region about *322,000 years before present (BP)*, CO_2 concentrations decreased from 300 to 260 ppm, and temperatures did the same, during the same period, by between 2.8 °F (1.58° C) and 6.5 °F (3.6° C). However, it does not matter here which one went down or up first - the point is their ups and downs do not correlate at all, as suggested by the UNEP and the IPCC. While CO_2 was decreasing steadily and smoothly, the temperature stopped its descent towards the end of the period, rose a few tenths of degrees, went down again, and up once more - then it began a long and sustained descent until the year 308,000 BP. On the other hand, while the temperature was *decreasing uniformly*, CO_2 levels *stopped their descent, went up a little and fell down again.*

Then, there is a lack of correlation between increase and decrease of CO_2 levels and increase and decrease of temperature, possibly due to other factors acting independently on those quite wide variations. What could have been those factors? Perhaps an increase or decrease in volcanic activity, a variation in the tilt of the Earth's rotation axis, in the precession, and other astronomical factors, most notably the known variation in the length of solar magnetic cycles and activity of the corona. (In order to learn more about the influence of the Sun on Earth's climate, please read the scientific study by Dr. Theodor Landscheidt (www.john-daly.com/landscheidt) This means that the *"apparent correlation observed"* between CO_2 and temperature, is not a net *"cause and effect correlation"* as there are other factors exerting their influence and destroying such *"cause and effect" correlation."*

Let us go to the example marked by the letter **C**. What happened here, people in the IPCC? Temperatures *began to go down*, and CO_2 *levels kept going for about 1800 years more!* Then, while CO_2 levels remained stable (in a clear, wide plateau during about 8,000 years), the temperature went down, kept quite stable, went down again, up, and down once more *before* CO_2 *levels started to decrease.* But, as in the case **B**, changes in temperature occurred *before* CO_2 levels followed the "correlation."

The same lack of correlativity is present in example **D**, where temperatures go down rapidly, while CO_2 levels keep stable for a while, and then go down in a manner and intensity that differ with other parts of the chart, showing CO_2 is not the important GHG pretended by the IPCC and the "global warmers." But, above all, from the analysis of the UNEP and IPCC data, what came out clearly is—leaving aside the imprecision and lack of adequate scaling—that correlation between CO_2 and temperatures is quite poor and mostly contradictory. It shows that there are other factors affecting the temperature increases and decreases, and scientists ought to reach an agreement, once and for all, about which are those factors.

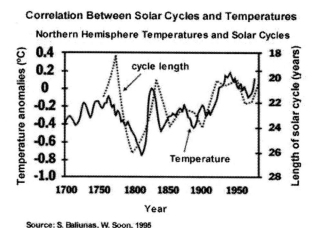

Correlation Between Solar Cycles and Temperatures

Source: S. Baliunas, W. Soon, 1995

More correlations, this time with the Sun

The UNEP and the IPCC like to speak about correlation between *"global temperatures and CO₂,"* but they never speak about correlation between solar activity and global temperatures because, they say, the Sun's activity has a *negligible influence* on Earth's climate—as if the planet were receiving heat from other more important sources!

Let us see what the UNEP and the IPCC have to say about the more than evident correlation between length of solar cycles and global temperatures. The graph corresponds to a study made in 1995 by astrophysicists *Dr. Willie Soon*, from the *Harvard-Smithsonian Center for Astrophysics*, and *Dr. Sallie Baliunas*, from the *Mount Wilson Observatory*, in California. There is not much we can add to the graph, so conclusions are quite obvious. To UNEP and IPPC discomfort and displeasure, *the cause and effect correlation* between solar cycles and terrestrial temperatures is incontrovertible. To the "warming industry" disgrace, in this case the *cause* is solar cycles and the *effect* is the temperature variations on Earth, simply because variations on Earth could never induce variations on the Sun's activity.

But, nothing is impossible for the IPCC and the Warmer Legion, and as they blame global warming for the freezing winter of 2003 in the Northern Hemisphere - and the June snow in Moscow; they will surely be tempted to blame global warming for the observed variations on solar activity. Now will have to watch how far it reaches their, up to now, unlimited ability to distort science.

Trends

The same website by the UNEP carries a page where a really pretty graph is displayed titled: **Trends in average global surface temperature**

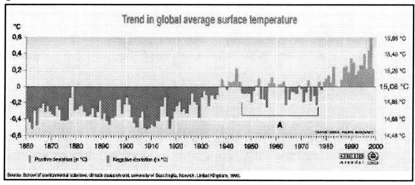

1. The figure shows the combined land-surface air and sea surface temperatures (in °C) between 1860 to 2000, relative to the average temperature between 1961 and 1990. The mean global surface temperature has increased by between 0.5 – 1 °F (0.3 – 0.6 °C) since the late 19th century and by about 0.4 – 0.6 °F (0.2 – 0.3 °C) over the last 40 years, which is the period with most reliable data. Recent years have been among the warmest since 1860—the period for which instrument records are available.

2. A question that springs to mind is, "Why are they choosing the average temperature of the period 1961 – 1998 as the "normal" one? Is this temperature considered the best for life on Earth? If that's so, why do climatologists call the period extending from 800 AD to 1250 AD *"Little Climatic Optimum"* (or "Medieval Optimum Climatic")? During this period, just

before the *"Little Ice Age"* (about 1300 – 1850), temperatures were about 3.6 °F (2 °C) higher than present, something that opened vast areas in Europe and Russia for agriculture and trading, and allowed the Vikings to colonize Greenland (because it didn't have the present thick ice cover) and the north of the eastern US coastline, which was warm and temperate. Those were not apocalyptic years, as shown by the huge leap forward experienced by mankind in terms of agricultural productivity, commerce and opening of new territories for all kinds of human activity.

3. If the "Medieval Optimum Climatic" temperatures were considered the best and most desirable for mankind, seeing the beneficial effects obtained in those days, all the catastrophe arguments presented by the IPCC and the UNEP are wiped out like a house of cards in a tornado.
   "The warming is evident in both sea and surface land based temperatures. Urbanization in general and desertification could have contributed only a small fraction of total global warming, though urbanization could have had an important influence in some regions. Indirect indicators such as temperatures obtained from ice cores and decrease of glaciers provide independent support for the observed warming. It should also be noted that warming has not been globally uniform. The recent warming has been greater between latitudes 40° N – 70° N, though some areas as the North Atlantic have cooled in recent decades."

4. This comment by the UNEP obviously leaves aside measuring errors due to inappropriate techniques, or old and inefficient instruments, as it has been demonstrated more times than the IPCC likes to remember. A 1 °F (0.5 °C) error in measurement made during the sailboat era, when canvas or metal buckets were used to pick the water from the sea surface; or by means of pipe intake feeding the boilers of early 20th century ships, etc, are enough to invalidate (if those errors are not corrected) all sea surface temperature records prior to the 1950s.

5. The same applies to temperatures obtained over Earth's surface, where the location and orientation of the measuring weather station is vital. Temperatures are rising as cities were surround weather stations, adding a spurious 7 °F (4 °C) to the records. (A good source of information on this side of the question is John Daly's article about the *"heat island effect"* on his "Still waiting for Greenhouse" website [www.johndaly.com].

6. Why did the areas between 40° N – 70° N warm while some North Atlantic areas in the same latitudes cooled? The IPCC does not know how to explain this, much in the same way they don't know how to explain many things surrounding their absurd theory of anthropogenic warming. Simply because their hypothesis is just a hot air balloon full of holes, from where science is escaping aghast, ashamed to be used in such a dishonest way to enforce politics aimed to stop industrial and economic development in poor nations of the Earth.

7. I drew in the graph a horizontal key covering the cool period from 1947 to 1977, and marked it with the letter A. According to the IPCC, the rising levels of CO_2 anthropogenic emissions are responsible for the sustained temperature increase. Ergo, the bigger the concentrations of CO_2, the greater the warming. Period. And don't you dare to discuss this climatic papal bull.

8. There is something in this logic that doesn't close. Given that the famous CO_2 graph used by the warming industry is absolutely uniform, why did temperatures go down between 1947 and 1877, if CO_2 levels went up, up, and up during the same period? It looks somewhat silly, but not even Stephen Schneider nor his friends in the IPCC have ever explained this "anomaly." To attribute this to natural causes is out of the question, of course. For the IPCC there are *no* natural causes affecting the climate; only man-made CO_2 emissions can do it … if we are going to believe them.

9. But there is something else that throws the human-induced global warming theory in the garbage can. As the IPCC and its followers dismiss the *"urban heat island effect,"* and do not

include the necessary corrections in their records and charts, the cooling effect happened between 1947 and 1977 must have been much greater (at least by 3° C) than that declared by the IPCC, and the ensuing warming must have been smaller than the one claimed by the IPCC graphs.

10. Correlation between CO_2 and global temperatures is clear – but only in some part of the world's climatic history – and the attribution of "cause and effect" was done backwards: temperatures seem to drive CO_2 levels, and not the opposite as the IPCC and the "warmers" claim.

11. Correlation between solar cycles and temperatures on Earth has been proved beyond any doubt.

12. The trend toward warming is driven by another cause, and not by atmospheric CO_2 levels, since CO_2 levels rose uniformly during 30 years between the years 1947-1977, while mean global temperatures went their own way, totally ignoring CO_2 levels.

13. All this nonsense about man-made global warming through CO_2 emissions is based on a huge number of unknowns, ambiguities and uncertainties found in the so-called *General Circulation Models* (GCM), an issue too well known as to be treated here. However, if you have an inquiring mind, or still have some doubts about their validity and usefulness, please read the excellent scientific paper by Dr. Willie Soon, Sallie Baliunas, Sherwood W. Idso, Kirill Ya. Kondriatev, and Eric Postmentier, *Modeling Climatic Effects of Anthropogenic CO_2 Emissions; Unknowns and Uncertainties* at: http://mitosyfraudes.8k.com/INGLES/ModelSoon.html.

In an excellent story titled **Cosmic Ray Flux Zaps Pro-Kyoto Types**, printed on July 3, 2003, columnist for the *Edmonton Journal*, and reproduced with permission, Lorne Gunter put the final nail in the coffin. Under the subtitle: New study puts paid to overheated theories on climate change, *Gunter wrote:*

It's the Sun. And apparently the stars, too. But that shouldn't surprise anyone, since the stars after all are just other planets' Suns.

Fluctuating levels of solar and stellar radiation are the cause of climate change on Earth, ***not rising carbon dioxide levels***. Ebbs and flows in the Sun's energy raise and lower Earth's temperature far more than CO_2 ever could, according to an extensive new study by Jan Veizer, a University of Ottawa geologist and paleoclimatologist, and Nir Shaviv, an astrophysicist at the Hebrew University of Jerusalem.

Also, as our solar system passes through the galaxy's star nurseries—the coiling, cloudy tentacles of the Milky Way where there are dozens of infant stars—Earth absorbs unusually high levels of cosmic radiation. According to Veizer, ups and downs in this radiation - a variation known as the cosmic ray flux - *"is linked to climate variability."* At least 66 percent of the swings in temperature, violent weather and precipitation to which Earth is periodically subjected *"is likely due to solar system passages through the spiral arms of the galaxy."*

These findings correspond to those reached by a growing number of scientists at Harvard University and the Smithsonian Institute, at the European Space Agency and the renowned Lawrence Livermore National Laboratory in California, at the Schroeter Institute for Research in Cycles of Solar Activity, in Germany, and a variety of Canadian and international universities that *all the warming Earth has experienced in the past 150 years* can be traced back to the *Sun and its activities.*

Most convincingly, Veizer and Shaviv reached the same conclusions before they even knew one another. Veizer was finishing off his research last September, when he received an e-mail from Shaviv suggesting they compare notes. Both had examined climate changes dating back as much as 500 million years, independently of each other. Yet when they met in Toronto last October and laid their graphs one on top of the other, they were "awfully surprised" by the near match.

In his study, Veizer and Prof. Shaviv argue the "warming effect of CO_2 ... is potentially lower" than predicted by the UN's IPCC, the so-called overwhelming majority of scientists that is said to believe in the CO_2-warming theory.

Three years ago, after one of the most thorough studies ever of the possible correlation between CO_2 and climate change - one funded by our blindly pro-Kyoto federal government - Veizer concluded that *rising CO_2 levels followed rises in the Earth's temperature, not the other way around. "Atmospheric carbon dioxide concentrations were not the principal driver of climate variability,"* he wrote then.

At most, Veizer and Shaviv calculate that CO_2 *might* raise ocean temperatures by 3.6 °F (1.9 °C). *Might*. While that is a considerable warming, *it is far from the 9 °F – 14 °F (5 °C – 8 °C) warming* predicted by the global warming climate models cited by the UN and by Canada's own federal government.

The pro-Kyoto types are able to reach their hellfire levels of 9 °F – 14 °F (5 °C – 8 °C) only because they control all the inputs on their elaborate computer models, so they have added things called 'feedbacks' to their computations. The computer models—which, so far, are the *only* places where global warming has been 'proven'—all rely on *unknown mechanisms* that magnify the CO_2-forced warming they predict.

Most of these supercomputer projections see a doubling of CO_2 by this time next century. This doubling raises global temperatures by less than 3½ °F (2 °C), but the climate modelers then insist that this rise triggers *some as yet unknown feedbacks* (likely clouds and increased water vapor) that then raise temperatures an additional 5½ °F – 11 °F (3° C to 6° C).

However, the increase in atmospheric CO_2 witnessed since widespread industrialization has taken us nearly halfway to a total doubling of CO_2. Yet warming in the past century and a half has been less than 2 °F (1 °C), when, if the modelers were correct, it should have been 3.5 °F – 5.5 °F (2 °C – 3 °C).

Also this week, Dr. Madhav Khandekar, a former *Environment Canada* climatologist, revealed that *"in the higher latitudes of the northeast, from Baffin Bay to Labrador, extreme cold spells have increased in the last 50 years."* Far from warming, Canada's Arctic is at least maintaining its iciness.

Although studying different phenomenon than Khandekar, Igor Polyakov of the *University of Alaska* at Fairbanks came to a related conclusion. By combing through every weather record he could find from remote weather stations, exploratory expeditions, Christian missions and police outposts, he and his team announced last December *that the Arctic had actually cooled since the 1920s.*

Arctic snows, too, are increasing, not decreasing as the climate computers had guessed. Thankfully, Ottawa seems to have lost its interest in Kyoto, because there are *increasing doubts* about the global warming science.

Climate cover-up: A trumpeted consensus to the contrary is a global hoax

The website http://personals.galaxyinternet.net/tunga/OSGWD.htm reports that 17,000 scientists, engineers and physicians have signed a petition put out by the Oregon Institute of Science and Medicine, which opposes adoption of the Kyoto Protocol, so those who talk about the "universality of global warming as a fact of life" are just plain wrong or trying to deceive for some nefarious reason.

On Tuesday, May 17, 2005, I reported that six eminent researchers from the Russian Academy of Science and the Israel Space Agency had just published a startling paper in one of the world's leading space science journals. The team claimed to have compelling evidence that changes in *cosmic ray intensity* and *variations in solar activity* are driving much of the Earth's climate. They also predicted that increased cosmic ray intensity will lead to an increase of the global cloud cover which, according to their calculations, will result in "some small global cooling over the next couple of years."

In fact, the global mean temperature, as recorded by NASA's global Land-Ocean Temperature Index, has *dropped* slightly during the last couple of years despite higher levels of CO_2 emissions.

In looking at solar vs. human activity as the major climactic influence, I put the breakdown somewhere between $80/20 - 90/10$, so I was delighted to learn that the Russian and Israeli researchers allocate *much* of the climate change to solar variability rather than human causes.

The above website is also a gateway to literally hundreds of learned papers debunking global warming, so I was puzzled when a recent study published in the December, 2004 issue of *Science* categorically announced that skeptical papers simply don't appear in the literature. Someone smell a rat? Let's take a look.

In the article, Naomi Oreskes talked of, "Unanimous scientific consensus on the anthropogenic causes of recent global warming." Claiming to have analyzed 928 abstracts on global climate change, Oreskes said, "75 percent accepted the view that most of the recent warming trend was man-made." She goes further by claiming that, "No paper since 1993 has questioned this 'universal agreement.' This analysis shows that scientists publishing in the peer-reviewed literature agree with IPCC, the National Academy of Sciences and the public statements of their professional societies. Politicians, economists, journalists and others may have the impression of confusion, disagreement or discord among climate scientists, but that impression is incorrect."

Two quotes at random from articles accessible through the above website are revealing:

National Center for Policy Analysis: "Scientists from the Harvard-Smithsonian Center for Astrophysics say the hypothesis that increases in carbon dioxide (CO_2) in the atmosphere due to industrial activity have caused global temperatures to rise over the past century and, if unchecked, will cause catastrophic warming is incorrect."

Science and Environmental Policy Project: "Climate science is not 'settled'; it is both uncertain and incomplete. The available observations do not support the mathematical models that predict a substantial global warming and form the basis for a control policy on greenhouse (GH) gas emissions. We need a more targeted program of climate research to settle major scientific problems."

Add to those voices the Russian Academy of Science, the U.S. Association of State Climatologists, and the American Association of Petroleum Geologists, who all formally reject the view that anthropogenic factors are the main trigger of global warming. So there we have it. The Oreskes article is thoroughly debunked. But for the time being, the damage is done. Activists, campaigners and scientific organizations with their own agendas routinely cite the article as proof that the world agrees that the debate is over and that: *Human activity is solely responsible for climate change.* And in a scary turn of events, the British media is under pressure to not report any contrary point of view.

Lubos Motl, assistant science professor at Cambridge, MA, replicated Oreskes' survey and came up with completely opposite conclusions: "Quite a number of the papers emphasise that *natural factors* play a major if not the key role in recent climate change. My analysis also shows that there are almost *three times* as many abstracts that are skeptical of the notion of anthropogenic climate change than those that explicitly endorse it."

A major player in the global warming agenda is *Science* journal itself. The editors routinely reject articles critical of the Great Global Warming Myth, while publishing articles such as that by Oreskes that claim universal support for the Myth. Why the editors of *Science* are deliberately misleading the world is a puzzle because it contravenes every principle that science is sworn to uphold. And it fosters skepticism, even cynicism, about how politicians have hijacked science and are using it as a battering ram to drive through their own self-serving agendas. The editors and scientists who go along despite mountains of evidence to the contrary have sold out for their 'thirty pieces of silver' and done incalculable harm to their discipline in the process.

In a May 20, 2005, I posted on ECTV an article titled ***Another Black Eye for Global Warming Cult,*** by science writer Roger Highfield:

The world's largest ice sheet is growing due to increased snowfall caused by climate change, scientists announce today.

The study of the east Antarctic ice sheet will be seized on by skeptics to dispute claims made about sea level rises caused by global warming. However, scientists point out that melting glaciers in other regions, especially the smaller but more rapidly changing west Antarctic ice sheet and in Greenland, will more than offset the effects reported today.

The study, described in the journal *Science* by scientists from the Desert Research Institute and Universities of Missouri and Arizona in America, and Edward Hanna at the University of Sheffield, used satellite measurements to assess the thickness of ice from 1992-2003.

They also used weather forecast models and ice core data to study trends in snowfall during the same period.

Dr Hanna said: "We found that, while the west Antarctic ice sheet was thickening in places and thinning in others, the east Antarctic ice sheet showed significant thickening in many areas, specifically towards the centre.

"This thickening correlated very well with the snowfall modeling, showing that the increased snowfall is causing the ice sheet to grow in mass. We estimate that the ice sheet is holding an extra 45 billion tons of water each year, the equivalent of a sea level drop of 0.12mm a year.

"At the same time, the thinning of the Greenland ice sheet is contributing to a sea level rise of 0.2mm a year. This is being offset to some extent by the sea level drop caused by the thickening of the east Antarctic ice sheet.

"Global warming may mean a moister atmosphere and therefore a wetter climate that increases snowfall on the east Antarctic ice sheet," he said, adding that natural climate variations cannot be ruled out without more data.

The 'Broken' Hockey Stick

This theory is at the heart of the current global warming hysteria— the argument that the last 10 years are the hottest in the last thousand, and that there was no such thing as the "Little Ice Age" or the "Medieval Warm Period." The graph presented to the UN IPCC shows a slight cooling trend for 900 years, from 1000 – 1900, and then a sudden, rapid 100-year warming trend. Because its shape resembles a hockey stick, the name has stuck.

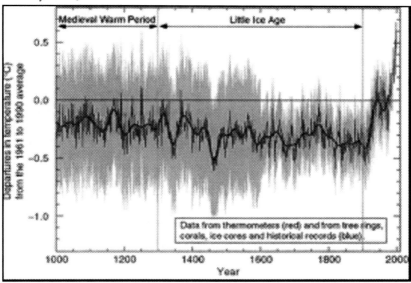

Mann's theory gained strong support in the IPCC, but a growing number of climate experts are questioning it. However, it led to the Kyoto Protocol, aimed at curbing greenhouse gases, and most nations have ratified it. Canada, for example has committed $10 billion to implementing it.

The demise of the Hockey Stick began in January 2005, when a University of Guelph economics professor, Ross McKitrick, and a Toronto mineral exploration consultant, Stephen McIntyre, published an article in the journal, *Geophysical Research Letters*. The article's main findings were:

- Many teams have tried to independently replicate the above chart, but none has succeeded, yet the IPCC inexplicably accepted the theory as scientific fact.
- McIntyre asked Mann for his original data and was told, "We've forgotten where we put it." And amazingly the IPCC never actually verified the data.
- Mann has been vague and evasive on which "proxies," such as tree rings, he used. Initially it was 112, but then in 2003, Mann suddenly increased the number to 159.
- When asked, Mann refused to provide the original computer code for his model, but McIntyre found evidence that Mann had worked backwards from the hockey stick graph to determine which tree rings to select.
- Climatologists know *for a fact* that the weather in the 15th century was actually warmer than in the 20th century, but Mann's model completely ignores it.

Other researchers show what appears to be a serious computer programming error in the original calculations, affecting a crucial step, and that the method used by Mann et al. in fact mines a data set actually looking for 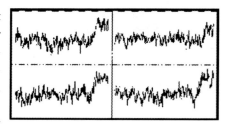 hockey stick patterns. Even from meaningless random data, the model nearly always produces a hockey stick. For example, three of the four hockey sticks shown here were produced from random numbers in lieu of actual temperature readings.

Professor Richard Muller of the University of California at Berkeley examined their work and reported, "The findings hit me like a bombshell, and I suspect it is having the same effect on many others. Suddenly the hockey stick, the poster-child of the global warming community, turns out to be an artifact of poor mathematics."

The bottom line is that neither Hansen's model nor the Mann reconstruction of it are usable for comparing 20th century climate to earlier periods. We found that the distinctive hockey stick shape was due simply a strong 20th century growth spurt from a small group of bristlecone pine trees in the western USA, which was reflected in wider tree rings. So, contrary to previous understanding, the Mann reconstruction cannot support claims that the Earth is experiencing unprecedented climate change.

So, Watson, the game is afoot, and there's no telling how it's going to turn out. Time will tell, however.

In this war over the hearts and minds of the world's opinion over socalled global warming, the first victim has clearly become "science itself." Scientific data has been hijacked for the use of personal agendas. As we have witnessed over this last decade, corporate-funded organizations with highly paid scientists are coming forward and spoon-feeding you erroneous data, telling you that *you* are the cause of our wicked weather. *You* are causing earthquakes, volcanoes, hurricanes, floods, and yes, it was *you* who caused the Indian Ocean tsunami, killing a quarter million people. The message is clear: "We must attack and eliminate the "evil doers" who are killing the good people. So we'd better pass laws and stop them before they destroy the Earth."

Having established that the planet is in dire straits, the savor is introduced a couple of years from now: "Hi, I'm from Shell Oil. I'm here to save you. Yes, we have new developments that can clean the water and suck the CO_2 and other fossil fuel pollutants right out of the air. In fact, my partners BP Oil, Standard Oil, GM, and Ford. have all come forward at this very time to help you. We wanted you to know we stand firmly behind you (former 'lemming,' now wise consumer). We are here to put ourselves on the front line to fight the 'evil doers.' And guess what! We can do all this for only $70 billion. And we'll only tax you a small amount to subsidize our miracle technology that we've developed to save you. Oh, and our $63 million 'management fee'? Don't worry, it's already factored in."

That's right, it is the fascist, cooperate conglomerates who are the promoters of the very environmental zealots they pretend to fight. Now how wicked is this! And unfortunately look how successful this model has been. It's straight out of Machiavelli's handbook: (1) Initiate a problem, (2) Rush in with a solution, (3) Sell weapons to both sides. Just think tobacco! Now do you get the picture?

The eminent climatologist John Daly (1934 – 2004) put it well: "Climate and climate change have been a lifelong study of mine since my early days as a ship's officer in the British Merchant Navy. I have lived through and traced the progress of the 'Ice Age' scare of the 1970s, the 'nuclear winter' scare of the 1980s, and now the 'global warming' scare of the present. All these scares have advanced the interests of what was a small academic discipline 30 years ago to become a mammoth global industry today. It is my view that this industry has, through the 'politics of fear' which it has promoted, acted against the interests of the public."

Well, said, John. Your sharp, inquiring mind will be missed. (John's website: www.john-daly.com is mandatory reading for anyone interesting in the global warming debate.)

Stopping Climate Change

Putting things in perspective, geologists tell us our present warm climate is a mere blip in the history of an otherwise cold Earth. Frigid Ice Age temperatures have been the rule, not the exception, for the last few million years. If Earth is heading back into another Ice Age, do we even want to limit carbon dioxide emissions into the atmosphere, where they might sustain habitable temperatures for an extra century or so.

In Chapter 4, we saw how we're halfway into a 25,000-year warming phase and have maybe 12,000 years until it peaks. Then we slide into cooling phase that may well be colder than the last phase because the big picture is that we're going back in a multi-million-year mega-Ice Age. Each 100,000-year cycle may see colder low and cooler high temperatures, but for now, we're looking at a 2 – 3 °F warm-up for maybe 10,000 years, but *not* because we're pumping CO_2 into the atmosphere.

Global climate cycles of warming and cooling have been a natural phenomena for hundreds of thousands, even millions, of years, and dramatic climate change *is* part of Earth's big picture. Planetary warming and chilling is just part of Earth's life, and we must direct our limited resources to finding ways to adapt to global cooling and warming, and the inevitable fluctuations in ocean levels and precipitation.

238

Supporting this view is British scientist Jane Francis of the School of Earth and Environment, University of Leeds, who maintains: "What we are seeing really is just another interglacial phase within our big icehouse climate." Dismissing political calls for a global effort to reverse climate change, she said, "It's really farcical because the climate has been changing constantly ... What we should do is be more aware of the fact that it is changing and that we should be ready to adapt to the change."

In May 2005, some recent nuggets dismissing global warming found on the website www.globalwarming.org put out by an informational body, included:

- A *Sunday Telegraph* article on May 1, 2005 challenged *Science* magazine over its current complete lack of articles questioning the axiom that: "Human activity alone is responsible for global warming." The article also revealed that *Science* refused to publish the results of a survey finding that less than 10 percent of scientists believe in the axiom.
- Regarding the landmark NASA study on global warming that predicts based on imperfect models, University of Alabama scientist Roy Spencer believes the debate is on shaky ground without 50 to 100 years of accurate satellite readings of the Earth's radiation budget. Without that data, we have no idea of the role played by clouds, water vapor, deep ocean heat storage, and other processes.
- A new NASA study, released on April 28, 2005 reveals that NASA scientists have further revised downwards their estimate of how much temperature will rise in response to more energy trapped in the atmosphere, from their earlier prediction of 1.1 °C down to 0.6 °C.
- Warnings of mass extinctions as a result of global warming have been cast into doubt by new research that shows fish adapt well to changing temperatures. It was believed that fish lose their ability to adapt to changes, but a study of Antarctic fish shows that they adapted well to very cold waters. The lead researcher writes, "The effect of climate change on species distribution and extinction may be overestimated by current models of global warming."

The Word from Theodor Landscheidt

Let's turn to Theodor Landscheidt, of the Schroeter Institute for Research in Cycles of Solar Activity for the last scientific word on this silly debate that just won't go away. His landmark paper, *Solar Wind Near Earth: Indicator of Variations in Global Temperature* reveals a distinct correlation between solar activity and global temperature, albeit with a lag of 4 to 8 years. Allowing for this temperature lag, an outstanding geomagnetic peak around 1990 could explain the high global temperature in 1998. After 1990 the geomagnetic data show a steep decline comparable to the decrease between 1955 and 1967, followed by falling temperatures from 1961 through 1973 in spite of growing manmade CO_2 emissions. This points to decreasing global temperature during the next 10 years, he claims.

Landscheidt points out that the total magnetic flux leaving the Sun, dragged out by the solar wind, has risen by a factor of 2.3 since 1901, and global temperature has increased by 0.5° C. The energy in the solar flux is transferred to the near-Earth environment by magnetic connection and directly into the atmosphere by charged particles, where it affects the weather within days after solar eruptions

He then quotes a number of sources to show a linear relationship between solar magnetic flux and solar irradiance. On average, this has risen in energy by 1.65 watt/m^2 which forces an energy rise in our atmosphere by 0.3 watt/m^2. This forcing corresponds to an increase in temperate of 0.23° C, which potentially accounts for nearly half of the change in the Earth's global temperature over the 20th century.

Landscheidt goes on to assert that the strongest contributors to the solar wind intensity are CMEs, solar flares, and eruptive prominences, which create the highest velocities in the solar wind and shock waves that compress and intensify magnetic fields in the solar wind plasma. Coronal holes have a similar effect. So the key question is: Are periods of strong plasma ejections on the Sun connected with temperature on Earth?

He compared indices of geomagnetic disturbances for those eruptions that actually affect the Earth with Northern Hemisphere land air and sea surface temperatures, and found a promising positive correlation. He argued that if there were a causal connection, temperature should lag the geomagnetic index. There was. The correlation reaches a maximum when temperature lags the geomagnetic disturbance by 6 years. This is in contradiction, he point out, to assertions that there is only a negligible effect of solar activity on temperature in the second half of the 20th century and especially in the two last decades.

In his chart, the vertical axis on the left measures yearly global surface temperature anomalies (from Jones, Parker et al.) against the index.

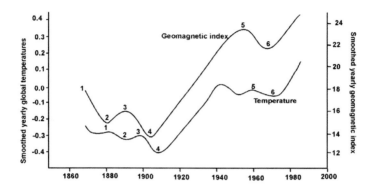

Temperature lags the index by 4 to 8 years, but follows the undulations of its curve. Identical numbers highlight the connection between the leading index extremes and the following temperature extremes.

As this result is based on the data that have already been shown to be highly significant, it can be considered valid. Temperature lags geomagnetic index on the average by 6 years, with only one exception. After 1942, temperature did no longer follow the rising index and formed a shallow trough. It could be that between 1942 and 1952, we saw the steepest rise in volcanic activity since 1860

The lag of the temperature data suggests that the process by which some of the excess energy linked to solar activity is stored and accumulated in the climate system takes years, possibly due to the thermal inertia of oceans may offer an explanation.

What does this mean for long-range forecast of global temperature? The results suggest that future change in global temperature may be read from the leading geomagnetic data. The following chart shows the repeatedly smoothed yearly global land and sea surface temperature anomalies and geomagnetic index after 1985. Around 1990 the index reached the highest maximum since the beginning of the record in 1868 (marked by the number 7). Allowing for a lag of 8 years, the corresponding maximum 7 of global temperature could have occurred in 1998 with the highest temperature measured since the establishment of regular meteorological services.

After 1990 the index declined steeply, although the current sunspot cycle has reached its maximum, which points to global cooling during the decade after temperature maximum 7.

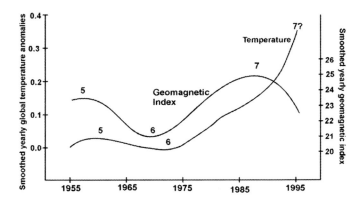

So a maximum in the curve of global temperature could have occurred around 1998, the year with the highest temperature observed since the establishment of international meteorological services. In 1999 the temperature was considerably lower, especially in the Southern Hemisphere. This relationship points to global cooling for at least 10 years.

Actually the global temperature in 1999 was much lower than in 1998, especially in the Southern Hemisphere. As the correlation seems robust, we should see falling temperatures at least during the next ten years. The decline in the geomagnetic index after maximum 7 is steeper than after maximum 5. So global temperature should fall at a faster rate than after temperature maximum 5.

Manmade CO_2 contributions should not be an obstacle to such decrease, as temperatures were falling from the early sixties through the early seventies in spite of the fast rise of manmade CO_2 emissions. The increase in surface temperature from 1910 to 1940 was steeper and smoother than in the current warming phase, although the rate of manmade emissions at that time was only 10% of the present rate. The next decade should reveal the degrees to which solar activity and human greenhouse gas contributions force global temperature.

Climate Change: It's the Sun, Not 'Man-made Doom'

Long range forecaster and astrophysicist Piers Corbyn of Weather Action spoke at a recent two-day conference on *Food Crops and Changing Climate* at Britain's Royal Society, and predicted that *global cooling is likely by 2040.*

"Climate change has always been happening, but the decisive cause is particles from the Sun not man-made CO_2," Corbyn said. "Our 'Solar Weather Theory' explains climate change *scientifically* over time scales from decades to many thousands of years, and enables long range weather forecasting many months ahead, down to time scales of a few days for extreme events – as will be shown by heavy rain, thunderstorms and strong winds in Southern England later this week, which we forecasted 8 months ahead."

"The current man-made CO_2 global warming dogma is fundamentally flawed and is being used as a cover for the promotion of nuclear power," he said, speaking about the developments in research by himself and co-workers presented in Moscow last year and unveiled in more detail at the Institute of Physics on February 2, 2005 (see http://groups.iop.org/EG/05/03/050314a_e.html)

"World temperatures and climate are controlled by particles from the Sun and changes in the Earth's magnetic field. Particle activity of the Sun and the motion of the Earth's magnetic pole will keep the world's warmth a few more years and then major cooling is likely to take place and be important by 2040.

"Temperature changes relate much more closely to particle effects from the Sun than they do to CO_2. This means the Sun must be the driving force of what we see. Man's CO_2 could not be driving what the Sun does!

"Claims that the effects of the Sun have been 'proved' to be not important are false because these judgments are made essentially considering sunlight rather than the Sun's particle and magnetic effects, which show great variations and which we have shown are the key to Sun-Earth climate links. "The so-called 'fingerprint' of man-made CO_2

in rises in sea temperatures which supposedly proves they are caused by man is not justifiable. The truth is probably the opposite. There is *no actual evidence of a causal link.* The fact is, there is more CO_2 around now than the 'global warmers' can explain by man's activity. The reality is probably that this extra CO_2 is a *result*, not a *cause*, of the extra warmth, which in turn is caused by—and so a fingerprint of—increased solar particle activity over the last 80 years.

"Other greenhouse gases are more important. Water vapor, ozone, methane, etc. are much more important than CO_2 and man's contribution to the flow of CO_2 in and out of sea and land is only 4% of total flow. The Kyoto carbon controls concern changes in the 4% of CO_2, which itself is only about 25% of total greenhouse effect. Even the most drastic 60% reductions of man's CO_2 (which would ruin the world economy) would reduce world temperatures *by only 0.2 °C!*

"The extinction threat is invalid. The idea is invalid that polar bears and other species could be wiped out by the temperature claims of the 'global warmers.' The Arctic was much warmer a thousand years ago than now, which is why Greenland was so named ... because it was warmer when discovered by the Vikings. Yet polar bears, walruses and all other species they say are now threatened, survived then and for the six thousand years before then which were also notably warmer than now."

The Story Unfolds

On July 3, 2005, I wrote an article titled **Sunspots Everywhere - What's Going On With the Sun?** in which I said, "Today's sunspot count has jumped to 168. The Sun is peppered with spots covering most of the Earth facing surface. Sunspot region 783 poses the greatest threat of M-Class flares."

Then, on July 4, Dr. Gary Sharp put out a news release:

There is a high risk of tornados and floods hitting Britain in the period July 8-11, say Weather Action long range forecasters. "Damage is likely and we warned of this 7 months ago using predictable aspects of particle and magnetic influences from the Sun," said Piers Corbyn. "Weather fronts in that period will be more active than traditional meteorology forecasters will expect."

This Weather Action forecast comes hard on the heels of a double whammy success by Weather Action, which predicted both the major thunderstorms in June that hit North Yorkshire and Glastonbury.

"Of course, the Global Warming groupies around the G8 will claim these events are caused by man-made CO_2. They are not, so we are announcing this forecast to let everyone know. The Global Warmers claim almost every weather extreme is man-made but they have no evidence and neither have they evidence of any dangerous weather being caused by man-made CO_2.

"Our revolutionary Solar Weather Technique has real proven predictive power. The 'global warmers' can predict nothing. They are a modern substitute for religion. Climate change is fundamentally driven by solar activity, and not by CO_2 levels that in the long run are driven by temperatures, and not the other way around.

There is a second window of raised tornado and flood risk this month, between July 21 -24," said Mr Corbyn. (Extract from Weather Action Long range forecast, issued December 2004):

July 8-11, 2005: Heavy rain and sharp thunderstorms with hail. Tornado type events likely.

Heavy rain sweeps in from the West with sharp thunderstorms developing in many parts. Local flooding.

Active cyclonic thunder systems attacking from the West and driving towards South Scandinavia and the Low Countries. Auroras likely.

A Weather Action Press Release
[Contact information: **News Release Weather Action,** Delta House, 175-177 Borough High Street, London SE1 1HR. Tel +44(0)20 7939 9946 Fax +44(0)20 7939 9948, info@weatheraction.com, Contact: Piers Corbyn 07958713320]

Freak Storms Scares are 'nonsense' say long range forecasters
Claims that the thunderstorms and floods such as happened at Glastonbury and Yorkshire earlier in June would be more frequent due to man-made global warming were today criticized as 'pre-G8 hype and nonsense' by Piers Corbyn of Weather Action long range forecasters.

"The timing of this particular thunder breakdown and specifically the warning of 'thunderstorms and floods likely in West' was forecast by Weather Action back in May … and came just one day early. This and the earlier event which gave floods in Yorkshire confirmed both of Weather Action's two forecasted thunderstorm/flood high risk periods this June.

"We predicted these two and only these two periods (June 11-13 and 25-28) for the highest risk of serious '*thunderfloods,*' and they were both confirmed," pointed out Mr Corbyn.

"These two events were caused by predictable aspects of particle influences from the Sun. Surely Baroness Young or her advisers cannot seriously think that man-made CO_2 is increasing the activity of the Sun!" added Mr Corbyn.

"The caption under a photograph published in *The Independent* on Sunday June 26, 2005, accompanying an article by Sir John Houghton reads: '*Extreme* weather typified by the Devon storm last week is triggered by burning fossil fuels,' is untrue. Those storms were demonstrably and predictably triggered by solar activity effects. It is solar particle and magnetic effects—not mankind—which are the drivers of weather patterns and climate change.

"The truth is that a *scientific look at storm developments* over the last 50 years shows that there have been *fewer* not *more* major storms around the world, and there is no evidence of more weather extremes, but only more *reportage* of events and more tragedies due to poorly advised positioning of new building.

"Baroness Young, her advisers and a self-serving so-called community of Western European climate scientists are engaging in a massive exercise in spin and scaremongering assertions for which they have no evidence. It is a scandal that they never name even one scientist with any physical observations which back up claims.

"Sir John Houghton's claim of more heatwaves being caused by man-made CO_2 is also without evidence. When speaking in Moscow last July, he agreed that there was no evidence of a connection (and it was noted that such heatwaves in Western Europe are often associated with colder weather in Russia). The fact is that heatwaves are caused by specific pressure patterns, and the enhanced brightness of the Sun due to clean air measures (i.e., less 'dimming') and continuing de-forestation in Europe (which enhances surface temperatures) mean that any heatwaves that occur can be a bit hotter."

Mr Corbyn warned, "This is 'bonanza week' of Global Warming hysteria in the build-up to the G8 summit. The fact is that there has been no increase whatsoever in the last 20 years in 'dangerous weather events' that are the supposed reason for the Kyoto Protocols. The frequent 'crazy' claims that any weather event is proof of Global Warming is dishonest spin in the run-up to the G8, and intended to promote nuclear power and Carbon Credit trading to the disadvantage of poorer nations.

"Scientists who actually look at the *observed facts* resent very much being accused of being in the pay of the oil lobby. I receive no such funding. We want to discuss the science , not see the truth drowned in spin. Furthermore it should be noted that, as Sir John Houghton himself points out in last Sunday's *Independent,* a number of very big oil companies are now publicly 'on board' with Global Warming. The reason is simple. Global Warming hype will enable them to gain considerable incomes for extracting CO_2 from the atmosphere and 'recycling' use of their old oil platforms to inject solid CO_2 into the sea bed (where it will poison fish)—termed *'Carbon sequestration'* in the name of saving the planet at taxpayers expense.

"Claims that **climate change in Africa** is threatening food production there are **just another manipulation of the plight of the poor** to boost the Global Warming lobby. It was revealed (e.g., in a presentation by James Verdin at the Royal Society meeting on *Food Crops in Changing Climate* April 26-27, 2005) that the main threat to food supply in Africa is caused by variability in production due to short-term attitudes of farmers -on top of corruption, wars and failure to tackle AIDS. That is nothing to do with any real or imagined extra variability due to man's CO_2 (for which there is no evidence).

Mr Corbyn concluded, "If the G8 members care about the poor of the world, they will refuse to go down either the dangerous nuclear route or the Global Warmers' anti-industry schemes that will curb the growth of the developing world and cause more otherwise avoidable poverty and the deaths of millions of children.

"I hope there IS a G8 fudge about Global Warming; they should not even spend time talking about it but instead get on with tackling real pollution from chemical and industrial waste."

Obituary: Gerard C. Bond, Climate Change Geologist

Dr. Bond's studies show a *direct connection* between solar activity and climate. A marine geologist at the Lamont-Doherty Earth Observatory at Columbia University, he conducted novel studies of earth's climate changes by interpreting sediments taken from beneath the seafloor.

Trained as a classical geologist, Dr. Bond shifted his interests to the ocean floor in the early 1990s, when he began to look at samples of sediments retrieved from the North Atlantic. With other scientists, he concluded that relatively recent and unusual layers of limestone and other sediments had been deposited by the melting of 'armadas of icebergs' that originated in eastern Canada.

In further studies, involving iron-stained quartz grains within the sediments, he found that a cycle of warming climates released the glaciers every 1,400 – 1,500 years, an occurrence leading to a periodic cooling of ocean waters by several degrees. He traced the warming and cooling cycle back 100,000 years, compared evidence of a correlation in Greenland's ice and, along with a team of other researchers, published the results in the journal *Nature* in 1993.

G. Michael Purdy, director of the observatory, said, "Dr. Bond had helped translate an incredibly rich source of information about the Earth's history and a fabulous tape recorder of millions of years of that history and the climate."

Wallace S. Broecker, a professor of geochemistry at Columbia, said, "In the late 1990s, seeking to understand the causes of the 1,500-year cycles, Dr. Bond theorized that variations in solar activity—the appearance of sunspots and changes in the emission of solar radiation—might be driving them."

Michael Crichton's *State of Fear*

Let's end this chapter on an entirely different front—best-selling author Michael Crichton who weighs into the Global Warming arena with his latest book *State of Fear*, a masterful blend of good science and great fiction in the style of *Jurassic Park* and *The Andromeda Strain*.

Crichton has his characters make the following points, all of which come from impeccable, cited sources (from the website of The Heartland Institute, a group critical of global warming):

- Most of the warming in the past century occurred before 1940, before CO_2 emissions could have been a major factor (p. 84);
- Temperatures fell between 1940 and 1970 even as CO_2 levels increased (p. 86);
- Temperature readings from reporting stations outside the U.S. are poorly maintained and staffed and probably inaccurate; those in the U.S., which are probably more accurate, show little or no warming trend (pp. 88-89);
- Full professors from MIT, Harvard, Columbia, Duke, Virginia, Colorado, UC Berkeley, and other prestigious schools ... the former president of the National Academy of Sciences ... will argue that global warming is at best unproven, and at worst pure fantasy (p. 90);
- Temperature sensors on satellites report much less warming in the upper atmosphere (which the theory of global warming predicts should warm first) than is reported by temperature sensors on the ground (p. 99);
- Data from weather balloons agree with the satellites (p. 100);
- "No one can say for sure if global warming will result in more clouds, or fewer clouds," yet cloud cover plays a major role in global temperatures (p. 187);
- Antarctica "as a whole is getting colder, and the ice is getting thicker" (p. 193, sources listed on p. 194);
- The Ross Ice Shelf in Antarctica has been melting for the past 6,000 years (p. 195, p. 200-201); "Greenland *might* lose its ice pack in the next thousand years" (p. 363);
- The Intergovernmental Panel on Climate Change (IPCC) is "a huge group of bureaucrats and scientists under the thumb of bureaucrats," and its 1995 report was revised "after the scientists themselves had gone home" (p. 245-246);
- James Hansen's predictions of global warming during a Congressional committee hearing in 1988, which launched the global warming scare, were wrong by 300 percent (.35 degrees Celsius over the next 10 years versus the actual increase of .11 degrees); in 1998, Hansen said long-term predictions of climate are impossible (pp. 246-247);

- There has been no increase in extreme weather events (.e.g., floods, tornadoes, drought) over the past century or in the past 15 years; computer models used to forecast climate change do not predict more extreme weather (p. 362, 425-426);
- Temperature readings taken by terrestrial reporting stations are rising because they are increasingly surrounded by roads and buildings which hold heat, the "urban heat island" effect (p. 368-369); methods used to control for this effect fail to reduce temperatures enough to offset it (p. 369-376);
- Changes in land use and urbanization may contribute more to changes in the average ground temperature than "global warming" caused by human emissions (p. 383, 388);
- Temperature data are suspect because they have been adjusted and manipulated by scientists who *expect* to find a warming trend (p. 385-386);
- Carbon dioxide has increased a mere 60 parts per million since 1957, a tiny change in the composition of the atmosphere (p. 387);
- Increased levels of CO_2 act a fertilizer, promoting plant growth and contributing to the shrinking of the Sahara desert (p. 421);
- The spread of malaria is unaffected by global warming (pp. 421-422, footnotes on 422);
- Sufficient data exist to measure changes in mass for only 79 of the 160,000 glaciers in the world (p. 423);
- The icecap on Kilimanjaro has been melting since the 1800s, long before human emissions could have influenced the global climate, and satellites do not detect a warming trend in the region (p. 423); deforestation at the foot of the mountain is the likely explanation for the melting trend (p. 424);
- Sea levels have been rising at the rate of 10 to 20 centimeters (four to eight inches) per hundred years for the past 6,000 years (p. 424);
- El Niño is a global weather pattern unrelated to global warming and on balance tends to be beneficial by extending growing seasons and reducing the use of heating fuels (p. 426);
- The Kyoto Protocol would reduce temperatures by only 0.04 degrees Celsius in the year 2100 (p. 478);

- A report by scientists published in *Science* concludes "there is no known technology capable of reducing [global] carbon emissions ... totally new and undiscovered technology is required" (p. 479);
- Change, not stability, is the defining characteristic of the global climate, with naturally occurring events (e.g., volcanic eruptions, earthquakes, tsunamis) much more likely to affect climate than anything humans do (p. 563); and
- Computer simulations are not real-world data and cannot be relied on to produce reliable forecasts (p. 566).

Thank you, Michael. I rest my case.

Chapter 14

Life after Earth Changes

The newspaper headline reads "Dramatic Increase in Number of Natural Disasters," but is this true, or does it just seem that way because of increased coverage, as when hundreds of camcorders were on hand to capture the S.E. Asia tsunamis? Where were they when up to 5 million died in China during the 1920s flooding?

In May 2005, New England was hit by a Nor'easter, with temperatures in the 40s, and a wind chill dropping that to about freezing point, making it the coldest May 24 since 1967. The NNE winds, blowing at about 30 mph, gusting up to 50 mph, drove a mixture of sleet and rain almost horizontally. This extremely rare situation was caused by a huge high pressure system over Quebec and a jet stream to the south that guided one low pressure system after another over New England. On the same day, the temperature in Las Vegas soared to 103 °F, breaking the old record of 101 °F. Las Vegas also broke the record of 7 days in a row of 100+ °F days in a row in the month of May by having 9 of them in a row.

If you're thinking unusual weather has been occurring in your area, you're right. A series of "record-breaking" weather has hit just about every continent on the Earth. Right here at the ECTV studios, an abrupt 'weather warning' was broadcast to warn people of severe heat as we climbed into the 90's in May, while 'normal' is about 63 °F. Some areas hit 'record lows' showing a 30 degree shift in temperatures.

Why all the extremes? The Sun, of course. It fired off an M-Class flare on May 28 from sunspot region 767, with a following CME that was Earth-directed. So today, and right on schedule within 48 to 72 hours, we are under a severe geomagnetic storm, as the Kp index for 5/30/05 shows.

On July 6, 2005, the 2005 Hurricane Season got off to a blazing start when Tropical Storm Cindy roared onshore and dropped up to 6 inches of rain on the SE states before weakening to a Depression. Meanwhile, Tropical Storm Dennis strengthened into Hurricane Dennis and took aim at Jamaica, where up to 12 inches of rain was expected. NOAA issued a 'life-threatening flood' warning.

Natural Disasters

A Google search on 'natural disasters' yields over 20,000 pages, the first of which is NASA's disaster database at: http://ndrd.gsfc.nasa.gov.

Behind each of those images in the screen shot reside dozens of informative articles about what steps NASA is taking to mitigate disasters of that type.

Another excellent database that lists natural disasters from November 1981 to May 2000 is at: http://www.reliefweb.int/w/rwb.nsf. For each incident, ReliefWeb backs it up with maps and photographs, as in this screen shot of the Situation Report on Hurricane Adrian that ripped through San Salvador in May 2005 (see below).

NASA's Disaster Database

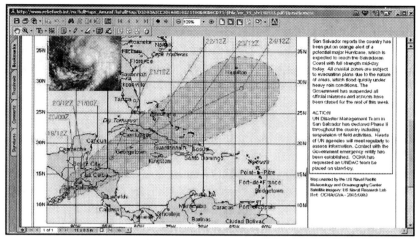

Typical ReliefWeb screen

Another information goldmine is the USGS database called IRIS. The home page shows a global map with all seismic activity in the last five years. In the screen shot, note all the activity around Sumatra in the aftermath of the December 2004 event.

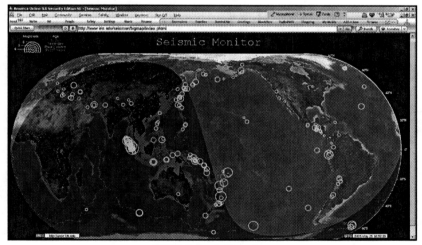

IRIS Seismic Database

The IRIS database, available at www.iris.edu/seismon, is updated every 24 hours. Among the fascinating facts revealed is that 18 volcanoes have erupted since January 1, 2000, some more than twice.

The Earthquake Hazards Program within the USGS has excellent lists of seismic events, and can be found at http://wwwneic.cr.usgs.gov/neis/bulletin/bulletin.html, while the sister site, http://wwwneic.cr.usgs.gov/neis/qed/qed.html offers outstanding maps. According to those sites, we are experiencing an average of 100 significant seismic events per week!

In an article I posted to the ECTV website on May 27, 2000 titled *Dramatic Rise in Frequency of Natural Disasters Worldwide*, Deborah Janveaux analyzed the almost 12,000 disasters that have occurred between 1900 and 2000. The Law of Averages says that we should have seen about 120 per year during the last century, but the first 83 years (1900 – 1983) saw on average a mere 55 a year (4,557 disasters). However, the 16 years between 1984 – 2000 saw a whopping 455 a year (7,281). And this is just the count of events, and not actual loss of life or property damage.

All this tells me quite clearly that something is going on. The Earth seems to be getting restless, and preparing for ... *something.* Let's preview what Earth might look like on the other side of that 'something' or even 'somethings.'

In the millennia-old aboriginal view of the universe, all things are made up of four elements: Earth, Air, Fire, and Water. All animals, plants, stones, emotions, inanimate objects, and energies are combinations of these elements, just as we are. Everything has its own unique blend of the four elements in it: that which has substance has earth in it; that which has energy in it has fire; that which flows and/or has feelings has water; and that which involves sound, thinking or communication has air in it.

As anyone will tell you who has been through a major quake, when the earth moves, the changes are in your face in a heartbeat, so let's begin there.

Earth Changes: Earth

A powerful earthquake occurs less than once every two years, but about 40 moderate earthquakes occur every year, and cause damage. Over 8,000 minor earthquakes occur each day without causing any damage, with only about 1,000 being strong enough to be felt.

Monster quakes (over 9 on the Richter Scale) have occurred recently in Kamchatka, Russia (1952), Aleutian Islands (1957), Southern Chile (1960), Alaska (1964) and Sumatra (2004). Ironically, earthquakes rarely kill people directly. Instead, falling objects, collapsing buildings and other structures, fire and explosions from broken gas or power lines, spilt hazardous materials, falling power lines and tsunamis are the real killers.

What interaction can solar activity have upon the Earth? Intuitively, there should be *some* interaction. After all, if you've ever used one bar magnet to push another around, you know the force that the first applies to the second. Likewise, when a CME barrels towards Earth, its magnetic field exerts a force on the planet's magnetosphere, which in turn will push back onto its source—the core of the planet. It would seem reasonable that the CME's magnetic field is therefore pushing the core backwards, which would exert a force on the mantle on the opposite side of the planet. If that region coincided with a tectonic boundary, that extra force could disturb the dynamics of the boundary and trigger a seismic event. Making matters even more complex, different areas of the mantle contain different concentrations of ferric materials, which would also be affected by the force field of a geomagnetic storm.

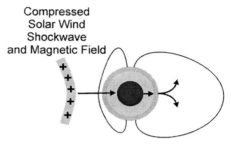

Compressed Solar Wind Shockwave and Magnetic Field

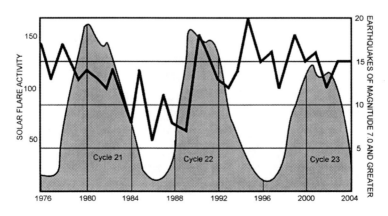

On the basis that more CMEs would occur during Solar Maxima, I plotted the number of major (7.0 – 7.9) and great (8.0+) earthquakes for the last three solar cycles to see if there was any correlation. Admittedly a sample of just 30 years is tiny, but it would tell me if what was intuitively reasonable is born out in fact. As you can see, it isn't. As is apparent, 1995 saw the greatest number of seismic events (20), which coincided with the Solar Minimum between cycles 22 and 23. (If anyone wants to plot earthquake events against actual CME occurrences, I would love to see the results.)

One obvious effect that the Sun does have on the Earth is gravitational, although the Moon exerts 2½ times more gravitational force on Earth than does the Sun. During a Lunar Eclipse, the Sun and Moon are on opposite sides of the Earth, and exert forces that pull against each other. During a Solar Eclipse, they are on the same side, in a direct line, and are therefore pulling together, causing a different kind of strain on fault zones. Also, because the Earth's core is solid and tends to move within the more liquid outer core, gravitational forces tend to move the core relative to the mantle, again causing stress on fault lines.

For example, an earthquake in Iran on September 16, 1978 was the most devastating one of that year and killed more than 25,000 people. It occurred just 3½ hours before a total lunar eclipse was visible there. Coincidence or not?

"Coincidence," most seismologists say. "The lunar cycle (full moon or new moon) does not increase the frequency or intensity of earthquakes. There is no recognizable pattern between full moons and earthquakes, despite the incredibly sensitive equipment in the U.S.," according to the USGS site. One geologist claims success in predicting strong earthquakes based upon the alignment of the Moon and Sun with the Earth, such as during eclipses, but strong earthquakes also occur when Sun and Moon are in no particular alignment, so there is no cause-and-effect at work.

So it would seem that the impact of Solar Rain on the Earth's physical body is not all that significant.

A Google search on "Earthquakes sunspots" yields a couple of hundred pages, which is nothing in today's Internet. So what's striking about this is that so few papers dealing with the earthquake-sunspot issue have been published. If there were even a tenuous correlation between earthquakes and solar activity, then I should have found thousands of pages. This suggests that there is at best a very weak correlation, and at worst, no correlation between solar activity and earthquakes.

However, on August 11, 2003, I wrote a piece titled *Is NASA Preparing Us For Earthquakes?* although it wasn't what you're thinking:

There is something about this timing that is a bit unsettling. A public announcement was just released moments ago, telling us NASA is ready to predict earthquakes. That's right, predict earthquakes. It was just last year, NASA went public shunning the possibility of predicting earthquakes. Why the sudden turnaround?

NASA makes this announcement "High above Earth where seismic waves never reach, satellites may be able to detect earthquakes—before they strike." NASA claims they have satellite technology which can detect tectonic plate movement. NASA says they are working hard to have a system in place "giving the public and emergency planners time to prepare." (NASA)

"There are several satellite-based methods that show promise as precursors to earthquake activity," says Jacob Yates, a researcher at NASA's Goddard Space Flight Center. "One method is Interferometric-Synthetic Aperture Radar (InSAR). Basically, InSAR is when two radar images of a given tectonic area are combined in a process called data fusion, and any changes in ground motion at the surface may be detected."

Folks, the "Super-duper Doppler Weatherman" is alive and well. It just may be, even with the down time of SOHO, we will see our local and national weather personalities giving forecast which includes space weather such as solar flares, CME's, geomagnetic storms, and now ... earthquake predictions!

NASA reports one of their methods is to monitor "slow fluctuations in Earth's magnetic field." Scientists doing research with magnetometers just before major earthquakes have serendipitously recorded tiny, slow fluctuations in Earth's magnetic field. One example happened during the Loma-Prieta earthquake that devastated San Francisco in 1989. Almost 2 weeks before the quake, readings of low-frequency magnetic signals (0.01-0.02 Hz) jumped up to 20 times above normal levels, and then spiked even higher the day of the quake.

It's all about magnetics! Just as the equation can predict extreme weather, such can be monitored for electro-magnetic flux as outlined above. We do indeed live in exciting times.

So here, we were talking about magnetic variation as a *symptom* of some underlying seismic process, and not its *cause*.

Earth Changes: Air

Odd stuff is air. We can't see it (hopefully), but we can feel the impact when it moves, and we can't exist without it for more than a few seconds. And as we'll see, air's fluidity makes it far more susceptible to impact by Solar Rain. Air effects run the gamut from gentle summer breezes to F5 tornadoes, with winds topping 300 mph that will drive a drinking straw through a two-by-four like a nail through butter.

Let's briefly review some of air's more destructive forms and then superimpose earth changes due to Solar Rain on them.

Derecho, or Straight-Line Wind. On October 26, 1997, 20,000 acres of prime Colorado timber country were flattened by 100 mph winds that swept down from the skies. The effect often happens when air is being sucked into a rotating system that can be several miles away. There is no rotational element to the wind flow, which proceeds in a straight line. It is possible that solar activity could increase the speed of the jet stream or push it lower in altitude, intensifying the effect on the ground. Or it could direct the jet into more southerly latitudes so that the cold-air low pressure systems it guides interact with warmer air further south, also intensifying the effect.

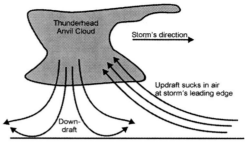

Micro-bursts. Air within a thunderhead rises very quickly, cooling from, say, 80 °F to -40 °F. It then forms a dense column that falls at between 25 – 100 mph, which spreads out as it approaches the ground. Usually this has little effect, other than to flatten crops, but when it happens just as an aircraft is in the extremely vulnerable state during take-off, it can be disastrous.

On August 7, 1975 at Denver's Stapleton Airport, Continental Flight 426 was taking off at 4:10 p.m. on runway 35L when a microburst crossed the runway seconds after it had taken off. At 50 feet, flying into the microburst gave the Boeing 727 an extra 25-knot headwind, for an airspeed of 160 knots. But 13 seconds later, at 150 feet, that headwind became a 25-knot tailwind, which suddenly killed much of the lift from the wings. Despite the engines being on maximum power, because the wind also had a vertical downward component, just five seconds later, the plane slammed down hard onto the runway, landing on its belly. Of the 124 passengers and 7 crewmembers headed for Wichita, 15 were injured, but with no fatalities. The hull was written off as a total loss, however. The diagram shows what happened.

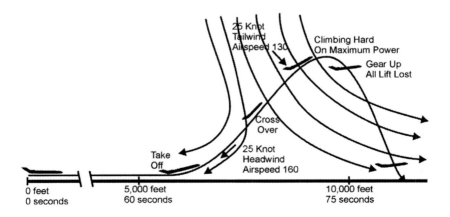

Tornadoes. The more powerful tornadoes (2 and above on the Fujita Scale) are spawned from a supercell. Wind shear begins to rotate a large thundercloud mass associated with heavy rain and hail, which is created by frozen raindrops being repeatedly carried up to about 50,000 feet, where more water freezes onto them each time. The rotating storm could be several miles across, but down on the ground, the rotational effect is squeezed into a vortex maybe only a half-mile across. The updraft creates an area of super-low pressure that pulls in even more air, so that the twisting effect becomes self-sustaining. Solar activity could increase the incidence of upper-level wind shear, which would create more supercells, and increase their rotational speed, making for more frequent and more powerful tornadoes.

Those lower on the Fujita Scale are not spawned from supercells, but from the co-incidence of ground-level vortices created by windshear from two opposing air masses *and* normal late afternoon thermal updrafts. If an updraft and a vortex "get lucky" and encounter each other, a spiral element is introduced into the upflow and a twister is born. If solar activity increases, these encounters could happen more frequently.

We are grateful to Fujita, the father of tornado research, for the six-level classification according to the damage done:

- **F0** (Wind speed < 73 mph) *Light damage.* Downed chimneys; branches broken off trees; shallow-rooted trees pushed over; billboards damaged.
- **F1** (73 – 112 mph) *Moderate damage.* Tiles blown off roofs; mobile homes pushed off foundations or overturned; moving autos blown off roads.
- **F2** (113-157 mph) *Considerable damage.* Roofs torn off frame houses; mobile homes demolished; boxcars overturned; large trees snapped or uprooted; light-object missiles generated; cars lifted off ground.
- **F3** (158-206 mph) *Severe damage.* Roofs and some walls torn off well-constructed houses; entire trains overturned; most trees in forests uprooted; heavy cars lifted off the ground and thrown, trucks blown over.

- **F4** (207-260 mph) *Devastating damage.* Well-constructed houses leveled; structures with weak foundations blown away some distance; cars thrown and large missiles generated.
- **F5** (261-318 mph) *Catastrophic damage.* Strong frame houses leveled off foundations and swept away; automobile-sized missiles fly through the air for long distances; trees debarked, road surfaces scoured off.

Photo credit: National Weather Service

The above NWS photo shows the damage caused by an F4 tornado. If this had been an F5, all the rubble would have been in the next state, leaving just bare concrete foundation slabs.

To test the linkage between sunspot activity and tornadoes, I superimposed NOAA's totals for F4 and F5 events in the U.S. for the years 1976 – 2000 on top of the chart for Cycles 21, 22 and 23 (see next page). As can be seen, the correlation is certainly evident. As the Sun becomes more active, so does the atmosphere over the United States, in terms of the ability of supercells to spawn F4 and F5 tornadoes.

Hurricanes. This phenomenon has been covered thoroughly in an earlier chapter, where we saw how solar activity could in fact reduce the number of hurricanes by destabilizing them early in their creation.

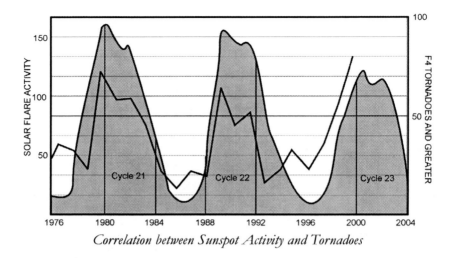

Correlation between Sunspot Activity and Tornadoes

The atmosphere surrounding Earth is fluid and subject to many influences. Some 'experts' believe that the human activity of burning fossil fuels introduces increasing amounts of carbon dioxide into the atmosphere, which increases the so-called greenhouse effect. However, as we saw in the previous, this has been proven insignificant compared with the impact of solar activity, and is being pursued for political and economic purposes, and not because of good science.

If solar activity continues to build, so will the impact on our atmosphere, and we may see increases in the number and intensity of storms. Life after earth changes may prove to be a lot more 'hit-and-miss' than it is today.

Turning from the impact of short-term solar activity such as flares and CMEs on short-term weather to the impact of longer cycles on climate, the level of sunspot activity results in long-term changes in the mean temperature of our planet. During the Maunder Minimum of very little sunspot activity between 1640 – 1720, mean temperatures in Northern Europe fell by almost 2 °F, plunging the planet in the 'Little Ice Age,' during which, for example, the River Thames in London froze each winter. To put things in perspective, that effect was double the impact that 'global warmers' worry about and occurred over about a decade, not a century.

Following that minimum, the Earth's average temperature rose again to 59 °F (15 °C), and advocates of so-called global warming claim that the average is now edging towards 60 °F (15.5 °C) due to CO_2 levels increasing from 280 ppm in 1860 to 360 ppm today. However, as we've seen, there are many more variables in play than just the concentration of atmospheric CO_2.

A return to the Maunder Minimum level of sunspot activity could drop Earth's mean temperature by 2 °F. Or the opposite effect of a doubling of sunspot activity could increase Earth's mean temperature over a couple of years. Now that would *really* melt glaciers, raise sea levels, and redistribute rainfall, creating new tropical regions and new deserts. For example, if we never saw another El Niño again, Indonesia would receive torrential rain every summer, and Peru might never see rain again.

Ozone, the greenhouse gas that absorbs UV radiation, also plays an important role in regulating the planet's temperature. A reduction in stratospheric ozone allows more solar radiation to reach the troposphere, which adds to warming. However, by not absorbing that radiation, the stratosphere is cooler, and emits less infrared energy (heat) to the surface, with the two effects tending to cancel each other out in terms of temperature. But higher levels of UV striking the surface reduce the biosphere's production of CO_2. However, apart from the release of CFCs into the atmosphere, the impact of human activity on the ozone levels is trivial compared with that of the Sun. Following its record huge size in 1993, the hole in the Antarctic ozone layer is on the way to mending itself, which points to the validity of the worldwide ban on CFCs. At least we did *something* right.

Earth Changes: Water

Life after earth changes will focus on one precious, even essential, resource. According to the World Bank, it is already in critically short supply in 80 countries, where the shortage threatens health because over 2 billion people do not have access to sanitary supplies of it. And it triggered the 8-year war between Iran and Iraq. Of course, we're talking about something most Americans take for granted—water. And it's only going to get worse. While the world's population doubles, demand for water increases six-fold. Also, dozens of countries find their main supply of water originates in a neighboring country with whom relations are strained. These include countries such as Botswana, the Sudan, Israel and Syria.

The health of the Dead Sea is a good bellwether of the state of planetary water affairs. In an article titled **For the Dead Sea, a Slow and Seemingly Inexorable Death**, John Ward Anderson, a correspondent for the *Washington Post*, wrote on May 19, 2005 that the Dead Sea's water level has dropped so drastically over the last 20 years that the shoreline is three-quarters of a mile away from the health spas, and a tractor hauls customers back and forth in covered wagons."

"The sea is just running out, and we keep running after it," says resort manager Boaz Ron, "and in another 50 years, it could run out another kilometer."

Apparently the Dead Sea is dying, having dropped over 80 feet and lost one third of its area over the last 50 years. In addition, the water table is also dropping, impacting indigenous flora and wildlife reserves that shelter 500 million birds migrating between Europe and Africa, and allowing sinkholes to appear that damage roads and buildings.

The reason? The River Jordon, water source for the region's population, agriculture and industries, is running dry due to upstream draw-off. In addition, 180 million gallons of water disappear every day (about 66 billion gallons a year) from evaporative pools on the Dead Sea shoreline, operated to extract nutrients, minerals and chemicals. Some are already talking about building a 120-mile pipeline to pump salt water from the Red Sea to the Dead Sea.

Ironically, about half the flow of the River Jordan (the river the Bible tells us John the Baptist baptized Jesus in) is today raw sewage, according to environmentalists. Without the sewage, the river would dry up in summer months.

With a population of over 6 million, Israel has installed ingenious water-conserving technologies and desalination plants (a technology in which they lead the world, to the shame of the U.S.). However, water withdrawal still exceeds supply, and over-pumping of aquifers along the coast allows seawater to pollute drinking water.

Rival neighbors Jordan and Israel are jointly dependent on the Jordan River for their fresh water. Interestingly, the words 'river' and 'rival' have the same root, with 'rival' actually meaning 'someone who shares the same river.'

Syria, Israel and Jordan often rattle their sabers at each other over the water issue, which could easily be the touch paper for war in this century as population and demand rises, but supply actually dwindles due to earth changes.

Also in the Middle East, Egypt's population of 68 million may reach 97 million by 2025, all of whom rely on the seasonal flooding of the Nile River. However, that river originates in Sudan and Ethiopia, both of which are experiencing shortages themselves, and are looking into building dams to average out wet and dry years.

"The Nile is one I worry about," says Sandra Postel, director of the Global Water Policy Project. "Egypt is militarily powerful but vulnerable, and hydro-politics might favor military action, because Egypt is so heavily dependent on the Nile. It's already virtually tapping out the supply, and Ethiopia is now getting interested in developing the headwaters."

Another Middle East flashpoint is the network formed by the Tigris and Euphrates Rivers, both of which originate in Turkey and flow through Syria to Iraq, supplying the bulk of agricultural needs and drinking water. However, the countless bodies of dead household pets, not to mention dead people, plus all the raw sewage make it unappetizing, if not downright dangerous. Turkey is talking about damming the headwaters for its rising population and hydro-electric projects. If Turkey proceeds, diplomacy may give way to military intervention.

Things are no better in the two other hugely populated nations of India and China. India's 1 billion people are over-pumping the aquifers so that wells are running dry, and the soil is growing saltier through contamination by over-salinated irrigation water. A projected population of 1½ billion by 2050 simply cannot be supported by existing water supplies, let alone what might happen as a result of earth changes. Ironically, flooding is one of the leading causes of death in India, because the ground simply cannot hold tropical downpours of 20 inches a day, so massive runoff occurs, and the fresh water is lost to the oceans.

China's 1¼ billion population is probably the scariest story on the planet. Marq de Villiers, author of *Water* says, "In dry Northern China, the water table is dropping one meter per year due to over-pumping, and the Chinese admit that 300 cities are running short. They are diverting water from agriculture and farmers are going out of business. Some Chinese rivers are so polluted with heavy metals that they can't be used for irrigation. Rivers are disgraceful, unusable, industrial sewers, and as farmers go out of business, China will have to import more food."

Japanese belligerence in the 1930s that caused it to invade most of S.E. Asia was driven by the lack of raw materials, especially steel, oil and rubber, and the intent to seize and control those countries rich in what it needed. And that was a tiny country with a population back then of about 75 million. If China ever decided to take what *it* needed, with a 2,000,000-man army, it would be the proverbial 900-pound gorilla.

Many futurists are projecting that by 2025, three billion people—half the Earth's population—will be short of water. And that's just for drinking, not watering the lawn, washing the car, or filling the swimming pool. That means children drinking out of rain puddles or streams polluted with runoff chemicals such as arsenic and mercury, which cause blindness and death, or polluted by human waste, which spreads disease such as dysentery.

Ron Suskind's book *The Price of Loyalty* tells of Treasury Secretary Paul O'Neill's trip to Africa, where he visited village hospitals with no running water, with river water being bucketed in. He calculated that a mere $25 million would provide wells for 10 million people—$2.50 a head—in countries such as Ghana. He returned to the States all fired up about actually doing something concrete for the Third World, and was rebuffed by the White House. Bush said something to the effect that, "If we succeed, everyone will want a well, and if we fail, we'll be a laughing stock." And, of course, Ghanaians won't be voting in the next presidential election. Of course, Bush fired O'Neill, so nothing got done, and the children still die.

The problem is not just in the Third World. In the 1920s, heavy snowfall in the Rockies and warm spring temperatures caused massive runoff in the Colorado River that inundated the Imperial Valley in California, wiping out the year's crop. That, plus the Great Depression triggered the building of Hoover Dam near Las Vegas. The resulting Lake Mead Reservoir served as a dampening effect in wet years, and held water over for dry years, so that the flow of water could be regulated. However, that puts Arizona, Nevada and California at each others' throats over how much water each state can draw off per year. And because Mexico gets whatever is left over, it's also an issue of international diplomacy.

On May 21, 2004, NASA's Patrick L. Barry penned an interesting article titled **Shifting Ocean and Jet Stream Currents is Cause of Warmer Globe** that explored why the western half of the U.S. is facing yet another summer of severe drought. Science provides some answers — and some baffling questions.

The article noted that little precipitation typically falls in the West during summer months, so these regions depend on winter storms to stock the mountains with snow, which melts in summer and replenishes water supplies. However, the snow pack in April 2004 was only 40 – 75% of normal.

While the drought isn't as bad as the Dust Bowl drought of the 1930s, when 70% of the U.S. was dry and precious topsoil blew away, the West is seeing widespread water use restrictions. "So what causes such severe droughts?" the article asked, "And are they predictable?"

Bob Oglesby, a climate dynamicist at NASA's Marshall Space Flight Center, said, "A key factor is the temperature of water in the Pacific Ocean. Sea surface temperatures (SSTs) in the Pacific alter the course of the jet stream as it flows eastward over North America. This high-altitude 'river' of fast-moving air is like a conveyor belt for storms, so the path it takes across the continent has a strong effect on where rain and snow will fall. By steering the jet stream, the Pacific Ocean directs weather patterns across North America. For example, a strong El Niño pattern of warm Pacific surface waters near the equator will drive storms into California, while the opposite La Niña pattern steers moisture-bearing storms further north to Washington state and Canada. One causes drought, the other alleviates it. But there must be more to the story: While a mild La Niña lurked in the Pacific during the onset of the current drought—as would be expected—a shift to a weak El Niño in 2003 did not reverse the drought.

"It's a really active area of research right now as people are trying to decipher exactly what's causing what. Part of the difficulty in understanding drought lies in the fact that weather involves many feedback loops that complicate its behavior and defeat simple cause-and-effect explanations. Soil moisture creates such a feedback loop during dry weather. Once you get into a dry pattern and you start to dry the ground out, that reduction in soil moisture can help to intensify and perpetuate the drought. Normally, the evaporation of soil moisture consumes much of the energy contained in the summer sunshine; without this moisture, that energy heats the ground instead and raises temperatures even further. Warmer temperatures create high pressure systems which, in turn, block storms from coming into the area. Drought begets drought.

"Drought is a natural part of cyclical weather patterns in North America," says Oglesby. "Physical clues about ancient weather, such as tree rings and lake sediment cores, show that dry spells such as the Dust Bowl and a similar drought in the 1950s typically occur a few times per century. The historical record also reveals a 'mega-drought,' longer and more severe than any recent episodes, 500 or so years ago."

So while the ongoing dry spell is not as severe as the Dust Bowl of the 1930s, the S.W. U.S. got a real taste of what would happen if a La Niña pattern got locked in for a decade or so. And burgeoning population has greatly increased demands on the water supply, which accounts for the 80-foot ring around Lake Mead, for example. Climatologists eagerly awaited winter 2004/5, wondering if it would bring much snow, or was the West facing another year of drought.

The answer was reported in the *Rocky Mountain News* on April 2, 2005 by Jerd Smith in a story titled **2005 snowpack signals light at end of drought's tunnel.** In the story, he quoted the words of state climatologist Roger Pielke Sr., "Colorado's snowpack rose above average April 1 for the first time in seven years, signaling an endpoint in the drought. From a precipitation deficit standpoint, the state has recovered. Still, 20 percent of Colorado remains dry enough to qualify as drought-stricken, but that's down dramatically from the 85 percent of lands so classified in 2002. However, Colorado's largest population center, the Front Range, remains dry, although it is improving."

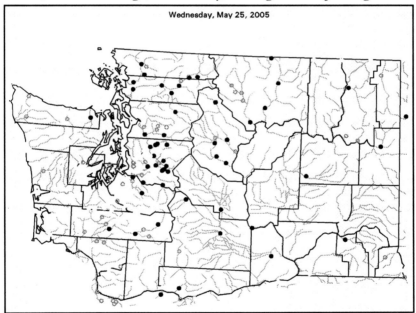

Wednesday, May 25, 2005

Pielke cautioned, "Droughts are, by definition, difficult to predict and characterize. And if you're in the 20 percent of the state that remains dry, then it isn't over for you."

The website of the Natural Resources Conservation Service reports the April 1 snowpack as a percentage of normal: Gunnison – 127%, Arkansas River Basin – 112%, Upper Rio Grande River Basin – 140%, San Juan Mountains – 138% and Statewide – 107%. Looks like the SW dodged a bullet in 2005. Up here in the Pacific NW, however, we're still deep in drought, as the map shows, for the 7 days ending March 25, 2005. Each black dot represents a stream or river that's flowing at less than one-quarter capacity, some below 5 percent normal, so we're looking for the next La Niña year.

Earth Changes – Fire

The 2004/2005 record-breaking rainfall in the SW was great for agriculture, but paved the way for a far more serious risk. Heavy winter and spring rain meant extreme ground cover that the warm spring temperatures dry, providing ample tinder for lightning strikes to start wildfires.

On May 25, 2005, a brush fire broke out near Palm Springs, CA, and threatened a windmill farm. Riverside County Fire Department and CDF scrambled a helicopter, air attack plane, and an air-tanker that stomped out the 50-acre blaze in an hour. However, Capt. Doug Cade said, "We're not looking forward to the season. We never have grass on the hills, but this year we have twelve inches. It just makes for a nightmare."

He was right. The average acre normally has 300 pounds of groundcover, but the SW went into the long, hot summer with 3,000 pounds per acre—10 times normal. So while Spring 2005 was an excellent growing season across the West, summer 2005 turned out to be a year to remember in terms of 'the West burning.'

By June 30, 2005, the so-called Duzak fire had consumed a whopping 280,700 acres, cutting a huge swath across Southern Nevada, and confining 'at risk' residents of Las Vegas to their homes. The authorities issued 'unhealthful air' warnings for the entire population. Elsewhere in the state, dozens of smaller fires had consumed hundreds of thousands of acres, sparked by dry lightning storms. Meanwhile, near Phoenix, AZ, the Black Canyon blaze charred almost 200,000 acres and threatened four communities plus Interstate 17, the main artery between Phoenix and Flagstaff to the north.

The 2012 Countdown

We end this chapter by recalling the theme of Chapter 5 on Ancient Wisdom. The following article by Will Hart appeared on the website of The Daily Grail [www.dailygrail.com/node/861] and is reproduced here with permission.

After 25 years of research and at several key breakthroughs I decided to publish my findings regarding the Maya (2012) Long Count calendar. I wrote two articles that were published in *Atlantis Rising*, in which I predicted an upsurge of natural disasters.

There are two aspects of the Maya cosmology and calendar system that one needs to know to make any sense out of my work:

1. They had a cyclical view of time and of solar output. In other words they saw history moving through a circle of ages that they called Suns. In their system we are in the 5th Sun. The 4th Sun was said to have ended in a deluge, the 5th would end with mounting earthquakes, that is why they called it the Sun-of-Motion or Wind.

2. Venus also plays a key role in the Maya cosmology. This fact long puzzled researchers, including this author, until I made the right scientific connections.

Several yeas ago I was examining the sunspot cycle and realized that the next solar maximum will come in 2012. That seemed a pretty striking coincidence. I had done research into the sunspot cycle and its relation to many different types of cycles on Earth including human behavior.

It seemed to me that the Maya solar-priests were on to something. One could wonder how they could so well calculate their complex calendar systems to synchronize the sunspot cycle with their 2012 end date, when sunspots were only discovered in the 17th century.

My research took a new course.

My gut had long told me that sunspots and natural disasters were linked. It stands to reason. Solar physicists track solar activity on a daily basis because X-flares, sunspots, etc. can increase the solar wind, which can disrupt the earth's magnetic field and cause radio and telecommunications storms.

Is it such a quantum leap to assume that these bursts of high particle energy also impact the earth and human beings in a variety of ways? Nonetheless, what I found still surprised me, a definite link between solar maxima and natural disasters.

I know that Gilbert and Cottrel discovered that the sunspot cycle was embedded in the Maya calendar. But they did not make the link between solar maxima and natural disasters and that is a big part of the 2012 forecast.

There is another key factor. The Mayan model suggested that solar output swings up and down in long-term activity/rest cycles. It was only within the last 3 months that a scientific study confirmed this, and the findings have stunning implications.

When the researchers found that our Sun has been more active over the past 70 years than at any time in the last 8,000 years, the puzzle pieces started to fit together. I went back through the studies of the 11-year sunspot cycle and found a rather startling fact staring back at me in the data. In 1640, following the second leg of the (1631-1639) transit(s) of Venus, the sunspot cycle dropped to zero and stayed there for 70 years.

That period is known as "the little ice age." Then in about 1710, sunspots appeared again and the solar activity level climbed to peak in 1960 when about 190 sunspots were counted. Now, is it a coincidence that this increasing solar output has been accompanied by a warming trend?

That is not all that has accompanied the steep rise in solar activity that has been taking place since the 1930s. Natural disasters have been surging since 1960. In fact, seven out of ten of the largest earthquakes that rattled the 20th century occurred after 1960. The next finding was really more of a shock to me since I have studied the Maya calendar since 1980. While looking through astronomical tables three years ago, I stumbled upon the table showing the transits of Venus.

Sure enough, the next pair of transits came in June 2004 and December 21, 2012. The latter date is the precise end of the 5th Sun according the Maya.

I cannot go into all the details and volumes of data that I've been pouring through these past few years. The upshot is that I decided to write about a steep rise in natural disasters partially due to the June transit. The recent wave began in July 2004.

This is not Y2K smoke and mirrors garbage. I have never written an article before predicting anything. I also made similar predictions based upon the models derived from the Maya calendar, on Whitley Strieber's radio show the month before the earthquake and tsunami. These assertions can be documented.

There is far more to this than a simple cosmic alignment and a global transformation into a new age of spiritual enlightenment. The Sun and the earth are going through massive shifts right now and these birth pangs are not going to be painless or stress free.

My interpretation of the Maya term "Passage of Venus" and the fact they embedded the transit of Venus into the calendar is that we are in the 2004-2012 window now. Venus is the key.

Will it trigger the solar off switch and shut down the sunspot cycle again?

On May 27, 2005, I posted a relevant article on the ECTV website titled **Mayan Prophecy and Modern Science**.

Much has been said about our ancestors' accuracy of today's time. What was mentioned hundreds and even thousands of years ago is proving itself by scientific facts right here, right now, and in our lifetime.

Just ten or twenty years ago, would we ever have considered the weather phenomena we are witnessing today? For those less aware of scientific discoveries and ongoing research, I would say this time frame would be more accurate to reflect a very short period of maybe the last 18 – 24 months.

What appears to be shocking news of "unexpected and unusual" solar events such as the most recent event of January 20, 2005 of which NASA said, *"The most intense burst of solar radiation in five decades accompanied a large solar flare on January 20, shaking space weather theory and highlighting the need for new forecasting techniques. This flare produced the largest solar radiation signal on the ground in nearly 50 years,"* said Dr. Richard Mewaldt of the California Institute of Technology in Pasadena, a co-investigator on NASA's Advanced Composition Explorer (ACE) spacecraft. *"But we were really surprised when we saw how fast the particles reached their peak intensity and arrived at Earth."*

[Full Article: www.earthchangestv.com/secure/2005/article_8046.php]

Then of course we have almost every single day a new report of "record-breaking" temperatures, or floods, or snow, or hail, or sandstorms, or hurricanes, or tornadoes, or drought, and the list goes on and on. In short, the Earth is experiencing extreme weather changes, the like of which has not been seen in at least two generations, and in many cases centuries.

Does this tell us we must be doing something wrong? Well some would like to think so, however, science tells us a different story. We see from ice and lake bottom sediment cores, and tree ring samples that the Earth has indeed experienced very similar events many times before. But guess what. The current extreme changes we see today, and most likely will certainly escalate, are actually at the lower end of significance compared to larger more extreme shifts of the past. It appears the science of cycles holds the most accuracy and authority in defining historical data and future events. And guess what. It appears most of our ancient text and cultures rely most heavily on the prophecy of specific events which our outlined in documents such as the Mayan Calendar, the Bible, Hopi petroglyphs, Dead Sea Scrolls, Egyptian hieroglyphs, and many other ancient recordings. The bases for their historical data is the reference of cycles. Cycles of the past … and cycles yet to come.

Yes, it is true. Many in the scientific community do, in fact, reference and factor in ancient text into current trends and even future projections. And yes, many of the major scientific bodies such as NASA, NOAA, Space Weather Center and (shhh, don't tell anybody, but our Military and National Defense) are included and do indeed utilize what our ancestors had recorded, much of which tells us of our current times today.

I can't tell you how exciting it is for me to be part of this once in a lifetime experience of witnessing and actually participating in the uniting of the (old) ancient text and the (new) science. On some of our older websites, we used to have on our front page from 1997 to 2001 the statement: "Here on Earth Changes TV, we build the bridge between science and the esoteric." I have since dropped the word 'esoteric' because it lends itself to certain belief systems that are not consistent with our premise. Since 2001, I used the phrase "ancient text."

I will often interchange 'ancient text' with 'our ancestors.' This best defines what I believe we are witnessing in this very moment.

Will There Even BE Life after Earth Changes

This chapter is titled "Life after Earth Changes," but is it possible that there would *be* no life, or *no life as we know it?* We've seen how asteroids did a number on the dinosaurs about 60 mya, and a number on almost *everything* about 220 mya. However, these events are extremely rare, and the growing number of 'asteroid watchers' improves our chances of spotting an extinction-threatening near-Earth object (except for sneaky ones that approach the Southern Hemisphere, where there are fewer watchers and observatories).

More likely are events that don't erase all life on the planet, but dramatically change the climate, and in turn change civilizations. Yellowstone National Park, for example, is an active caldera, and getting more active every day. Is there a precedent for what could happen up there? Yes. Let's take a trip back in time.

What Happened in 1650 BCE? Earth's Dark Age

Around the year 1650 BCE, several of the world's major civilizations mysteriously vanished:

- Egypt's Middle Kingdom fell to nomadic Asiatic plunderers called the Hyksos and remained under the conquerors until the New Kingdom asserted itself and restored control about 1550 BCE. What happened that rendered the Egyptians vulnerable to attack? We don't know because there was no documentation or record kept for that missing century?

- Bands of Indo-Europeans named Hittites swept down through Asia Minor, conquering and settling a vast area, from which they attacked the powerful Babylonian empire, ending the great Hammurabi Dynasty and plunging the region into a Dark Age that lasted until 1500 BCE.

- The sophisticated Harappan civilization, dating back to 3100 BCE, in the lush Indus Valley was wiped out by bands of marauding Aryans, sweeping down from Europe. All cities were either destroyed or abandoned, but no record exists of the Aryan occupation—another Dark Age.

- The highly advance Minoan civilization, based on the island of Crete simply vanished overnight, leaving few traces that it had ever existed.

Three other mysteries also hinge on this landmark date:
- In China, the powerful Xia Dynasty suddenly fell for reasons unknown, and the Shang Dynasty took control.
- In England, the huge monoliths of Stonehenge were regularly adjusted to remain in synch with the Sun's position, but this activity mysteriously stopped around 1650 BCE.
- Across the Atlantic, the Andean city of Caral had been occupied since 3000 BCE, as a religious and administrative center, and was mysteriously abandoned around 1650 BCE, leaving the way open for the rise of the Inca.

What single major planetary event could have plunged Earth's civilizations into chaos, leaving them vulnerable to invasion? We got a clue in August 1883. The eruption of Krakatoa, Indonesia, ejected more than six cubic miles of rock, ash and pumice, and generated the loudest sound ever recorded by human ears, being heard up to 3,000 miles distant across the Indian Ocean. Ash fell as far away as 5,000 miles and created such spectacular atmospheric vivid red sunsets that people in U.S. routinely called out the fire department. It also lowered global temperatures by over one degree for five years. Tsunamis of about 120 feet high killed over 36,000 people and wiped out 165 coastal villages. Traveling at over 300 mph, the wave reached Aden in 12 hours, a distance of 3,800 miles. The air pressure wave circulated the planet for five days after the explosion, going around as many as seven times. The volcano spewed rafts of floating pumice, thick enough to support men and animals, which crossed the Indian Ocean in 10 months, and were still afloat two years after the eruption. However, Krakatoa pales in comparison with the explosion in 1650 BCE of the Mediterranean island of Thera (today named Santorini).

Thera, about 10 miles in diameter, was a major seaport of the vast, thriving, sea-going Minoan civilization, based on the island of Crete just to the south. That year, in the eruption of Thera's volcano, almost the entire island exploded in one of the largest events in the last 10,000 years. The blast ejected about 7 cubic miles of magma as high as 25 miles, and generated a large tsunami. Ash fell over the eastern Mediterranean and Turkey, and remained in the atmosphere long enough to cause a global climate change. But, as with Krakatoa, that was just Act One. Things got really interesting after that.

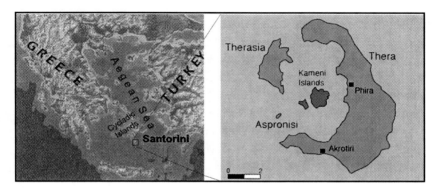

The ejection of such a large volume of magma caused the volcano to implode into its own caldera. Billions of tons of sea water poured into the huge opening, which the remaining magma turned to steam. The resulting explosion created a mega-tsunami, which devastated the entire Mediterranean region, especially the Greek Islands, ending the Minoan civilization in seconds.

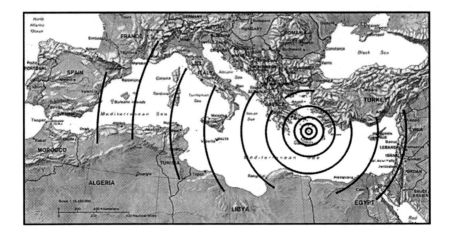

To the north, tsunamis estimated at 500 – 1,000 feet high (*ten to twenty times* the height of waves in 2004's S.E. Asia event) raced up the Aegean Sea, wiping out hundreds of coastal villages and reaching far up into the mountains of Turkey and Greece. They may even have crashed over the land bridge into the Black Sea.

To the east, the waves traveled unimpeded over Cyprus, to the coasts of today's Syria, Lebanon and Israel, going far inland to swamp the Jordan Valley and down behind the Sinai Peninsula.

To the south, Crete was destroyed almost immediately, and the waves then had a clear shot of the coasts of Libya and Egypt, over-running the low-lying Nile Delta, along with Alexandria, hitting up against the mountains of the Sinai Peninsula, meeting up with the flood waters coming down the Jordan Valley.

To the west, they roared unimpeded into Sicily and the toe of Italy, and swamped Tunisia's coastline. Then on to Corsica and Sardinia, and finally expending themselves against the mountains of Spain and France. Whether they managed to get out into the Atlantic is unknown.

All told, this disaster could have wiped out, or at least disrupted, half the world's population of the day in just hours, the Mediterranean being the planet's most heavily populated area. The volcanic winter would have resulted in crop failure for several years, leading to massive numbers of deaths due to starvation.

The chaos following the tsunami would have left a huge vacuum in the defenses of all impacted civilizations, which could easily have been exploited by hordes of invaders from the north, who had not been impacted by the catastrophe. History records that the invasions actually *did* happen but they are not well-documented because no one was around to document them, certainly not the illiterate invaders themselves. (The Roman Empire, scrupulous documenters of everything, was still a thousand years in the future.)

Could it happen today? Sure. There are plenty of volcanoes surrounded by water that could explode the entire island to create the first tsunami, and then implode into itself to create the steam explosion triggering the second, much larger tsunami. Of course, we would have some warning via seismic events, in the same way that the 1995 eruption of Mt. St. Helens was no real surprise.

Another Culture Killer

Slower but just as deadly as volcanoes are climate changes that render civilizations untenable. In a *Science* article titled **How Climate Change Kills Societies**, writer Becky Ham points out that just as the colonists were trying to establish the first permanent English settlement in the New World on Roanoke Island in 1587, they were confronted with the region's worst drought in 700 years. Conflict over meager resources aggravated their relations with the local Native Americans, and by 1590, the ill-fated colony had vanished without a trace.

Over the past 12,000 years, Earth's civilizations have staggered under droughts that have persisted for centuries. Was it drought that caused the Maya to abandon their huge cities? Or how about the ancient Akkadian Empire in Mesopotamia (today's Iraq)? Established around 2300 BCE, the Akkadian Empire extended from the Persian Gulf north into Turkey, and was heavily agrarian, with sophisticated irrigation Then, almost overnight, the empire collapsed. Was severe drought responsible for its demise?

According to archeological digs, we know that around 2170 BCE, a mass influx arrived from the north, where settlements were abandoned, covered by a thick layer of windblown dust. Core samples from the Gulf of Oman also indicate drought and a 300-year period of windblown dust that originated in Mesopotamia. Atlantic deep-sea cores suggest that the ocean cooled (we know that this affects the jet stream), which guided rain storms away from Mesopotamia and halved rainfall totals.

Two thousand years later, on the other side of the world, the Tiwanaku (Tiahuanaco) culture in South America may have faced a similar fate. Between 300 BCE – 1100 CE, the Tiwanaku were a society in south Peru on the Altiplano about 12,500 feet above sea level. (The enormous stone buildings of Tiahuanaco were already ancient ruins when the Tiwanaku arrived.) The Tiwanaku Empire developed through military conquests, farming, fishing and herding, and Lake Titicaca was their main water source. Their social complexity was beyond that of any other society of its time, but suddenly, about the year 1100, the cities and fields were abruptly abandoned.

Was drought responsible for the Tiwanaku collapse? Apparently so. The ice core from 125 miles from Lake Titicaca reveals the start of an increasingly dry spell around the same time, which lasted several centuries, while Lake Titicaca itself suffered a 33-foot drop in level.

The obvious question is: If it happened again today, how would we respond? The 1930s American Dust Bowl drought lasted only six years, yet it devastated a generation. Perhaps the next hot career should be 'weather engineer.' We may need them sooner than we think.

Chapter 15

Preparing for Earth Changes – Physically and Emotionally

Surviving a disaster actually begins long before there is even a threat. The keys to survival in the event of a catastrophe, be it an annoying power outage to TEOTWAWKI (The End Of The World As We Know It), are *knowledge* and *preparation*.

Do you want to be prepared? Or do you want to be surprised by just how unprepared you actually are?

Preparation for Survival

Preparedness is made up of three basic elements: (1) the survival mindset, (2) material preparation, and (3) skill assessment and acquisition. You must have all three in order to be properly prepared for a crisis situation. You, as an individual, must determine what your risk situations are, and how to prepare for them. You must consider what skills and materials you'll need to survive each of your risk situations; then you'll need to work to acquire them.

The next logical question people ask is: "When am I prepared enough?" The answer is never the same, because each of us has differ-

283

ent situations. You're the only one who can determine when you've prepared enough. Others can help you assess your situations, or recommend goods and gear for a particular risk situation, but only you can determine when you're ready to survive. One way you can make this determination is to test yourself. If you feel you'll need camping skills to make it through a time of crisis, go camping for a few days and see how you make out. Or, if you believe you'll need to pack the car and leave in a hurry, try it. See if you can fit everything in the car you thought you'd be able to, and see how long it takes. If you're happy with the result, then you're prepared. If not, keep working at it until you are.

Preparedness is a mindset that must become a part of your life. It shouldn't dominate everything you do, but it should always be in the back of your head. You should approach each situation in life with a few questions, two of which are: "What are the possible risks involved?" and "What information, skills, or materials can I gain from this that will help me get by in risk situations?" Once you begin to look at life from a survivalist's point of view, you'll view many situations differently than you do now. Only after you've practiced using the survival mindset will you truly understand what I'm referring to. But always remember to keep reading, keep learning, and keep stocking up. Prepare for the worst, pray for the best.

So let's hear from three survivalists, beginning with Philip Hoag. Next, I recently posted on the ECTV site an article by Douglas Good, contributor to ECTV, on the concept of survival. Then Bob Gilbert goes into more detail with his article.

Philip Hoag: No Such Things as Doomsday

Philip L. Hoag, author of *No Such Thing as Doomsday: How to prepare for Power Outages, Terrorism, War, and Other Threats*, includes a chapter titled 'Earth Changes,' in which he writes:

> Beyond the threat of man-made disaster is the issue of extreme weather patterns, large-scale natural disasters or cataclysm. The recent buzzword for this category of threat is called 'earth changes.' People tend to view natural disasters as isolated events. They consider them to be one-time anomalies. The concept of earth changes evaluates events in relation to the wider spectrum of earth's meteorological and geological history. Over the long history of the planet,

changes have been the rule as opposed to the exception. A reality check involves looking at the broader picture. The question is not if events will occur, but when will they occur.

The short span of recorded human history on this planet has been a period of geological and climactic stability. However, scientific evidence clearly shows that on numerous occasions the earth's topography and climate have experienced radical change and the earth's magnetic poles have repositioned. Fossil evidence indicates that the present northern latitudes were previously tropical. Many of today's dry areas were once under sea and the continental masses have moved across the face of the globe. Science confirms that on at least three different occasions, catastrophic events have exterminated the majority of life on this planet.

The idea of earth changes should not be ignored as a possibility. Earth change scenarios include dangers from asteroid impacts, coastal flooding, unusual temperatures, severe earthquakes, volcanoes and extreme surface winds. The impact of such earth change activity could cause a significant reduction in earth's population. If the future materializes any of these events, the need for preparedness, and even below ground sheltering, is obvious.

Extreme Weather Patterns

The frequency of large natural disasters worldwide during the last two years is three times greater than it was twenty years ago. Over the last several years the United States has experienced an increase in extreme weather patterns. The total annual severe thunderstorms between 1991 and 1996 increased from 6,504 to 9,175. According to the National Weather service, the annual total for hailstorms with stones three-quarters of an inch or larger increased from 2,749 to 9,636 between 1984 and 1996.

1998 went on record as the worst year for the planet in terms of large-scale natural disasters. Here in the U.S. we saw the Florida wildfires, the Texas heat wave, the North Dakota floods and a record number of tornadoes. January 21, 1998 was the most violent day on record for tornadoes since 1975 here in the U.S. There were 55 tornadoes in one day, 38 of which were in Arkansas and a total 1,000 for the entire year. We are seeing freak windstorms in unusual places. On several occasions in 1998 the jet stream came down to the Earth's surface in the U.S. with wind speeds of up to 130 mph. World wide, there have been a total of 240 disastrous windstorms and 170 disastrous floods in 1998. The biggest event for 1998 was Hurricane Mitch that hit Central America and killed 9,200 people.

Solar Storms
Cycles of increased sunspot activity occur about every 11 years. Sunspots are building up to an expected peak in the second half of 2000. As the number of sunspots increases, so does solar storm activity. Severe space disturbances are expected in 1999 and 2000. These electromagnetic storms erupt from the Sun and swirl out into space. Solar disturbances can disrupt communications, cause electrical power blackouts and damage satellites. In 1989, a solar storm caused an electrical blackout in Quebec, Canada. There is speculation in some circles that a six-planet alignment that will occur on May 5, 2000 could trigger off the largest occurrence of solar flares in the past 60,000 years. An extreme eruption of solar flares could expose the earth to a dangerous proton bombardment. The concern here is that such a bombardment would disable the immune systems of humans and animals. One theory suggests that such a solar flare occurrence caused the disappearance of dinosaurs from the planet. Humans and animals with greatly depressed immune systems would succumb to diseases that are not normally life threatening.

Earthquakes
The frequency of earthquakes on the planet has been increasing since the 10th century AD. During the course of recorded history, earthquakes have killed an estimated 74,000,000 people. Seismic activity has been steadily increasing on the planet over the last two hundred years. Earthquakes have become a more frequent part of life during the last two decades. For many Californians, the specter of the 'big one' continually lurks in the shadowy recesses of the subconscious mind. When we look at the threat of earth quakes, the question is not whether or not they will occur but rather when and where will they occur. I say this not from the position of being a fatalist but from a position of geological/scientific reality.

Douglas Good: What is Survivalism?

This is a commonly asked question, with no easy answer. *Survivalism* has many facets, and takes many forms. It means something different to everyone. Keep this in mind as I attempt to give you my best answer to this famous question.

The Survival Mindset

At its most basic level, survivalism is a mindset with the goal of keeping an individual alive through adverse circumstances. These circumstances could be lots of things, from a devastating flood or earthquake to a nuclear attack or civil war.

Each survivalist has a mental list of *risk situations* that he or she has determined to be a possible threat. These threats could vary from *imminent* to *slight*. In any case, there is a chance of the risk situation occurring. The difference between a survivalist and any other person is that the survivalist has considered the threatening situations and has taken steps to prepare in case they occur, whereas others have chosen to ignore the situations, or don't perceive them as threatening.

It's probably easier to give examples to illustrate my point. Let's say I live in Iraq. With only a few moments of thought, I can come up with a list of things that threaten my survival—war, famine, drought, terrorism, and earthquakes.

Now that I've determined the risk situations, I need to figure out which are most likely to occur, and which are less likely, so I rank them like so:

1. Drought
2. Terrorism
3. War
4. Earthquakes
5. Famine

The above list is in order of *probability*, not *severity* of the threat. In other words, I would be more afraid if my country broke out in a war than if we had a drought, but I believe the chances of a drought occurring are far greater than chances of a war breaking out.

Now that I have a list of risk situations, in order of probability of occurrence, I can make preparations in case one or more of them occurs.

Once you understand the thought process that the above example shows, you understand the *"survivalist mindset."* You've assessed your risks and are now ready to prepare for them. How you prepare is up to you. The fact that you are preparing makes you a survivalist.

Material Preparation

One motto of the survivalist is "Prepare for the worst, pray for the best." Each person must determine how they will prepare, and what lengths and expense they will go to with their preparation.

For some people, keeping a week's worth of canned goods and a kerosene heater around the house may be their way of preparing for a blizzard. For others, they may want not only the food and the heater, but a snowmobile, as well. Still others may decide that if it looks like a terrible snowstorm, they'll take a trip to their house in a warmer climate before it hits. In each example above, the person perceived the blizzard as a threat. The lengths they would go to were all different. The first person decided extra food and a second heat source were enough, while the last person has a second location to escape to.

No one can tell you how you should prepare for a disaster, because all of us have different situations we must take into account. The important thing is that you assess your threats, and determine how you can prepare for them if they occur. You must do what you feel is necessary. If you feel comfortable knowing that a week's worth of food and water is stocked up in your kitchen, you're prepared. If you buy a house in, you're prepared.

Many survivalists pick the worst possible scenario to prepare for. Others choose to prepare for moderate occurrences of their risk situations. Often times, preparing for the worst involves a lot of time and money. As with all other aspects of survivalism, to what level each individual prepares is up to them. I may feel comfortable with a week's supply of food on hand, you may want enough for a month. Or a year. It's an individual choice that only you can make.

Skill Assessment and Acquisition

Preparation doesn't only involve acquiring material items, but also means acquiring the skills you need to survive. Anyone can buy material goods and "survival gear." But if you don't have the skills and knowledge necessary to use that gear, your chances of survival in any type of crisis lessen substantially. Two examples illustrate my point:

One man lives in the city, and feels that one of his risk situations is rioting. In order for him to survive, he feels he'll have to leave his apartment and get to his "safe house," which is a friend's place in the country 75 miles away. Our second person lives in the country, and feels his primary risk situation is loss of electricity during a storm or blizzard.

In the first case, the city dweller may need to travel on foot for those 75 miles if the streets are blocked with traffic and rioters. The skills he'll need are navigation, hiking, outdoor cooking, stealth, and possibly caching for storing food along the way. He'll also need to plan several travel routes to his destination in case one is in a particularly bad state. He'll need to consider that the riot could happen at any time of the year, so cold weather survival skills could come into play.

Our second example has a different situation. He feels that a power loss is his biggest threat, so the skills he'll need revolve around that. He should know how to cook over a fire, how to preserve food without a refrigerator, how to use oil lamps and kerosene heaters to keep warm during winter, and he should have an alternate water supply set up so he can get water into his home without using an electric pump.

In these two examples, both survivalists need knowledge and skills that are unique to their situations. After you determine what your risk situations are, and begin stocking up on supplies for them, you need to assess your skills and learn what you feel you need to know.

Conclusion

Survivalism, as I see it, is made up of three basic elements: (1) the survival mindset, (2) material preparation, and (3) skill assessment and acquisition. You must have all three in order to be properly prepared for a crisis situation. You, as an individual, must determine what your risk situations are, and how to prepare for them. You must consider what skills and materials you'll need to survive each of your risk situations; then you'll need to work to acquire them.

The next logical question people ask is: "When am I prepared enough?" The answer is never the same, because each of us has different situations. You're the only one who can determine when you've prepared enough. Others can help you assess your situations, or recommend goods and gear for a particular risk situation, but only you can determine when you're ready to survive. One way you can make this determination is to test yourself. If you feel you'll need camping skills to make it through a time of crisis, go camping for a few days and see how you make out. Or, if you believe you'll need to pack the car and leave in a hurry, try it. See if you can fit everything in the car you thought you'd be able to, and see how long it takes. If you're happy with the result, then you're prepared. If not, keep working at it until you are.

Survivalism is a mindset that must become a part of your life. It shouldn't dominate everything you do, but it should always be in the back of your head. You should approach each situation in life with a few questions, two of which are: "What are the possible risks involved?" and "What information, skills, or materials can I gain from this that will help me get by in risk situations?" Once you begin to look at life from a survivalists point of view, you'll view many situations differently than you do now. Only after you've practiced using the survival mindset will you truly understand what I'm referring to. But always remember to keep reading, keep learning, and keep stocking up. Prepare for the worst, pray for the best.

Bob Gilbert: Disaster Preparations at Home

Why? Oh, how about floods, tornadoes, blizzards, etc. Electric power goes down, phone communications quit, no water, possibly no fuel and no help on the horizon for at least some time.

Won't happen with modern technology, you say? Bet me. Just recently here in Minnesota and the surrounding states, we have been hit by repeated blizzards. Power lines have been done for more than a week. People are trapped in their houses (or at least on their own property) for days. People are stranded in vehicles for 40 plus hours before being found, etc. Not a lot of fun with a wind chill of -80 to -90 degrees. For those of you who can't imagine the situation, the snow was blowing so strong and the white-out was so complete that people were disoriented and got lost within a couple hundred yards of places with which they were familiar.

A few years ago, the company that I work for sent me to Missouri to assist local telephone workers during massive flooding. Power was out over areas serving many tens of thousands of homes, only in isolated places did phones still work. Think a cellular phone is the answer? Sorry, the cell antennas require power to pick up your call and pass it on. And a cell phone will only reach a couple miles max. I found people living on the top floor of 2-story houses, and in houses on a hill totally cut off from anywhere else by the water.

Medical assistance? In our last storm, one doctor, attempting to reach a woman needing a cesarean delivery, required two snow plows to escort him and even then, it took him 8 hours to get 40 miles. Many people had to settle for local first aid.

I was in San Francisco when they had their big earthquake (1989). Food supplies were disrupted in some areas for over a week. Some places had no gas, electricity or water for several weeks.

So preparation is something that all of us should keep in mind. Being prepared is not something suitable only for those waiting for TEOTWAWKI (The End of the World As We Know It). Things to consider fall into seven areas: 1. Shelter; 2. Food; 3. Heat; 4. First Aid; 5. Clothing; 6. Protection; and 7. Communication.

Shelter

I listed this first as it is often vital. If you are cold and/or wet, it is difficult to collect your thoughts, organize and get the rest you will need to survive. In some disasters, lack of shelter will kill you straight off.

My home, as do most in Minnesota, has a basement. We have a reinforced 'gathering corner' down there, away from any glass and likely to survive the collapse of the house (verified by the architect). It also has an escape hole which I installed. In this corner are stored supplies of water, food, a first-aid kit, pack of dry clothes (sealed), flashlights, a couple of hurricane lamps, radio, batteries, etc. Also a small toolkit of essentials and a pry bar. In case we have to abandon the house, each of the two major family vehicles has a first aid kit, winter survival kit, small tool box, flashlights, etc.

Go to a hotel, you say? One may not be available and even if it is, you may not be able to get to it.

Ready to grab at home we also keep a lock-box with some cash and valuable papers, such as copies of insurance policies. A copy of those valuable papers is kept at a relative's house some distance away.

Food

We buy canned goods and paper goods by the case and store in the basement. Don't tell me you can't afford it. Just takes discipline. I and my wife have been doing this since we were poor newlyweds. We also do home canning and drying. I have a large and a small freezer always full. Probably overkill. We could probably last 6 months at least with no worries. After that I'd have enough of everything except meat for another six months. I would suggest that a family keep at least a couple of weeks' worth of food in the house.

Beans and cornbread might get old but they will keep you alive. Not that we would have to 'rough it.' If the house is intact, we have the stuff and know-how to make candies, pizza, and other goodies that make life good. We have always been ones who enjoyed made-from-scratch stuff. Cooking? Natural gas stove. If that fails, electric pans. If that fails, Coleman oven with spare fuel. If that fails, coal barbeque pit. If that fails, homemade wood burner.

Water? I'm on a well system but also keep 3 five-gallon containers in the basement, 5 gallons in the shed and have installed a 200-gallon water tank behind the house, kept full by an electric pump. It has a hand pump attached in case there is no power. I flush this tank regularly.

For extended periods of water outage due to power loss, I have both a portable hand powered pump and a battery powered pump (12v car battery) on hand, a nearby lake, a cart with a water tank. The cart is actually used for my gardening but I have a 30-gallon plastic, inflatable water tank to fit it and a portable filtration system I made to attach.

Heat

Natural gas forced air furnace. If the electricity fails I have a small 2kw generator. I modified the electrical hook up to the furnace so that the cable bringing 120v power to it terminates in a standard male plug. This is plugged into a female receptacle at the furnace. I make a double male extension cord for the generator. Cheap arrangement. If the power fails, I unplug the normal power at the furnace. Start the generator and plug it into the furnace. The old plug has a cover in case normal power is restored. The generator is large enough to power the fan on the furnace. It also has enough extra juice for me to run an extension to give limited light and power a radio or TV. I keep 30 gallons of fuel in various sized containers in a shed away from the house and have buried an extra 20 gallons.

No natural gas? I keep two kerosene heaters and 30 gallons of kerosene in the shed, along with kerosene-burning hurricane lamps. I also have about 30 lb. of assorted candles. You would be surprised at how warm you can keep one room of a house, even in Minnesota, with very little heat. One winter when power was lost and a blizzard was blowing, I decided to wait till morning to fire off the generator. I brought everyone into one bedroom, covered the windows with a vapor barrier (sheet plastic), and kept the door closed to the rest of the house. At -24 degrees outside, with 40 mph winds blowing, the body heat of four of us in a sealed room kept it above 50 degrees. Comfy sleeping!

**I always keep rolls of heavy mil sheet plastic around ... great stuff!

First Aid

I keep current in my certification as a First Responder. All members of my family have had first aid training. Besides the first aid kits for emergencies in the basement and vehicles, we have a main first aid kit in the house, loaded with everything—gauze, bandages, disinfectants, scissors, pain pills, antibiotics, etc. A comprehensive first aid book serves in case I can't remember something (or I'm the victim).

We rotate from the stored kits to the main kit as things are used. I don't know what will work for you but we have a sympathetic doctor who, once a year, fills a prescription for me for antibiotics. He knows why I want them and gives me the old lecture about their use. I don't load the kits with a lot of fancy appliances, as I don't want to spend the money nor do I see the need for fancy collars, inflatable splints and such. Anyone who cannot figure out how to make a sling or splint out of any handy materials should probably just stick to Band-Aids.

Clothing

We keep a full set of cold weather clothing in water proof packaging in the basement and in each car—thermal underwear, heavy shirts and pants, boots with extra liners, gloves, socks, hats, face masks. If it is warm outside you just put on less. With these are an assortment of blankets and sleeping bags.

Protection

I have installed lots of outside lighting, and steel doors with deadbolts. It's a rural area where everyone knows everyone else and keeps an eye on their neighbors (neighbors are very important). I have three unfriendly dogs. Yes, I know a grown man can kill a dog but these aren't attack dogs. However, they won't let anyone or anything within a hundred yards (even when they are indoors) without raising a ruckus. The alarm system has panic buttons with battery back-up which flashes lights. A very loud set of sirens outside alerts neighbors. My wife and son are trained with pistols to shoot and keep on shooting, reloading if necessary, until whoever it is stops twitching. I am not into assault weapons, and see no need. A .22 rifle and pistol for small game hunting, plus two very good pellet rifles for target practice and varmint dispatch, .308 bolt action rifle for larger hunting, 410 and 12-gauge shotguns, also for hunting. A shortened pump action 12-gauge with 3-inch magnums, and a double ought serve in case I don't like whoever it is who trying to pay me a visit—looters, IRS agents and other no-good types. ;-). (To any federal types reading this, send in the local deputy sheriff first. I know them and will talk first. One of them is a neighbor, I'd probably have a hard time shooting him. Decent guy with a wife & kids.)

Communications

As you may have gathered, I work for a phone company. So if it is possible at the time, I know how to fix phone lines. I also maintain CB radios in each vehicle, and a base CB in the house. I have an amateur tech radio license and a ham transceiver. I also have a very capable scanner that picks up most things, including the "illegal to monitor" bands. In addition, several battery powered radios, including shortwave are scattered about, including a battery powered TV.

Miscellaneous

Besides the 120v generator, I keep a 1350 cranking amp, deep draw marine battery charged. It is trickle charged from the commercial power source so that it is always ready. In a couple of spots about the house I have installed 12v outlets. This is used to provide additional means to power the radios and battery-powered TV. I also have on hand a couple of 12v lamps to plug in. The battery can be kept charged by my portable generator or by a car. I rigged up a special battery cable to hook to a running car on one end, and on the other end, clamps to plug into the big battery to charge it.

In the back of my property, I have buried a section of 3-foot diameter drainage pipe, sealed on both ends. It has a removable cap and is water tight. This cache is used to store dry and canned food, a toolbox, clothes, and other necessities in case the whole house goes. Fire, flood, etc.

We have a trailer permanently placed on a lake, way out in yonder country, as a summer fishing and vacation place and as a bug out spot if that should ever be necessary. It is completely stocked. In addition, we have a complete camping set packed and ready to be loaded in minutes if needed. It's not just for a bug-out. If a tornado blows the house away, we are ready to set up temporary lodging … plus we enjoy camping.

Thoughts

Finally, the most important tools to survival are knowledge and the skills to use it.

By profession I do heating and air-conditioning repair, electrical power repair, alarm systems repair, plumbing, locksmithing, carpentry, electrical generator repair and so on for a telephone company. By way of hobbies, I do repairs, upgrades and programming of PCs; small engine repair; amateur electronics; ham radio; welding; vegetable gardening; home canning; food drying; fishing; hunting; camping and hiking. I also fill in on an as needed basis for a local emergency response squad. I am a pack rat and gatherer of 'stuff.' In my shed are tools for virtually any type of job, lumber, metal stock, rolls of electrical wire, cable, chain, hose and rope, plus virtually every type of electrical fitting, nail, screw, bolt, hose fitting, tubing fitting and pipe fitting needed.

It may seem like a lot but flea markets and garage sales are wonderful things. The cost is not nearly what you imagine. The 2kw generator, for instance was sold to me as broken. It required about $15 in parts and the time expended in a tune up to put it in operation.

Family and friends used to make fun but after uncounted times of them calling and my being able to fix the problem, they no longer laugh. One of the reasons I view the Internet as such a valuable resource is that it provides an almost unlimited access to a world of knowledge—a survivor's best friend.

Used with permission on the Project EPSILON Survival Page
http://www.ezonline.com/ditto/index.html

The Red Cross: Survival Experts

Now let's turn to the Red Cross—the organization that really knows about dealing with earth changes, but before we do, there are some important things that many people overlook. First, remember your pets because they depend totally on you for their survival and may be in panic-mode if they don't know what's going on, so always factor them into your plans. And second, if you're a computer user, have all irreplaceable data already backed up on CD-ROM, with the disks in a place where you can grab them quickly in the event of immediate evacuation.

Finally, get into survivalist mode. With this country's seismic and meteorological instability, you never know what's going to happen. And planes fall out of the sky, trains and tanker trucks carrying hazardous materials crash, and chemical plants blow up. Get Murphy's Law firmly in your mind: "The worst possible thing can happen at the worst possible time." You want to *watch* it on the news, not be *part* of the news.

Red Cross Preparedness Check List

Disasters happen anytime and anywhere. And when disaster strikes, you may not have much time to respond. A highway or train wreck, or a hazardous material spill could mean evacuation. A winter storm could confine your family at home. An earthquake, flood, tornado, or any other disaster could cut water, electricity, and telephones ... maybe for days.

After a disaster, local officials and relief workers will be on the scene, but they cannot reach everyone immediately. You could get help in hours, or it may take days. Would your family be prepared to cope with the emergency until help arrives?

Your family will cope best by preparing for disaster before it strikes. One way to prepare is by assembling a Disaster Supplies Kit. Once disaster hits, you won't have time to shop or search for supplies. But if you've gathered supplies in advance, your family can endure an evacuation or home confinement.

Prepare Your Kit

Review the checklist below and gather the supplies that are listed. You may need them if your family is confined at home. Place the supplies you'd most likely need for an evacuation in an easy-to-carry container. These supplies are listed with an asterisk (*).

There are six basics you should stock for your home: water, food, first aid supplies, clothing and bedding, tools and emergency supplies, and special items. Keep the items that you would most likely need during an evacuation in an easy-to carry container—suggested items are marked with an asterisk(*).

Possible containers include a large, covered trash container, a camping backpack or a duffle bag. Keep items in airtight plastic bags. Change your stored water supply every six months so it stays fresh. Replace your stored food every six months. Re-think your kit and family needs at least once a year. Replace batteries, update clothes, etc.

Ask your physician or pharmacist about storing prescription medications.

Water

Store water in plastic containers such as soft drink bottles. Avoid using containers that will decompose or break, such as milk cartons or glass bottles. A normally active person needs to drink at least two quarts of water each day. Hot environments and intense physical activity can double that amount. Children, nursing mothers, and ill people will need more.

Store one gallon of water per person per day, and keep at least a three-day supply of water per person (two quarts for drinking, two quarts for each person in your household for food preparation/sanitation).*

Food

Store at least a three-day supply of non-perishable food. Select foods that require no refrigeration, preparation or cooking, and little or no water. If you must heat food, pack a can of sterno. Select food items that are compact and lightweight.

Include a selection of the following foods in your Disaster Supplies Kit, such as ready-to-eat canned meats, fruits, and vegetables, canned juices, staples (salt, sugar, pepper, spices, etc.), high energy foods, vitamins, and baby formula (if needed).

First Aid Kit

Assemble a first aid kit for your home and one for each car (see ECTV website for contents). Also include **non-prescription drugs such as** aspirin, anti-diarrhea medication, antacid (for stomach upset), and laxative. Keep a smaller version of the Disaster Supplies Kit in the trunk of your car.

For **Tools and Supplies,** Sanitation, Clothing and Bedding, **and** Special Items, see the ECTV website for a link to a suggested list to include.

Important Documents

Keep these in a waterproof, portable container that you can grab in a hurry. Store the container in a convenient place known to all family members.

The list of documents includes: wills, insurance policies, contracts deeds, stocks and bonds, passports, social security cards, immunization records, bank account and credit card account numbers and companies. Also make an inventory of valuable household goods, important telephone numbers. Include also family records (birth, marriage, death certificates)

Specific Threats

Now let's take a look at some specific threats, to see if you're prepared. In all cases, in case disaster occurs when some family members are not home, make sure you have a plan for where to meet, with back-ups in case roads are impassible or bridges are down. Make sure that everyone involved knows the plan, such as babysitters.

Also, learn First Aid and how to operate a fire extinguisher. The middle of a disaster is not the time to be learning basic survival. In all cases, include the Disaster Kit.

Earthquake

They're possible just about anywhere in the U.S. and you get no warning, so pre-select a safe place in every room, such as under a sturdy table or desk or against an inside wall where nothing can fall on you. Then practice DROP – COVER – HOLD ON at least twice a year. Drop under a sturdy desk or table, hold on, and protect your eyes by pressing your face against your arm. If there's no table or desk nearby, sit on the floor against an interior wall away from windows, bookcases, or tall furniture that could fall on you. Teach this to any children, too!

Eliminate hazards, by bolting bookcases, china cabinets, and other tall furniture to wall studs, by installing strong latches on cupboards, and by strapping the water heater to wall studs. Make sure you know the location of the main turn-offs for gas, water and electricity ... and that they are service-able (not painted over and unusable, say).

(When my co-writer owned an older house in San Francisco, he went to the trouble of securing the wooden base to the concrete slab by drilling holes and setting one-foot bolts into quick-drying cement.)

Hurricane

First you need to know that a Hurricane Watch extends out 36 hours, whereas a Warning is usually 24 hours, so the latter is more imminent.

In either case, plan ahead for possible evacuation—a friend's home in another town, a motel, or a shelter. Drive the roads so you know the way—road signs are often the first things to blow away. Plan alternate routes in case downed trees or power lines block your way. Monitor NOAA Weather Radio or local radio or TV stations for evacuation instructions. If advised to evacuate, do so immediately!

If a *warning* is issued, leave if the authorities tell you to do so, otherwise stay indoors, away from windows, and above possible storm surge.

Do not be deceived by the eye. The worst is yet to come because the wind is from the opposite direction, and will use any loose objects as battering rams. Also in the event of a tornado, go to the basement or center of your home, such as a closet or bathroom without windows.

If you're driving, do not try to drive through flood water. Just one foot of water can float the typical vehicle. If you're caught in rising flood water, get out of the car and climb to higher ground immediately.

Tornado

Tornadoes have been reported in every state. And while they generally occur during spring and summer, they can happen anytime during the year. With winds of over 200 mph, they can destroy just about anything in its path. Generally, ominous weather signs and warnings will alert you to the threat.

You may have a few minutes warning or none at all before it's upon you, so prepare in advance. Decide where to gather if a tornado is headed your way, such as a basement, a center hallway, bathroom, or closet on the lowest floor.

A tornado *watch* means a tornado is possible in your area, so listen to local radio and TV stations, and be alert to changing weather conditions. Watch for blowing debris or something that sounds like a freight train. A tornado *warning* means a tornado has been sighted and may be headed for your area, so go to your safe place. If you are outside, hurry to any sturdy building or lie flat in a ditch or low-lying area. If you are in a car or mobile home, get out immediately and head for safety.

Afterwards, watch out for fallen power lines. Turn off gas, water and electricity if necessary.

The Red Cross Disaster Preparedness pages on the ECTV website cover many other types of emergency, so I would suggest visiting those pages and printing them out for later reference.

An Ounce of Prevention ...

Of course, far better than surviving a disaster is to avoid it in the first place ... and there are many ways to do just that.

Let's start with flooding. Building a home or a whole community in a known flood plain is just crazy. Even if it's a 'hundred-year' flood plain, that year could be this one. And the river is not going to wait obediently another century before flooding again. The jet stream that parks itself over the Mississippi basin one year, bringing in one storm after another, could quite easily do exactly the same thing the next year. Some communities are even passing ordinances to block building permits in flood plains

We also need better building codes for the construction of homes and businesses to ensure that they can withstand stronger stresses from earthquakes, tornadoes and hurricanes. When hurricane Andrew devastated South Dade Country on August 24, 1992, it simply removed Homestead from the map, and then took aim at Florida City, then continued northwest across the Gulf of Mexico to strike the Louisiana coastline. The storm caused 15 deaths directly, 25 deaths indirectly and $30-billion in property damage, making it the costliest disaster in U.S history. Many of the houses in Homestead lost their roof because roof trusses were simply stapled together, and not nailed, so that the contractor could make more profit. Project Impact is a FEMA initiative in both hurricane- and tornado-prone areas, providing builders and homeowners with plans and assistance in making homes and buildings more resistant to disasters.

For example, coastal residents are encouraged to raise their homes up on stilts so storm surge waters can pass beneath them. If you live on the outer banks, maximum elevation four feet, and a 20-foot storm surge washes away your house, it makes no sense to rebuild the exact same house in the exact same place, while expecting taxpayers or other insurance policyholders to pay for your stupidity.

According to the president of the Reinsurance Association of America, the earth changes could bankrupt the industry. "With sea levels rising at a rapid rate, there is $2 trillion worth of insured property on the Atlantic and Gulf coasts at risk." It's true: a category 5 hurricane slamming head-on into Miami and then grinding up the coast to Jacksonville could easily do $100 billion in damages, with a huge cost in human life. Or a different track could take out Fort Lauderdale after Miami. (And with a category 5, there's no upper limit to wind speed—it's just a minimum of 156 mph.)

More deadly storms and higher populations mean more disruption and damage For example, recovering from Andrew took Florida a staggering 10 years, and some areas were never rebuilt, such as Homestead AFB, which never reopened after being 97 percent destroyed. However, toxic contamination levels prevented its conversion to any other use ... an issue that's still outstanding.

If the next Solar Maximum delivers higher sunspot activity, and more flares and CMEs, the combination of warmer oceans, higher sea levels from melting glaciers, and increased energy being pumped into the atmosphere could result in a rash of mega-weather events. In that case, everyone's survival skills will be tested, most of all, our adaptability.

To Know or Not Know

Suppose observatories around the world have identified a large aster-oid on a certain collision course with Earth, due to hit one year from now. It will probably impact in the Pacific Ocean, and you live on the coast of California, where the half-mile high tsunami will certainly take your life. Would you want to know? Do you think the authorities are obliged to inform you? Or would you prefer to live out your last year in ignorant bliss?

The topic of disclosure versus omission came up again in the con-text of mentally preparing for earth changes. In an ECTV article titled **My Battle Between 'Disclosure vs. Omission,'** I wrote:

It is my belief ECTV will be sending out what will appear to be extraordinary breaking news which involves 'earth changes.' I feel it is most important to maintain a sense of balance and empowerment. I am aware upcoming articles will be alarming, and there is the risk of setting off inherent defense triggers that every human possesses. It is a necessary 'fight or flight' defense mechanism that is 'hard-wired' into us for our survival. However, it is this very human and compul-sory reflex that can work against us. As a mental health therapist, I know that most of the DSM-IV diagnoses of 'stress and anxiety dis-order' I work with are directly related to over-use or misuse of this very natural reaction to life.

It will be up to each and every one of us to stride toward minimiz-ing—or perhaps better stated, preparing for—events ahead that could trigger distorted cause-and-effect reactions based on past experiences, or on an inability to handle rapid change. It is my belief we will need to practice innate skills and powers of adaptability. It is for this rea-son, I emphasize not placing importance on *where you live*, but *with whom you live.*

With events that may be unfolding in the coming months and years, it will be more important than ever to sharpen our coping skills and survivor instincts. This preparation involves the whole being:
- Physical (basic survival equipment)
- Mental (ability to handle stress, anxiety, fear, bewilderment)
- Spiritual (having a sense of purpose, understanding process, evolution, transition, and synchronicity*).

Something Called PTSD (Post Traumatic Stress Disorder)

Most often there is a connection to past trauma experienced as a child, or later in life as an adult following a shocking and unexpected, traumatic experience, such as being physically attacked, in a serious accident, in combat, sexually assaulted, in a fire, or experiencing a disaster such as a hurricane, earthquake or a tornado. After traumatic experiences, people can find themselves having problems they didn't have before the event.

People who go through traumatic experiences often have symptoms and problems afterwards. How serious the symptoms and problems are depends on many things, including a your life experiences before the trauma, your own natural ability to cope with stress, how serious the trauma was, and what kinds of help and support you get from family, friends, and professionals immediately following the trauma.

Because most trauma survivors don't know how trauma usually affects people, you may have trouble understanding what's happening to you. You may think it's your fault that the trauma happened, that you're going crazy, or that there is something wrong with you because other people who were there don't seem to have the same problems. You may turn to drugs or alcohol to make you feel better. You may turn away from friends and family who don't seem to understand. You may not know what you can do to get better.

Who is most likely to develop PTSD?

1. Those who experience greater stressor magnitude and intensity, unpredictability, uncontrollability, assault, victimization, real or perceived responsibility, and betrayal.

2. Those with prior vulnerability factors such as genetics, early age of onset and longer-lasting childhood trauma, lack of functional social support, and concurrent stressful life events.

3. Those who report greater perceived threat or danger, suffering, upset, terror, and horror or fear.

4. Those with a social environment that produces shame, guilt, stigmatization, or self-hatred.

What Are the Consequences associated with PTSD?

PTSD is associated with a number of distinctive neurobiological and physiological changes. PTSD may be associated with stable neurobiological alterations in both the central and autonomic nervous systems, such as altered brainwave activity, decreased volume of the hippocampus, and abnormal activation of the amygdala. Both the hippocampus and the amygdala are involved in the processing and integration of memory. The amygdala has also been found to be involved in coordinating the body's fear response.

Psychophysiological alterations associated with PTSD include hyper-arousal of the sympathetic nervous system, increased sensitivity of the startle reflex, and sleep abnormalities.

People with PTSD tend to have abnormal levels of key hormones involved in the body's response to stress. Thyroid function also seems to be enhanced in people with PTSD. Some studies have shown that cortisol levels in those with PTSD are lower than normal and epinephrine and norepinephrine levels are higher than normal. People with PTSD also continue to produce higher than normal levels of natural opiates after the trauma has passed. And the neurohormonal changes seen in PTSD are distinct from, and actually opposite to, those seen in major depression.

PTSD is associated with the increased likelihood of co-occurring psychiatric disorders. In a large-scale study, 88% of men and 79% of women with PTSD met criteria for another psychiatric disorder. The co-occurring disorders most prevalent for men with PTSD are alcohol abuse or dependence (52%), major depressive episodes (48%), conduct disorders (43%), and drug abuse and dependence (35%). The disorders most frequently co-morbid with PTSD among women are major depressive disorders (49%), simple phobias (30%), social phobias (28%), and alcohol abuse/dependence (28%).

Herein lies my dilemma: Several studies have been done on how the public at large would react to sudden, shocking, and possible life threatening scenarios: (1) Nuclear attack, (2) Asteroid heading directly at earth, and (3) Extreme weather phenomena.

Just hours after the 9-11 WTC attacks, we saw live on TV, government officials fighting over the issue of disclosing or withholding factual information. We heard it was unwise to disclose information to the public that would "panic" people out of fear of anarchy, violence, suicides, and general civil-unrest. It was argued that the better way to "minimize" panic was through informing the public of very real and ongoing events, thereby giving the public a chance to understand, prepare and adjust to whatever threats announced.

My studies have directed me to the latter. I believe it is far better to assist in minimizing shock and surprise through education, information and preparation. The theory of 'omission' to better serve the public is simply out-dated, assuming it was ever useful at all. I believe we have evolved significantly in our abilities to acquire and process news as it occurs, regardless of its imminent dangers.

Therefore, I have decided to disclose information to you as I receive it. I trust that you can, and will, use your gift of discernment. Yes, it is true that many could be prone to suffer negative reactions such as PTSD consequences, but at this time, I believe it is better to be 'aware and prepared.' In fact, studies state clearly that it's the action of being aware and prepared that will minimize the effects of shock, denial and bewilderment.

Animals in Disaster

In some ways, they are instinctively better prepared than humans, as we saw during the S.E. Asia tsunamis, but their dependence on humans can leave them panicked if those humans are missing. Then, the impact of a disaster on pets and other animals is often far more devastating than the impact on the human population. Animals are not allowed in shelters, and their owners often have little or no time before the disaster strikes to make other arrangements for their pets' safety and security.

After departing from the area of the disaster, the animal owners will often try to re-enter the now secured area of the disaster, only to be stopped by police, whose job it is to prevent looting. So the survival of a beloved pet or valuable livestock then will often depend on the plans you make in advance.

Pets and livestock should have a collar, with up-to-date tags, or an implanted microchip. It is vital that dogs have a current rabies tag, because if a rabies alert is issued, your pet may be put to death if it is found as a stray without a tag. If you must leave your animals behind, set out at least a five-day supply of food and water.

After a disaster, first look for your animals around your home. They may be traumatized by the disaster and be in hiding. Most lost pets will stay close to their home so, if they are not immediately found, put some dirty laundry around the outside of your home to provide a familiar scent.

Then contact nearby shelters because rescuers may have picked up your animals and taken them in. You'll also need flyers containing the pet's name, photo, description, last known location, and your name and contact information. Because the power might be out when you return, make these up in advance of the disaster (given enough notice).

So, Are You Ready?

Having read this chapter, let's look at how an entire state was caught off-guard by an uncommon but not rare phenomenon—a Hurricane Floyd-type event.

In September, 1999, Mother Nature delivered a one-two punch to the East Coast. First came Hurricane Dennis, which took a swing at the Carolina coast before ducking back out to sea and returning as Tropical Storm Dennis on September 15, dumping torrential rains and packing 70 mile-per-hour winds. Then ten days later came the knockout punch—Hurricane Floyd—and North Carolina went down for the count.

As a Category 3, Floyd's winds clocked at 130 mph, but this was no ordinary hurricane. Floyd was **enormous**, almost 600 miles across, dwarfing Florida as in this NASA photo—and almost *twice* the size of a typical Atlantic hurricane. A low-pressure trough of air from Canada threatened to steer it towards central Florida, where it would have created enormous destruction. In fact, an evacuation order was issued ... and harshly criticized in hindsight. Over two million Floridians evacuated pointlessly, which turned many in that state against mandatory evacuation.

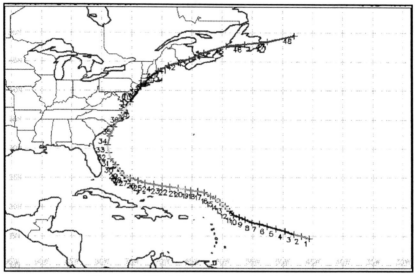

Hurricane Floyd Track, September 7-19, 1999

However, other forces steered the hurricane abruptly north, with North Carolina in its sights. After teasing Florida, Georgia and South Carolina, Floyd made landfall at about 0300 on September 16, near Cape Fear, NC. In the first 12-hour period, it dumped up to 20 inches of rain on top of the 6 inches dropped by Dennis. Even though Floyd was clipping along to the northeast, its sheer size meant that it was over the state for four days. And four days of torrential rain on top of water-saturated ground meant only one thing—flooding on an unimaginable scale.

North Carolina is criss-crossed with a dense network of rivers and streams connecting the Piedmont Hills to the Atlantic Ocean, and by nightfall on September 16, dozens of them overran their banks, spilling into urban areas, trapping sleeping people in upper stories of their houses. For thousands, their roofs were the only avenue of escape.

The rising waters flooded farms, drowning 4 million of the state's 22 million chickens, hundreds of thousands of the 10 million pigs, and thousands of the 1 million cattle. Flood waters swept through sewage plants, contaminating the water supply in many communities. Finally cresting at 24 feet above flood stage, water obliterated the town of Princeville.

The death toll was only 51, on the damage came in at $6 billion, making this only 'average' in terms of disasters, but it made life totally miserable for North Carolinians. Not only could they not drink or bathe in tapwater, they had to endure the odors from the contents of fuel tanks, pig waste lagoons, and human sewage treatment plants. Then came the odors of decay from millions of carcasses of pigs, chickens, and cattle.

In terms of property destruction, 7,000 homes were destroyed; 17,000 homes were rendered uninhabitable due to the noxious floodwater; and 56,000 homes were damaged. With over 500,000 customers without electricity, that meant that one in 16 residents were without power. Many proclaimed that it was the worst disaster since the Civil War, 140 years earlier, and that recovery could take a decade.

Could the state have been better prepared? "Yes," said the state's Disaster Center. For example, storm drains were full of debris, which hindered floodwater escape to the ocean. Another major vulnerability was the way swine wastes was stored in anaerobic surface lagoons. Not only did many of the state's 2,000 lagoons suffer structural damage, which hindered reconstruction, but the toxic spill polluted most of the state's ground water. With climatologists predicting ever-increasing hurricane activity in the years to come, the state will review the wisdom of livestock farming in the 100-year-flood plain.

"Dump the 'It can't happen here' attitude," authorities advise, "for this can be deadly when it keeps you from preparing your home, family, pets and business. Assume, 'Not only *can* it happen, but it *will* happen!', so plan for being without water and electricity for at least a week. Have a detailed evacuation plan for your family and pets, and have a disaster kit ready. The kit goes with you when you evacuate. If you stay at home, the kit will get you through those days when power will be off, the phone will be out, and emergency workers will be unable to reach you."

Georgia officials add: "Because it takes 26 to 30 hours to safely evacuate an urban area and the surrounding counties, you will be told by officials to put your family's evacuation plan in gear before the gale force winds actually get here. The entire county must be clear before the leading edge of the storm hits—generally 6 – 14 hours before the eye makes landfall. The sky may even be sunny as you drive away. You need to be ready to evacuate at least 36 hours before landfall or you could be trapped by rising water and high winds.

"There are two types of evacuations—voluntary and mandatory. In a *voluntary* evacuation (usually Category 2 or less), we recommend you leave the area, especially those living near any type of water, in areas prone to flooding and those living in mobile homes or other unstable construction. Alternatively, go to one of the shelters that are set up. A voluntary evacuation order is a word to the wise and should not be ignored. Do not wait for further instructions before deciding what to do. Be ready to leave before an order is issued. If you wait until an order is issued to begin preparations, you are putting your family at risk. In a *mandatory* evacuation (usually Category 3 and higher), the general public **must** leave designated areas. A mandatory evacuation order must never be ignored."

Because NCDOT, along with everyone else, thought Floyd was headed for landfall in Florida or Georgia, when it made its abrupt right turn, the state had only four days to prepare. Unfortunately, Interstate 95 was plagued by roadworks and already beyond capacity due to those further south fleeing north. Also, NCDOT did not have time to instigate a 'both directions north' plan that other states use, so half the Interstate 95 vehicle-carrying capacity was wasted.

Several agencies were involved in organization efforts, but there was no one 'command center' in charge, and when many agencies lost power, chaos set in. For example, when Interstate 95 was closed, NCDOT implemented a detour using U.S. 1 north of Raleigh. Unfortunately, local emergency service providers were not informed of the detour and did not expect the added traffic volumes on this route. Emergency responders, in particular, needed to know which routes they could use to aid in disaster recovery, but they were competing with the public for information via the eight hotline phones manned by volunteers.

Much was learned during and in the aftermath of Hurricane Floyd that will well serve North Carolina and the other eastern states in the event of a similar disaster ... which is only a matter of time.

Chapter 16

My New Mission

Those of you who have followed my work over the years know quite well I keep a firm footing in credible science. I have always believed this to be an essential component in my efforts to balance the (old) ancient text with the (new) science. Everything you have read in this book (except for chapter 5) is backed up by hard data and readied for peer review. However, it is at this junction I wish to present to you my most recent direction of passion. It came during my trip to Belize. Yes, it is of a more holistic nature, but then is this not what science may very well find at the end of the road?

For my science colleagues; don't worry, I have not by any stretch of the imagination abandoned my more left brain logical roots. I will continue my steadfast approach of providing ample documentation to support theoretical or applied theory. In fact, you will see I maintain a rather healthy dose of discernment with my more esoterically based colleagues. With this said, I present to you … my new mission.

On my return from the 2005 Mayan Cruise, I posted a three-part article on the Earth Changes TV website. Part Three is a poignant way to end this book. I let the article speak for itself in inspiring you to make whatever changes in your heart, mind and life that you feel are warranted.

Every now and then, we must take on external or internal challenges that keep us in alignment with our truth or journey. At times, this comes with great trepidation. As I now lay out what has come to me and is now a part of my mission, some may wonder why I believe this to be a hardship at all. Others will know full well of the turbulence ahead.

After consultation with Carlos Barrios, Mayan High Priest Elder, and he in consultation with his tribal council, it has been decided the time is NOW to make available sacred ceremonies which until this time have been kept secret from the public. Carlos and I believe that we are in a 'critical moment,' in which our collective world society can still make a difference regarding extreme challenges (earth changes) which are to come.

I cannot tell you the amount of energy I have spent in meditation and contemplation, all of which is focused on 'doing the right thing.' Anyone who makes a statement about "doing the right thing" can only be coming from a *subjective* point of view. In other words, "What *I* believe is the right thing may not be what *you* believe is the right thing." When we get into what one believes to be 'the truth,' it cannot help but be controversial. It could be no other way, for this, too, is part of the process.

So let me say up front that I do not pretend in any fashion to be the knower of truth, nor will you ever hear me suggest that I have some secret knowingness, or some special inside information that only a select few of us have. I do not! In fact, I go out of my way to often remind you that *no one* has any such thing, and 9 times out of 10, whoever is spouting such garbage is almost certainly a fraud and charlatan. The remaining 1% are probably sincerely thinking they are doing the 'right thing,' but it's my opinion that the 'true knowers' never claim to have the answers. They remind us that *we* have the answers, and to follow *our* truth, not theirs or anyone else's. But again, this is my truth, and just because I say it with passion and conviction does not make it 'the truth.'

Just like you, I am a seeker. A seeker of what? *Of what was, and is to come.* This is to say I believe in the wisdom of our ancestors. They have a message for us based on their experience and observation. Each generation prior to the 1800s (some would suggest in some areas and tribes it still happens today) passed on wisdom from their elders, telling of their past, and what was to come in their future. Most of this empirical wisdom was not based on *meaningless* folklore, superstition, and myths. I emphasize 'meaningless' because folklore, superstition, myths and storytelling were often filled with factual information. The style of storytelling knowingly or unknowingly; was a masterful method of passing on wisdom and experience of their tribe (community) in a way children and young adults would listen to and absorb. What stands out above all else and is found in *all* ancient text is the lineage of *patterns.* Now it is better known as the 'science of cycles.'

Many of us say it is time to reveal hidden treasures to the world community. To do otherwise is to surely nail the coffin shut on our potential growth and evolution. Parts of the 13 Mayan calendars tell us "we are in the time of transition." Our intuition shall rise to a peak, and we will have expanded insights and heightened awareness. Now I realize some of you will be reading this and scratching your head saying something like, "This sure doesn't sound like my Uncle Bob, or my brother, or my co-worker, or my oldest son, or my neighbor, and certainly not like the s.o.b. who just cut me off on the highway." Of course, you're correct. Not everyone is able, or perhaps more accurately, willing, to make the adjustments needed to facilitate or absorb the intense energy we have come into. And the intensity only goes up from here.

Our ancestors tell us, if we do not make the adjustments needed to strengthen our body and soul (spirit), we are likely to revert to our learned defense mechanisms. Defense mechanisms are learned behaviors that are most often derived from customized survivor skills often related to fear-based schisms manufactured to protect one's self-image or self-esteem. The less you feel about yourself, the more likely you are to compensate. Examples of defense mechanisms are: rage, (inappropriate) anger, drinking or drugging excessively for escape, workaholism, avoidance, controlling, jester (jokester). The point is to keep people at a distance, and—most importantly—to never let anyone really know how you feel about yourself.

The opposite of using defense mechanisms (low self-esteem/self-image) is to become "self-actualized," a term from Maslow's Hierarchy of Needs (http://web.utk.edu/~gwynne/maslow.HTM). Self-actualized people have evolved into their higher self, a state of acceptance of who they are, and who they are not; a drive to seek higher understanding and knowing they (we) are part of a whole. The concept of synchronicity and symbiotic relationships give weight to the new studies of quantum physics. But the 'new science' of quantum physics is really the 'old wisdom' of our ancestors, perhaps known as metaphysics, where 'meta' means 'situated behind.'*

Our Mayan Elders tell us we are in that time of 'self-conflict,' that we are at the proverbial fork in the road.' Down one path, we may find predictability, a familiar comfort zone, no change, sameness, assurance. However, this could be a cruel trick we will all have to face, for it is said that the road to sameness will ensure change. So the very thing these people are seeking is the very thing that will elude them.

Our ancestors from around the world, representing almost every single tribe known—from the Egyptians to the Dogon, to the Essenes, to the Hopi, to the Maya, to the Tibetans, and yes, to the Christians—all tell us one thing: *Life will change, and you will be different!* Some say this in a more dramatic fashion. The Christians say: "If you do not repent, hell will be bestowed upon you." The Hopi and Maya say: "We are coming into a time of transition. We must seek guidance and harmony with ourselves and our community. If we do not, Mother Earth will speak to us."

To take the alternative path at the fork in the road or (fork of life), we embrace our 'conflict,' and use it to steer ourselves back into harmony with ourselves, our community, and our world environment. To do otherwise is to ensure destruction. The elders tell me (us): "If we do not change our ways, we will experience 'earth changes' in a way our last many generations (hundreds of years) have not seen." Earthquakes measuring 10+ on the Richter Scale, eruptions of Mt. Rainier,

---

* Quantum physicists study, for example, how subatomic particles come barreling from 'nowhere' and seem to agree consciously to form matter. Metaphysicians, on the other hand, study the 'nowhere.'

Vesuvius, Colima, Popo, and yes, Yellowstone and Toga within the next 5 years. The Sun will present solar activity the Earth has not seen in centuries. And the worst disclosure of all, at least to this writer, is the demise of many civilizations *by man's own hand.* This is to suggest nuclear war may prevail but only because the many, who outweigh the few, choose this. We do have time to change the percentages, but not much.

I cannot affirm that any of the above events will come true. This is what many of our ancestral tribes are telling us, and I have no doubt it has happened before. Science proves that. It's all about cycles, and I have no reason to believe cycles will not continue as part of a natural rhythm. If we do what the Mayan and other ancient wisdoms tell us, I have no idea whether it would make a difference, but maybe it's a good idea to try. But this I can say, regardless of the influence we may have on future events—and I say this with full conviction—we will no doubt be better prepared spiritually, physically, mentally, and communally if we heed the wisdom of our ancestors. This is the very reason they passed on their stories, experience and wisdom. Just as in any family, they did not want us to suffer as perhaps they might have. As a father might say to his son, "Son, I've been were you are right now. I know it's confusing and fearful, but trust me and take advantage of my wisdom. Use what I say, so that you don't have to experience what I did. I say this not to scare you or control you, but because I love you and want to give you a chance that my father was unable to give me." (sigh, deep breath and tissue)

This brings me to *My Mission.* Although controversial, I have chosen the path of disclosure. I do this in full alignment with Carlos Barrios and with his appearance before his tribal council. Therefore, for the first time ever in history, you will be able to see ECTV's documentary of the Mayan Sacred Fire Ceremony, which was held at one of the most ancient Mayan temples ever to be excavated near the Belize-Guatemala border. I have over 9 hours of footage, some of which shows their most powerful sacred rituals, and never before made public. I will be making this available to you before Christmas 2005. The many hours will be made into a 90-minute documentary for the Discovery Channel, Travel Channel, and History Channel for possible world release. But my promise to you—the most sincere, supportive, and 'self-actualized' audience I am humbled to be a part of—is that you will be assured access to this documentary prior to *any* national or international distribution.

The time is NOW. To keep this incredible gift to only a select few, at this time, would be meaningless. In fact, many in the Mayan community have come forward affirming that their gift to the world has *always* been meant for disclosure *in this time*. So Be It!

Printed in the United States
81187LV00001B/1-36